F-CENTERS IN ALKALI HALIDES

SOLID STATE PHYSICS

Advances in
Research and Applications

Editors

FREDERICK SEITZ

Department of Physics
University of Illinois
Urbana, Illinois

DAVID TURNBULL

Division of Engineering
and Applied Physics
Harvard University
Cambridge, Massachusetts

F-CENTERS IN ALKALI HALIDES

JORDAN J. MARKHAM

Department of Physics
Illinois Institute of Technology
Technology Center
Chicago, Illinois

ACADEMIC PRESS · New York and London · 1966

ACADEMIC PRESS INC.
111 FIFTH AVENUE
NEW YORK, N. Y. 10003

United Kingdom Edition
Published by
ACADEMIC PRESS INC. (LONDON) LTD.
BERKELEY SQUARE HOUSE, LONDON W. 1

Library of Congress Catalog Card Number: 65-26403

PRINTED IN THE UNITED STATES OF AMERICA

To Lillian

Preface

The idea of writing a book on the F-center came during conversations with a colleague in the early hours of the morning when we were discovering new absorption bands by irradiating alkali halides at low temperatures. It was shortly after the war; the average American physicist had lost all contact with his German or Austrian brothers; and the only bridge left seemed to be the *Göttingen Nachrichten* and the *Wiener Berichte*. It seemed to us that these papers had a great wealth of information which had been almost lost, and there was a need to synthesize and put together all of the information buried in the Library of Congress. Our feeling was that although there were several reviews of these papers, a more detailed treatment was required. Since then, many changes have occurred, new equipment has appeared in every laboratory, and many new techniques have been applied to the F-center. The communication among the various countries is rapid, and visits are frequent. Nevertheless, in this field the hard core of facts still arises from these papers of Germany and Austria, and they can be traced back to the papers we enjoyed so much.

This book is an attempt to synthesize these works, adding many of the contributions that have been made elsewhere. No attempt is made to give a complete bibliography or to include the most recent measurement or theory. Indeed, the references have been kept to a minimum so that the reader does not assume any completeness. This is not a complete treatment of the F-center; the author has rather selected those properties he thought were of greatest interest. He believes most of the experimental aspects of the F-center are covered until about the middle of 1963. He has not presented every theory, but has attempted to give the basic ideas underlying most of them. This process is quite arbitrary, and some theorists may well feel that an alternate approach should have been employed. As the book goes to press, the author is aware of many important papers which are appearing and are not included. A few facts described here will undoubtedly be altered. Nevertheless, we hope that this book will be a good background for these new developments, and that it will assist the beginner in this field.

The author would like to thank the Zenith Radio Corporation, and Illinois Institutes of Research and Technology for making available time so that he could write this book. He owes a special debt to Dr. F. Seitz, who initiated him into this field and has helped clarify his thinking regarding many points over the last 15 years. The following are to be thanked for reading parts of the manuscript: Drs. J. Brophy, W. T. Doyle, A. Reinberg, J. Simpson, and C. A. Trapp; Messrs. T. N. Casselman, R. L. Gilbert, J. T. Ritter, J. Ring, R. Singh, and Mrs. J. Ritter. Thanks are due to Mrs. Bonnie Russell for typing and assisting with the manuscript.

Finally, the author expresses his appreciation to Professor R. W. Pohl for developing this field in physics with so much beauty.

JORDAN J. MARKHAM

Park Ridge, Illinois
July, 1966

Contents

F-CENTERS IN ALKALI HALIDES

I. The Optical Properties of the F-Center

1. Introduction

This book covers a very limited aspect of solid state physics—a particular imperfection in an ionic crystal (the F-center, to be defined in Section 2). It is believed that this imperfection occurs in all monovalent ionic crystals, that is, crystals made of singly charged positive and negative ions. We believe that it is the simplest imperfection which occurs in a crystalline system involving chemically strong forces—in this case the forces are between the ions that surround the imperfection and the electron trapped there. It most probably is a prototype of many imperfections which occur in ionic solids or solids which have some ionic nature. Hence, information regarding it will open a large field of knowledge concerning point imperfections in solids.

A knowledge of the perfect crystal will be assumed since several excellent treatments exist. The classic ones are: Born and Mayer,* Born and Huang, Seitz (1940, Chapter II), as well as Mott and Gurney.

The author's viewpoint on the F-center is best expressed by a statement made by Seitz (Seitz, 1946) a few years ago: "Almost every field of physics possesses a few problems which merit particular attention, both because they occupy a central position and because one has reasonable hope that, as a result of their inherent simplicity, they may eventually be understood in a complete fashion. The problems centering about the

---

* The method of reference used in this book is the following: Since the complexity of the subject requires the use of many advanced treatments, we shall in general refer to a book which, in the author's opinion, gives the most elegant treatment, although it need not be the "simplest." At the end, these books are listed as standard texts. Thus, for example, Born and Huang refers to the book of Professor Born and co-worker. Additional information, such as Born and Huang (1954) or a number, is of no value since there is only one book by Born and Huang listed in the general references. If an author has written two books or review papers, for example, Professor Seitz, then additional information is needed and the year of the publication will be given. A second type of reference (to a book or paper) will be employed. These are given at the end of every section, listed again by name of author and year when required. To separate the two we shall attach a letter S after the second type since they are limited to one section. This system is used to keep us from referring to the same book many times, as would be the case if we did not have a general list of references.

1

properties of atoms and molecules having one or two electrons occupied this position in the development of quantum mechanics; the problems centering about the properties of the very simplest nuclei occupy a similar position in nuclear physics. In the field of solids, the properties of the alkali halides have an enduring interest, since these crystals have continuously yielded to persistent investigation and have gradually provided us with a better and better understanding of some of the most interesting properties of all solids." The *F*-center, due to its simplicity, is in such a position relative to the field of color centers and the field of point imperfections in solids. This explains why it should be studied in greatest detail.

We shall discuss the properties in a general manner and shall not include every detail or experimental phenomenon. Some of the omitted data may be of only passing interest, while other data may introduce new properties of solids which are not presently understood. This selectivity is necessitated by the size of the field, which is growing very rapidly. We shall not attempt to include all literature references, since a bibliography of this field appears every year in the *Physics Abstracts*.

This field of science, like most others, has developed in stages. The first was primarily a descriptive one and established the existence of color centers, as well as the means of production. It started in the middle of the nineteenth century and lasted until World War I. The second stage, the period between the two wars, was one of discovering the phenomena associated with these types of imperfections. Finally, in the present stage the phenomena are used to understand more completely the nature of the alkali halide itself.

In the first period, one asked, "Do x-rays produce coloration?" Presently, however, one wants to know *how* x-rays produce coloration. Twenty years ago, one would have asked, "Do relatively simple equations describe the absorption observed?" Now, one wants to know the significance of the deviation from these simple relations. While it is useful to visualize stages of development, in reality the periods overlap, and one may not be sure where one stops and the other begins.

Most of this book concerns the second stage, which we understand most completely. Here and there we shall consider the more sophisticated point of view and, at times, there may be some slight inconsistencies, a reflection of the growth of the field. Indeed, data will be given without regard to when it was taken. The reader must remember that experiments done at one period may not be useful at a later time when refinements are required.

2. ELECTRON INJECTION IN ALKALI HALIDES

Most perfect alkali halides are transparent in the visible and near-visible region of the spectra. We should like to investigate optical absorption bands caused by the presence of excess electrons (electrons in excess of the ones in the filled shells). The most direct method of starting these investigations is to spray electrons into an alkali halide. The method used is illustrated in Fig. 2.1. We apply several hundred volts to a pointed

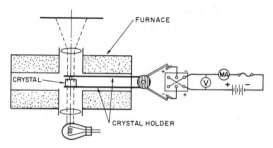

FIG. 2.1. Schematic of coloring apparatus.

platinum cathode (relative to the crystal). The resistance of the system consists of two parts: one due to the bulk of the crystal and the other due to the point—that is, the spreading resistance. As we raise the temperature, the bulk resistance of the crystal drops, and the field around the point increases. At an appropriate value, a color appears at the point. It may come like faint diverging blue rays, as in KI or KCl, or it may gush out in a deep red color, as in NaCl (see Fig. 2.2).

The temperature at which the injection occurs is not a precisely defined quantity, and it may depend on the purity and past history of the crystal. Some typical values reported by Hersh and Bronstein (S) are given in Table 2.1. The coloration is affected by various parameters. Overheating causes the electron injection to stop and the color drifts to the anode without further injection. Too high a voltage results in excessive current and the melting of the crystal. One may extract the color by reversing the external field on the crystal.

What has happened to the crystal during these experiments? At these temperatures, the crystal is a conductor, so that there is a large number of unassociated positive- and negative-ion vacancies. The term "negative-ion vacancies" may be replaced by "negative vacancies" or $\boxed{-}$; and likewise, use will be made of "positive vacancies" or $\boxed{+}$. The positive

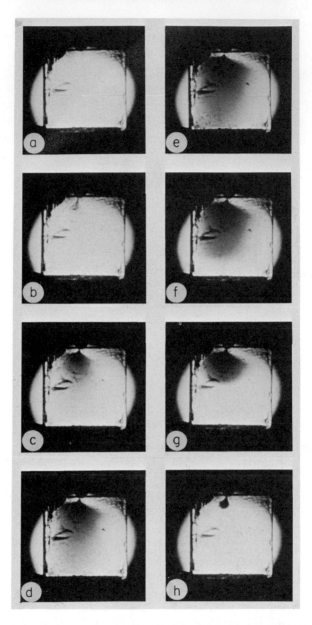

FIG. 2.2. Electron injection (a–d) and withdrawal (e–h) in KI (after Hersh and Bronstein, S).

vacancies are attracted to the plate, and some get destroyed (by the injection of an ion) with an out-flowing of negative charge.* We believe that an equal number of negative vacancies does not drift out at the point but that, instead, some electrons are injected into the conduction band.

TABLE 2.1. TEMPERATURE OF ELECTRON INJECTION[a]

Crystal	Coloration at 600° C	Optimum coloration temperature (°C)
NaCl	Red	640
KCl	Blue	625
KBr	Blue	600
KI	Blue	600
CsBr	Blue	450
CsI	Blue	450

[a] After Hersh and Bronstein (S).

The color is due to an interaction, or series of interactions, between excess electrons and negative vacancies since we have only added these quantities during the coloration process.

If the crystal is cooled to room temperature by removing it from the furnace, it changes its color; if the rate is slow, the final color in NaCl is blue or black. The electron attaches itself to a sodium ion which combines with other sodium atoms to precipitate out of the salt, forming a heterogeneous system. The precipitation occurs abruptly, as we may see by taking high-speed motion pictures of the crystal on cooling.

The study of the absorption caused by the precipitation of the metal belongs to another field of solid state optics, since the colloid is treated as a metal imbedded in a dielectric. The theory pertaining to this problem was developed by Mie and by Gans. A detailed treatment of this problem has been given recently by Born and Wolf (S) and by van de Hulst (S). Actual calculations on the properties of colloids of Na in NaCl have been carried out by Savostianowa (S). The data presented in Fig. 2.3 were taken from those calculations. The reader should note that we are dealing with two processes, scattering of the light beam and a real absorption, which decrease the intensity of the light going through the solid. The

* The positive vacancy has a negative charge and the negative vacancy has a positive charge.

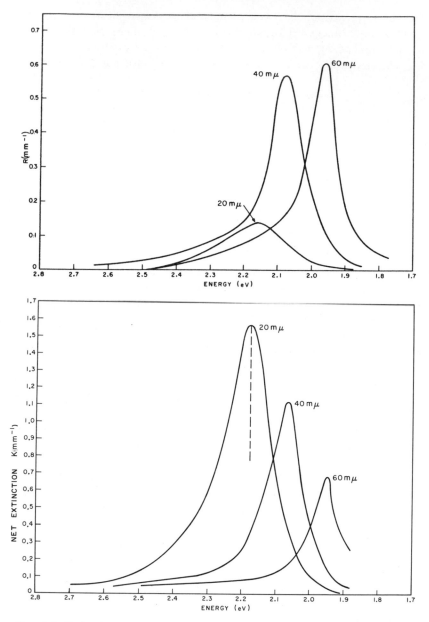

FIG. 2.3. Extinction curves for absorption K and scattering R in NaCl after the calculation of Savostianowa (S). The theory due to Mie was employed. One part per million by volume of sodium was assumed.

bands are asymmetrical, having a longer tail in the violet. The absorption in Na-NaCl cannot be lower than 2.25 ev. It is believed, and there is experimental evidence to support this conclusion, that the absorption and scattering from this type of imperfection is independent of temperature.

Rapid quenching of NaCl gives a dirty brown color which can be easily distinguished from crystals with colloidal particles. The tendency towards colloidal formation is less in KCl, so that when KCl is taken out of the furnace, the new type of coloration remains without quenching. There is no abrupt change in the color of this alkali halide, but rather a uniform color shift from the blue at 600° C to the magenta (bluish-red) at room temperature (RT).

This new type of coloration is caused by a combination of the injected electron or electrons and probably a negative vacancy or vacancies. It has no relation to the colloidal particle. Its absorption band is temperature dependent and peaks in a region to the violet of the curves shown in Fig. 2.3. This phenomenon will be extensively studied here. In the next section, we shall examine some of its simpler optical properties.

The band is known as the *F*-band, *F* standing for the German word *Farben*, and the imperfection that causes the absorption is known as the *F*-center. The model of this imperfection is discussed in Section 25, after its properties have been reviewed in great detail.

REFERENCES

M. Born and E. Wolf, "Principles of Optics," Chapter 13. Pergamon Press, New York, 1959.
H. N. Hersh and L. Bronstein, *Am. J. Phys.* **25**, 306 (1957).
M. Savostianowa, *Z. Physik* **64**, 262 (1930).
H. C. van de Hulst, "Light Scattering by Small Particles." Wiley, New York, 1957.

3. THE OPTICAL PROPERTIES OF THE *F*-CENTER

a. *General Features*

The absorption that causes the new color, representing the major induced absorption due to electron injection, is shown in Fig. 3.1.* The

---

* Actually, the data were not obtained on crystals colored by this method, but by techniques that are simpler to use, although not as illustrative. Section 3 describes the colored crystal with no regard to how it was produced. These problems are considered later. For completeness, we shall state how the coloration was obtained, although it is believed that the results are independent of the means of production.

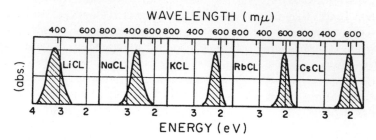

Fig. 3.1. The band in various alkali halides; y-axis is absorption (after Pohl, S).

effects of surface reflection and natural absorption of the crystal have been eliminated; the natural absorption in this spectral region is extremely small. The surface reflections can be calculated from the Fresnel equation

$$R = \frac{(n-1)^2}{(n+1)^2},\qquad(3.1)$$

where n is the index of refraction. Some typical values are given in Table 3.1.

TABLE 3.1. REFLECTION COEFFICIENTS

	n	R	$\log I_0/I_e$
NaCl	1.544	0.0458	0.0407
KCl	1.490	0.0387	0.0342
KBr	1.559	0.0477	0.0426
KI	1.677	0.0640	0.0492

In the last column of the table, I_0 is the intensity of the light falling on the sample, and $I_e = I_0(1-R)^2$, the light transmitted after two reflections. In all cases log is to the base ten while ln is to the base e.

The refractive index employed corresponds to the visible region of the spectra. All the alkali halides are transparent in this region. On the infrared side of this region occurs the absorption due to the out-of-phase vibrations of the positive and negative ions. (For KCl, this starts at 0.03 ev, and extends to the further infrared.) On the violet side, the edge absorption is due to the interband transitions and to the creation of excitons; it is well beyond the region of interest here (in KCl, this occurs beyond 6.5 ev).

Actual measured values of $\log(I_0/I)$ are larger than those reported in Table 3.1, and they depend on the treatment of the crystal, since rough surfaces scatter the light and one cannot apply Eq. (3.1) to obtain I_e. Some experiments change the surface only to a minor degree; others which require rapid cooling, modify the surfaces to a measurable extent. In an actual case, the last column has to be determined experimentally, and the quantity may have a wavelength dependence.

The absorption is defined by either one of the two equations:

$$I(x) = I_0 e^{-\alpha x} \qquad (3.1a)$$

or

$$dI/dx = -\alpha I. \qquad (3.1b)$$

Here $I(x)$ is the light passing through the crystal at the position x; I_0 the light falling on the crystal neglecting scattering and reflection losses; and α the absorption constant.*

No simple rule exists as to how to report the true absorption, and the data are treated differently in various experiments. All curves, such as Fig. 3.1, require an element of judgment as to how to eliminate the surface effects. Self-consistent accurate data require a uniform approach not always employed. In most experiments x is some standard distance such as the thickness of the crystal. Quite often, the values of the absorption are adjusted so that its maximum value is unity (relative scale, A_r).

Generally, we shall not use a wavelength scale, but report our values in electron volts; that is,

$$\epsilon = \frac{hc}{1.602\lambda \times 10^{-12}} = \frac{1240}{\lambda \text{ (in m}\mu)}. \qquad (3.2)$$

If the incident light after scattering is I_0, and the transmitted light is I, the true absorption α is defined by the equation

$$\alpha = -(1/l)\ln I/I_0, \qquad (3.3)$$

where l is the thickness of the crystal. Many times, the thickness of the colored portion of the crystal is unknown, and one uses

$$A = -\log_{10} I/I_0 \qquad (3.4)$$

instead of α. A is proportional to the absorption, since there is always an effective l. The reader should note a change in the base of the logarithm.

The striking feature of Fig. 3.1 is that there is a single large absorption

* We note the negative sign. In the most general case, both positive and negative α's can exist, in view of laser action.

band. The small absorption on either side may, to first approximation, be ignored (see Section 14.1). As stated, the large absorption band is known as the F-band. It will be described as a bell-shaped curve since, at present, no completely satisfactory analytical description of it has been found. (We shall discuss this problem in Section 33.) One may determine the wavelength at the maximum absorption ϵ_m, as well as the point to the red, ϵ_r, and to the violet, ϵ_v, where the absorption is half the maximum value. Use will be made of $H = \epsilon_v - \epsilon_r$, $\alpha(\epsilon_m) = \alpha_m$, and $A(\epsilon_m) = A_m$. In the old papers the wavelength has also been reported in terms of millimicrons; therefore, λ_m will also be employed.

F-centers can be formed in almost all alkali halides; in Table 3.2, we list ϵ_m and λ_m (in parentheses) for most of the alkali halides at room temperature. Table 3.2 is based on the early work of Mollwo (1933S). We have included the value of H and also some values of Avakian and Smakula (S). The starred ones have been checked by other workers, and the author believes they are reliable. In Table 3.2a, the data of Rabin and Klick (S) for the value of ϵ_m and λ_m at 5° K are presented. These seem to be the most complete data at this low temperature. Since Mollwo's work,

TABLE 3.2. ROOM TEMPERATURE VALUES OF ϵ_m AND λ_m
FOR F-CENTERS IN VARIOUS ALKALI HALIDES[a]

	F	Cl	Br	I
Li	4.96	3.22		
	(250)	(385)		
Na	3.65	2.67	2.30	2.11
	(340)	(465)	(540)	(588)
		0.46*		
K	2.72	2.20	1.97	1.81
	(455)	(563)	(630)	(685)
		0.35*	0.35	0.345*
Rb		1.98	1.72	1.60
		(624)	(720)	(775)
Cs		2.06	1.84	1.58
		(603)	(675)	(785)
		0.36	0.32	0.36

[a] After Mollwo (1933S). First figure: ϵ_m in electron volts; value in parentheses in millimicrons; third figure: value of the half width in electron volts. Starred values have been checked by other observers.

TABLE 3.2a. ϵ_m AND λ_m AT $5°\,$K[a]

LiF	NaF	NaCl	NaBr	KCl	KBr	KI
5.10	3.69	2.75	2.36	2.30	2.06	1.86
(243)	(336)	(450)	(526)	(539)	(602)	(666)

[a] After Rabin and Klick (S).

some modification of the values have been necessary, so that some recent values of ϵ_m are superior to those given in the table. Most are not; hence, Mollwo's work gives the most *complete*, over-all picture. If one averages all the values of ϵ_m in the literature, one assumes that a random error exists. After looking at the data a long time, the author sees no justification for this conclusion. The reason for this will be discussed at length later in this section. Mollwo (1931S) first reported a relation between ϵ_m and a parameter of the crystal—namely, the inverse square of the interionic distance, *a*. In Fig. 3.2, $\log \epsilon_m$ is plotted against $\log a$ for all the data given in Table 3.2.

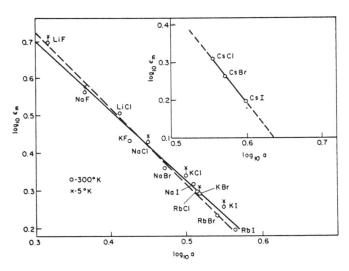

FIG. 3.2. Data from Tables 3.2 and 3.2a combined with the usual values of *a* (temperature effects are not included). —, Mollwo's equation; – – –, Ivey's equation (except for CsCl, CsBr, and CsI).

The reader will notice that the data fit a simple empirical relation discovered by Mollwo,

$$\epsilon_m \quad \text{(in ev)} = (20.7)\, a^{-2} \qquad \text{(for a NaCl structure)}, \qquad (3.5a)$$

fairly well, but an equation obtained by Ivey (S),

$$\epsilon_m \quad \text{(in ev)} = (17.6)\, a^{-1.84} \qquad \text{(for a NaCl structure)}, \qquad (3.5b)$$

gives a slightly superior fit. The foregoing relations do not apply to the Cs salts, which have a different crystal structure. The exponent on the interionic distance is of the order of 2.5 instead of 1.8. If one uses the method of least squares, the best curve through Mollwo's value of ϵ_m (Table 3.2) is

$$17.4 a^{-1.83}$$

while the best fit through the data of Rabin and Klick (S) (ϵ_m at 5° K) is

$$13.8 a^{-1.86}.$$

One may grow mixed crystals of KCl—RbCl with any proportion of K or Rb. The ϵ_m versus a relation is shown in a striking manner from the data on mixed alkali halides. Vegard (S), as well as Gnaedinger (S), have shown that a is proportional to the ratio of the molar fraction of the mixture. One may produce F-centers in these crystals, and Meissner (S) has shown that ϵ_m has approximately the same a dependence.

Recently, additional studies on mixed crystals have been carried through. Reitz et al. (S) studied mixed crystals made of KBr and KI. Smakula et al. (S) studied mixtures of RbCl and KBr, of KCl and KBr, and of KCl and RbCl. All these data roughly obey a Mollwo–Ivey relation, although the agreement is not perfect. Smakula (S) has indicated that the deviations from the Mollwo–Ivey relation are systematic, which shows that ϵ_m is not determined only from the distance between nearest neighbors.

The importance of Eq. (3.5) is that it indicates that the center is not a complex which has precipitated out of the crystal for, in this case, λ_m or ϵ_m would have no simple relation to a. If the electron interacts with a single positive ion, we would expect mixed crystals to have two or more F-bands. This is not the case; hence, the electron must interact with many ions.

b. Effects of Temperature

One requires somewhat more elaborate equipment to obtain absorption measurements below room temperature. The simplest method is to have the crystal in good thermal contact with a boiling liquid. Some commonly used points are

Helium	4° K	(HT)
Hydrogen	20° K	
Nitrogen	77° K	(NT)
Oxygen	90° K	
CO_2 (sublimes)	195° K	(DT)

The actual temperatures are usually slightly higher (1 or 2 degrees), which is generally of no importance; hence, the foregoing abbreviations will be used. The use of CO_2 requires special care and cannot be recommended.

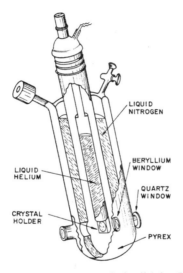

FIG. 3.3. Low-temperature optical cell (after Hersh, S).

To cut down on the evaporation rate, one must keep heat conduction, convection, and radiation to a minimum. The elimination of convection requires high vacuum; conduction is minimized by the use of glass or special steels; while radiation losses require that one shield the liquids (that is, H_2 and He are surrounded by O_2 or N_2) as well as special plating of the surfaces. Both metal and glass cells have been used for optical work. In the opinion of the author, glass cells are cheaper, require less upkeep, and usually do an equivalent job.

In Fig. 3.3, we show a typical helium cell designed by Hersh. It can be employed above room temperature by using an appropriate liquid with a heater. Cells that operate between boiling points have been designed and used. Details can be found in books describing low temperature techniques (see also Konitzer and Markham, 1960S).

Let us now turn to the data and ask the question, "Can one obtain a consistent set of data—that is, do data from various laboratories agree?" One must make such a comparison at low temperatures, since ϵ_m and H can be measured more accurately there. Actual values of H obtained by various observers show large variations at the same temperature. For example, Table 3.3 gives the values at approximately NT for KBr. The

TABLE 3.3. H FOR KBr AT APPROXIMATELY NT

Observers	H (ev)
Mollwo[a] (1933S)	0.22
Molnar[a]	0.30
Russell and Klick[a]	0.22
Duerig and Markham[a]	0.19
Meissner[a]	0.22
Mador et al.[a]	0.208–0.197
Smakula et al.[a] (1963S)	0.19

[a] See references under the name at the end of the section.

variations are well beyond experimental error and require an explanation before we may make any comparison with theory. The first question is, "To what accuracy can one measure H?" Mador and co-workers answered this question by taking a set of measurements on samples cleaved from the same block of KBr. They produced the coloration by means of soft x-rays (see Section 5) and made the measurements at NT. The probable error of H obtained from one block is about 0.0006 ev, while variations of 0.005 ev appear in H obtained from different blocks. The cause of the variations of H in Table 3.3 is not due to the technique of measurements or the subtraction of the background due to the scattering from surfaces.

The most probable explanation of this problem appears in a study by Konitzer and the author (1957S), who bleached the *F*-band with white and *F*-light. At RT, this causes the appearance of subsidiary bands to the red (see Section 14.2) and a shift of ϵ_v to the violet. Typical examples of the data for KCl (additively colored) and measured at NT are shown in Table 3.4. The time column has very little meaning, since the amount of bleaching depends on the time and the strength of the source. An examination of the data indicates that one or more bands have appeared right next to the F-band. Careful measurements can at times partially resolve a structure in the absorption structure indicating a second band. We shall refer to the broader composite as the B-band for reasons to be discussed in Section 14.2, and reserve the term F-band for the narrowest structure that can be obtained by the usual means (see Sections 5 and 6). The conversion from F to B can be extremely rapid when the crystal is exposed to F-light. To prevent this during an experiment requires some care.

TABLE 3.4. BLEACHING OF THE F-CENTER IN KCl AT RT
MEASURED AT NT[a]

Bleaching time	ϵ_v (ev)	ϵ_m (ev)	ϵ_r (ev)	H (ev)
0	2.411	2.304	2.215	0.196
15 min	2.439	2.308	2.206	0.233
1 hr	2.453	2.310	2.210	0.243

[a] From Konitzer and Markham (1957S).

The discrepancies in H in Table 3.3 appear to arise because some of the measurements were made on the B-band instead of the "pure" F-band. We shall place more reliance on experiments carried out with narrower bands and thus attach a greater significance to Mador's value of 0.197 instead of his value of 0.208 ev.

The detailed study of the temperature variation of ϵ_m and H has been made by Mollwo (1931S, 1933S), by Russell and Klick (S),* and by Konitzer and the author (1960S); Markham and Konitzer (1961S). First, the general features of the problem will be described; this is based to a large extent on the work of Mollwo. Then, some additional important details based on later studies will be presented. Figure 3.4 shows the

* Mollwo's data, as well as those of Russell and Klick, seem to pertain to the B-band; the data on the F-band show quantitative, not qualitative, differences. The studies of Mollwo as well as Russell and Klick are more extensive than those of Konitzer and Markham in the sense that more alkali halides were used. Konitzer and co-worker, however, made a much more detailed study of the F-band in KCl and NaCl.

F-band at several temperatures. $A(\epsilon)$ drops off faster to the red of the peak than to the violet. The shape looks more symmetrical at higher temperatures, and there seems to be no reason to assume that the asymmetry arises

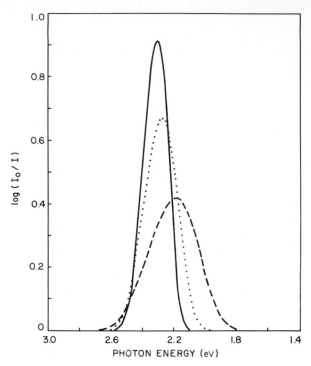

FIG. 3.4. Variations of the *F*-band in KCl with temperature (after Konitzer and Markham, 1960S).

from the nonharmonic effects in the lattice vibrations which are smallest at 80° K. Further, Mollwo's study indicates:

(1) ϵ_m and ϵ_r decrease with temperature, θ, while ϵ_v stays constant.

(2) $\epsilon_m(\theta)$ is not proportional to $a(\theta)^{-2}$ or $a(\theta)^{-1.84}$.

(3) $H(\theta) - H(0) \approx \int\limits_0^\theta C_p \, d\theta$ where C_p is the specific heat.

Mollwo stressed that $H(0)$ arises from the zero-point vibrations and lattice defects.

(4) If one plots the absorption $A(\lambda)$ against λ_m/λ, one obtains a single Lorentzian curve for all the alkali halides which only depends on the temperature of measurements.

The Lorentzian curve has the form

$$\alpha = \frac{b}{\pi} \frac{1}{1 + b^2(\epsilon - \epsilon_m)^2} \tag{3.6}$$

where

$$\int \alpha(\epsilon) \, d\epsilon = 1. \tag{3.6a}$$

Item 2 is particularly important because it indicates that Ivey's relation Eq. (3.5b) does not contain all the important parameters, a point stressed strongly by Smakula (1961S). Item 3 indicates the importance of the zero-point energy which has to be included in any theory. The Debye temperature (θ_D) for an alkali halide is about $250°$ K so that C_p is approximately constant above $100°$ K; hence, for $\theta > 100°$ K,

$$H(T) = \text{const} + a\theta. \tag{3.7}$$

Mollwo only used values of A greater than $0 \cdot 1$ to arrive at item 4 (on a relative scale where $A_m = 1$). If the smaller values are included, one sees that a Lorentzian curve is not a good description of the data. Attempts have been made by Hesketh and Schneider (S), to fit A to a Gaussian, that is,

$$A(\epsilon) = A_m \exp\{-b(\epsilon - \epsilon_m)^2\} \tag{3.8}$$

This does not lead to a major improvement unless one assumes two values of b; one for $\epsilon > \epsilon_m$, the other for $\epsilon < \epsilon_m$. Actually, no discontinuity exists at ϵ_m, and A deviates from (3.8) at the peak of the band. One must conclude that A can be approximately described by Gaussian curves with two values of b. The major differences between a Lorentzian and a Gaussian curve occur for large values of $|\epsilon - \epsilon_m|$ where A cannot be obtained accurately because of the background.

To characterize the absorption shape of the F-band in a better manner, we must consider the results of several recent studies. Konitzer and co-worker have examined the shape of the band in KCl (Konitzer and Markham, 1960S) and in NaCl (Markham and Konitzer, 1961S). One desires the true or the "pure" F-center where all the effects of surface scattering have been eliminated. The data as obtained from a spectrophotometer are shown in Fig. 3.5. It has not been adjusted to take care to Fresnel reflections as discussed previously. The rise in the base line in the violet is due to the scattering arising from the roughness of the surface and surface layers caused by the absorption of gases (corrections for this must be made).

A definite bump, which is known as the *K*-band, since it first appears
in absorption data reported by Kleinschrod (S), appears to the violet. Our
interest is in the "pure" *F*-center and we must find a way to subtract this
band. Any procedure used to analyze the data developed so far is arbitrary.
At low temperatures in KCl, this is no major problem since every reasonable subtraction procedure gives approximately the same results. This is

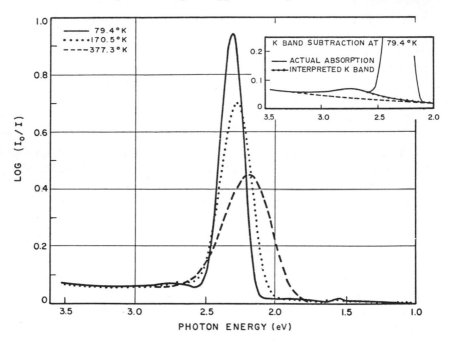

Fig. 3.5. The data as obtained from the spectrophotometer, and the method of
determining the base line and the elimination of the *K*-band (after Konitzer and
Markham, 1960S).

not the case for the *F*-center in KBr, KI, and NaCl and determination of
the *K*-band is a major problem. In these crystals one may not completely
resolve the *K*-band from the *F* to obtain the "pure" *F*-band. Hence,
there is a large uncertainty in the shape, particularly to the violet of ϵ_v. The
true ϵ_v can usually be obtained at low temperatures resulting in a fairly
reliable value. The measurements of Konitzer and Markham indicate that
even in KCl at RT, ϵ_v changes from 2.421 to 2.404 ev when one subtracts
the *K*-band. The change is of the order of 0.001 ev at HT. The indications
are that in NaCl the resolution of the *K*-band is so poor, even at low

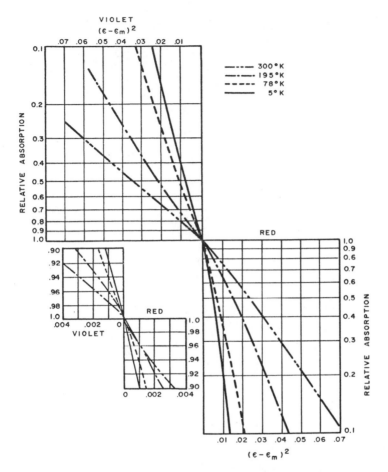

FIG. 3.6. Comparison of the system of the two sides of the F-band. Note the inversion of the scale of the red and the violet (after Konitzer and Markham, 1960S).

temperatures, that one cannot obtain reliable values of ϵ_v and H. The author believes it is impossible to obtain a "pure" F-band (without the K-band) in these alkali halides. A method adopted to subtract the F-band is shown in the figure. It is this subtraction procedure which resulted in Fig. 3.4.

Figure 3.6 indicates the type of fit one obtains when the double Gaussian is employed. The expected deviation around A_m is shown in the inset. The agreement is less satisfactory in NaCl. The double Gaussian

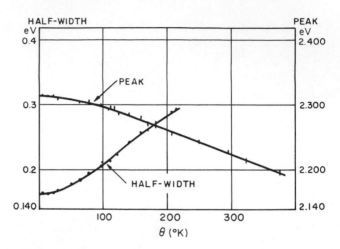

FIG. 3.7a. Plot of ϵ_m and H against temperature for the *F*-center in KCl (after Markham and Konitzer, 1958S).

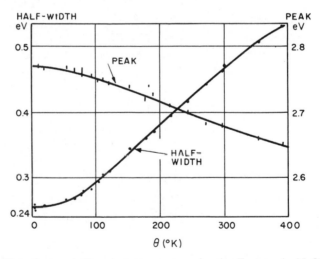

FIG. 3.7b. Plot of ϵ_m and H against temperature for the *F*-center in NaCl (after Markham and Konitzer, 1961S).

curve resembles one suggested by the calculation of Pekar. This curve (Poisson curve) is discussed in Sections 31–33.

The nature of the temperature dependence of ϵ_m and H is indicated in Fig. 3.7 for KCl and NaCl. One cannot explain the temperature dependence of ϵ_m by the Mollwo–Ivey relation Eqs. (3.5a) and (3.5b)—that is, the change in lattice distance. This was first pointed out by Mollwo. The explanation of the nature of the temperature dependence requires a detailed theory of the *F*-center. This problem has not really been completely solved. (For further details see Sections 30 and 31.)

TABLE 3.5. SMAKULA'S CONSTANT

Type of curve	a_s
Lorentzian	1.571 ($\pi/2$)
Gaussian	1.064
Poissonian[a]	1.07

[a] The Huang–Rhys factor (see Section 31) is assumed to be about 25.

We would intuitively expect that $\int \alpha(\epsilon)\,d\epsilon$ should be temperature independent. The integral is the zeroth moment of α, hence, will be denoted by M_0. The ratio $M_0(\alpha_m H)^{-1}$ will be referred to as Smakula's constant, a_s, and is a quantity of theoretical and experimental importance (see Section 4).* Using Eqs. (3.6) and (3.8), we obtain Table 3.5. For the Lorentzian and the Gaussian, the a_s can be calculated in a straightforward manner. The value of a_s for a Poisson distribution was obtained numerically (Markham, S); a_s as a function of θ has been determined for the band in KCl and NaCl. Some data are shown in Table 3.6. These data indicate

TABLE 3.6. M_0 AND $\alpha_m H$ AT VARIOUS TEMPERATURES FOR KCl

Temperature	M_0 (ev cm^{-1})	H (ev)[a]	$M_0/\alpha_m H$
RT 300° K	3.40	0.336	1.04
DT 195° K	3.51	0.275	1.04
NT 78° K	3.58	0.193	1.06
HT 4.5° K	3.65	0.163	1.05

[a] Average value—attempts were made to subtract the *K*-band.

* The theory is usually derived in terms of the frequency of a photon—not its energy. For this reason, one may also define the zeroth moment as $\int \alpha(\nu)\,d\nu$ and Smakula's constant as $a_\alpha \alpha_m \Delta\nu = \int \alpha(\nu)\,d\nu$. $\Delta\nu = 2.42 \times 10^{+14}H$, since H is in electron volts. The frequency will be used in Section 4.

that $\alpha_m H$ is temperature independent and proportional to M_0; $\alpha_m H$ can be obtained with much less effort since one measures α_m and H without any calculations. The most recent studies indicate that the shape of the F-band does not change with temperature to the degree of accuracy with which one can subtract the K-band. This is true in spite of the appearance of the curves in Fig. 3.4.

c. Effects of Pressure

Another macroscopic variable is the pressure. Jacobs (S) has made measurements of ϵ_m and H as a function of p for pressures below 8×10^3

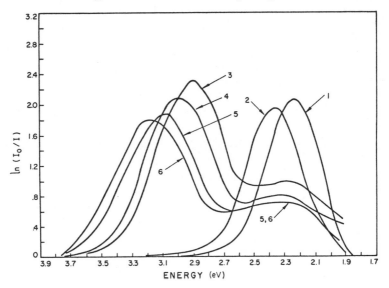

Fig. 3.8a. Variation of the F-center absorption with pressure in KCl: 1, $0k$ atm; 2, $8k$ atm; 3, $66k$ atm; 4, $79k$ atm; 5, $108k$ atm; $133k$ atm (unpublished data of Eppler).

atm. These measurements have been extended by Maisch and Drickamer (S) to 50×10^3 atm. We shall examine the latter data first, since they give an over-all picture of the phenomena, then return to the earlier data for some quantitative results.

KCl undergoes a phase transition from the NaCl lattice structure to the CsCl lattice structure at 19.5×10^3 atm. In view of the data in Fig. 3.2, we would expect a change in ϵ_m during this transition since the Mollwo–Ivey relation depends on the structure. No such transition appears in NaCl. The data of Drickamer and co-workers are given in Figs. 3.8a and 3.8b.

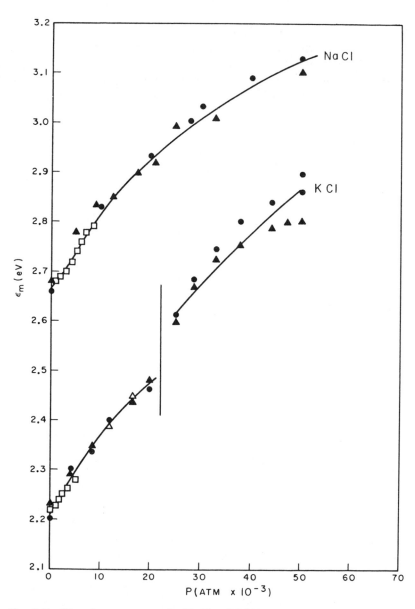

F$_{IG}$. 3.8b. Plot of ϵ_m *vs.* pressure for NaCl and KCl (after Maisch and Drickamer, S).

Figure 3.8a shows some absorption measurements taken at various pressures by R. A. Eppler at Drickamer's laboratory.*

Drickamer pointed out that there is some scattered light associated with these measurements, and that too much reliance cannot be placed on the absorption shapes. The H value is somewhat broader than the values usually reported. In view of the difficulties of such a set of measurements,

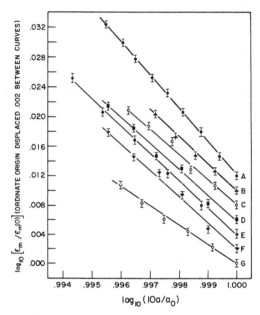

FIG. 3.9. Plots of $\log \epsilon_m$ against $\log a$, where a is the distance between nearest neighbors; ϵ_m is the peak absorption at a given pressure and $\epsilon_m(0)$ is the peak at "zero" pressure (1 atm); (after Jacobs, S). Scale displaced for various crystals: A, NaCl; B, NaBr; C, KCl; D, KBr; E, KI; F, RbCl; G, CsCl.

we shall not attach any importance to this. Above the transition point, the F-band shifts to the violet and seems to be broader. The F absorption seems to be broader at a pressure of 8k atm. Figure 3.8b indicates the variation of ϵ_m with pressure for NaCl and KCl. The reader will note that pressure mainly effects ϵ_m, while the major effect of temperature is on H. Jacobs reports that in NaBr, H decreases by 10 per cent, while Maisch and Drickamer have found a 10–15 per cent increase in some alkali halides. The present data indicate that H is somewhat pressure dependent, but a

* The author thanks Professor Drickamer for the use of Eppler's data.

sufficient number of measurements have not been made to establish the effect or effects. At high pressure, additional bands appear and disappear as one approaches the region where there is a change in the crystalline form.

In the low-pressure region, the region studied carefully by Jacobs, one may obtain relations between $\epsilon_m(p)/\epsilon_m(0)$ and $a(p)/a(0)$. Data taken from Jacobs's measurements are shown in Fig. 3.9. Ivey's empirical relation suggests that $\epsilon_m = 1/a^n$; n, however, does not have the value given in (3.5b).

Plots of $\ln \epsilon_m$ against $\ln a$ give straight lines when a is varied by three means: (1) changing the crystal; (2) varying θ; and (3) varying p; n, however, depends on how we change a. To examine these effects further, we define

$$n_\theta = \left\{ \frac{\partial \ln \epsilon_m(\theta, p)}{\partial \ln a(\theta, p)} \right\}_p = \left\{ \frac{\partial \ln \epsilon_m(\theta, p)}{\partial \theta} \right\}_p \left\{ \frac{\partial \ln a}{\partial \theta} \right\}_p^{-1}$$

$$= \frac{3}{\beta \epsilon_m} \left(\frac{\partial \epsilon_m}{\partial \theta} \right)_p . \tag{3.9}$$

Likewise

$$n_p = \frac{3}{K \epsilon_m} \left(\frac{\partial \epsilon_m}{\partial p} \right)_\theta , \tag{3.10}$$

where β and K are the volume coefficient of thermal expansion and compressibility. Some of Jacobs's calculated values of n_θ and n_p (extrapolated to room temperature and 1 atm) are given in Table 3.7. The variation of ϵ_m with temperature was obtained mainly from Mollwo's measurements. Some of the differences may be attributed to the experimental errors and the presence of structure along with the "pure" *F*-band. Other factors besides a influence the energy levels associated with the imperfection which is responsible for the *F*-band.

TABLE 3.7. VALUE OF n TO BE USED IN
A MOLLWO–IVEY RELATION

Crystal	n_p	n_θ
NaCl	4.4	4.0
NaBr	3.6	3.8
KCl	3.5	5.0
KBr	3.5	4.5

REFERENCES

P. Avakian and A. Smakula, *Phys. Rev.* **120**, 2007 (1960).
W. H. Duerig and J. J. Markham, *Phys. Rev.* **88**, 1043 (1952).
R. J. Gnaedinger, *J. Chem. Phys.* **21**, 323 (1953).
H. N. Hersh, *Phys. Rev.* **105**, 1158 (1957).
R. V. Hesketh and E. E. Schneider, *Phys. Rev.* **95**, 837 (1954).
H. F. Ivey, *Phys. Rev.* **72**, 341 (1947).
I. S. Jacobs, *Phys. Rev.* **93**, 993 (1954).
F. G. Kleinschrod, *Ann. Physik* **27**, 97 (1936).
J. D. Konitzer and J. J. Markham, *Phys. Rev.* **107**, 685 (1957).
J. D. Konitzer and J. J. Markham, *J. Chem. Phys.* **32**, 843 (1960).
I. L. Mador, J. J. Markham, and R. T. Platt, *Phys. Rev.* **91**, 1277 (1953).
W. G. Maisch and H. G. Drickamer, *Phys. Chem. Solids* **5**, 328 (1958).
J. J. Markham, *Rev. Mod. Phys.* **31**, 956 (1959).
J. J. Markham and J. D. Konitzer, *J. Chem. Phys.* **29**, 673 (1958).
J. J. Markham and J. D. Konitzer, *J. Chem. Phys.* **34**, 1936 (1961).
G. Meissner, *Z. Physik* **134**, 576 (1953).
E. Mollwo, *Gött. Nachr.* pp. 97; 236 (1931).
E. Mollwo, *Z. Physik* **85**, 56 (1933).
J. P. Molnar, Thesis, M.I.T. (unpublished 1940).
R. W. Pohl, *Proc. Phys. Soc. (London)* **49** [Suppl.] 3, (1937).
H. Rabin and C. C. Klick, *Phys. Rev.* **117**, 1005 (1960).
R. A. Reitz, W. D. Butler, and J. R. Brandenberger, *J. Chem. Phys.* **37**, 1893 (1962).
G. A. Russell and C. C. Klick, *Phys. Rev.* **101**, 1473 (1956).
A. Smakula, *Proc. Semiconductor Conf. (Prague)* p. 729 (1961).
A. Smakula, N. C. Maynard, and A. Repucci, *Phys. Rev.* **130**, 113 (1963).
L. Vegard, *Z. Physik* **5**, 17 (1921).

4. SMAKULA'S EQUATION

A relation between the measured absorption and concentration is desired. Smakula (S) found a simple equation which is of profound importance and which will be used in the description of the properties of the F-center; we shall derive it here. While it is useful to regard Smakula's equation as a result of theory, one may equally well consider it to represent an experimental law with an adjustable constant. Thus, future modification of the theory need not affect its use in experimental work. We shall derive the equation by a method due to Rauch and Heer (S). The more traditional or classical derivation is given by Seitz (1940) or by Mollwo and Roos (S).

Assume that we have an atom that possesses at least two bound electron states with eigenvalues ϵ_1 and ϵ_2. The energy absorbed per unit time in the frequency range dv (Heitler, Eq. 17: 19) is

$$S = \frac{8\pi^3}{3} \frac{e^2}{hc} \nu |\langle \psi_2 | \mathbf{r} | \psi_1 \rangle|^2 I(\nu)\, dv \tag{4.1}$$

where ψ_1 and ψ_2 are the wave functions of the upper and lower states and

$$\nu = \frac{1}{h}(\epsilon_2 - \epsilon_1). \tag{4.2}$$

The other symbols have their usual meaning. $I(\nu)^*\, dv$ is the intensity of the light in the frequency range ν to $\nu + dv$.† Equation (4.2) assumes the Bohr frequency condition. In this section, ν is used in place of the photon energy in electron volts. The results can be readily converted to the parameters used in reporting the experimental data.

In Heitler's derivation, one considers a single atom in an infinite vacuum. To apply this to an imperfection in a solid, several modifications must be made:

(1) The absorption response has a finite width. Equation (4.2) does not hold exactly.

(2) We replace I by I_L, the local intensity at the imperfection. I_L must be proportional to I, so one may write $I_L = aI$, where I is the intensity falling on the crystal (surface scattering being neglected).

(3) We introduce the oscillator strength, defined as

$$f = \frac{8\pi^2}{3h} \nu m |\langle \psi_2 | \mathbf{r} | \psi_1 \rangle|^2 \tag{4.3a}$$

$$= \frac{2}{3hm\nu} |\langle \psi_2 | \mathbf{p} | \psi_1 \rangle|^2 \tag{4.3b}$$

where the relation

$$\langle \psi_2 | \mathbf{r} | \psi_1 \rangle = \frac{i}{2\pi m\nu} \langle \psi_2 | \mathbf{p} | \psi_1 \rangle \tag{4.3c}$$

(Slater, p. 468) has been used. We see that f could have a frequency dependence of $\nu^{\pm 1}$ depending on the properties of the matrix element of $\mathbf{p}$ or $\mathbf{r}$.

---

* $I(\nu)$ is the light intensity in unit interval of ν. Throughout the literature $I(\omega)$ and $I(\epsilon)$ are used as well; they are not equivalent. Surface effects are neglected.

† In this section N_0 denotes the number of imperfections per unit volume. This notation is not used throughout the book.

Two types of broadening will be of interest; we shall now consider them in detail. The simplest type is:

(a) The effect of interaction between centers;* assume that it is possible to split the Hamiltonian into two parts, H_0 and H_1. H_0 is the energy of the electron bound to the center, while H_1 describes the interaction between centers. Consider a small region of the crystal whose size is only a fraction of the absorbed light's wavelength, but has a large density of centers.† Then Eq. (4.1) applies, where now ψ_1 and ψ_2 represent the total wave functions. When H_1 is neglected, ψ_1 has the form

$$\psi_1 = \phi_1(\mathbf{r}_1)\phi_2(\mathbf{r}_2)\cdots\phi_n(\mathbf{r}_n)\cdots\phi_N(\mathbf{r}_N) \tag{4.4}$$

ϕ_n is the ground state of the nth center and $\mathbf{r}_n$ is the position vector of the trapped electron there. N-centers are considered.‡ The excited state has the form

$$\psi_2 = \phi_1(\mathbf{r}_1)\phi_2(\mathbf{r}_2)\cdots\phi_n'(\mathbf{r}_n)\cdots\phi_N(\mathbf{r}_N) \tag{4.5}$$

where ϕ' corresponds to an excited state of an imperfection.

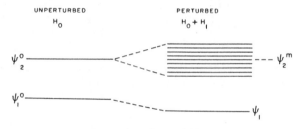

FIG. 4.1. Effects of H_1.

H_1 has only a small effect on the nondegenerate ground state. Let the new ground state energy be ϵ_1'. It changes the wave function and eigenvalue only slightly (it simply lowers or raises the energy of the level). Since ψ_2 is degenerate, H_1 may have a profound effect on it. H_1 effects the proper combination of excited wave functions differently so that the changes in energy will not all be equal. It may produce N nondegenerate

* This effect is not the primary one for our present problem. It is considered because of the insight it gives. The result will be used later.

† To use (4.1), we must be able to neglect the phase of the absorbed light of different centers; this is achieved by requiring that the region be small compared to the wavelength. Evidence exists that the centers can be 10 or 20 Å apart. Further, they are distributed at random; hence, this requirement can be satisfied in practice.

‡ The use of a better wave function than Eq. (4.4), such as a Slater determinant, will not change the nature of the effect described here.

levels. Let these eigenfunctions and associated eigenvalues be denoted by $\psi_2{}^m$ and $\epsilon_2{}^m$. In view of the large number of excited states, we assume that the $\epsilon_2{}^m$'s form a discrete dense set (see Fig. 4.1). From the theory of spectroscopic stability (Van Vleck, p. 137)

$$N|\langle\phi_m'|\mathbf{r}_m|\phi_m\rangle|^2 = \sum_m|\langle\psi_2{}^m|\mathbf{R}|\psi_1\rangle|^2, \tag{4.6}$$

where $\mathbf{R}$ is the vector sum of the $\mathbf{r}$'s, since the expression on the right refers to the whole system of N-centers.* For the limitation on this relation, the reader is referred to the derivation of the theorem given by Van Vleck.

Our interest is in transitions between the ground levels and those levels in the excited state where $(1/h)(\epsilon_2{}^m - \epsilon_1')$ falls in the frequency interval $\nu_m \pm \frac{1}{2}\Delta\nu$. The probability of such a transition is proportional to

$$\sum_{\nu_m - \frac{1}{2}\Delta\nu}^{\nu_m + \frac{1}{2}\Delta\nu} |\langle\psi_2{}^m|\mathbf{R}|\psi_2\rangle|^2$$

To relate this sum to the unperturbed matrix, we define $g(\nu)$ as follows

$$g(\nu)|\langle\phi_m'|\mathbf{r}_m|\phi_m\rangle|^2 = \frac{1}{N\Delta\nu} \sum|\langle\psi_2{}^m|\mathbf{R}|\psi_1\rangle|^2 \tag{4.7}$$

dividing by N to refer the matrix elements to a single center, and by $\Delta\nu$ to obtain an expression per unit frequency. g has the properties

$$\int g(\nu)\,d\nu = 1. \tag{4.8}$$

(b) The broadening may arise because the ψ's are products of electronic wave functions ϕ and functions associated with the lattice vibrations $\chi(q)$. As long as the lattice normal modes, q, are not influenced by changes in the electronic states, the χ's do not contribute to the broadening of the level and

$$h\nu = \epsilon_2 - \epsilon_1. \tag{4.9}$$

In Eq. (4.9), the ϵ's are the electronic eigenvalues. If, however, the q's are affected by the transitions, phonons may be absorbed or emitted during a photon absorption and (4.9) does not hold.† One may, in this case, also

---

* A more careful formulation of the problem starting with Heitler's Eq. (17.3) shows that $\mathbf{R}$ is not a simple vector sum but has a phase factor which arises from the phase of the light; see Markham (S), p. 970.

† The reader may be concerned with the meaning of ϵ for a state composed of an electronic and a vibrational part. This is a rather involved problem, which is treated in some detail in Section 30.

define a $g(\nu)$ (see Section 31) with the properties stated in Eqs. (4.7) and (4.8).

Thus, one may replace $|\langle\psi_2|\mathbf{r}|\psi_1\rangle|^2$ of Eq. (4.1) by $g(\nu)|\langle\phi'|\mathbf{r}|\phi\rangle|^2$. The experimental g obtained from absorption might be a result of the combination of items (a) and (b), especially in crystals which have very high densities of coloration. The broadening associated with the optical absorption of the F-center is, however, primarily of type (b).

Now, we combine the information in items (1), (2), and (3) following Eq. (4.2) with Eqs. (4.1) and (4.3) to obtain a relation between α and N_0, the density of centers. First consider a very thin slab having unit area and thickness Δx. Let I be the intensity falling on it. If the energy I falls on the first face per unit time, then $(I - S)$ is emitted from the second per unit time, where $S = \alpha I \Delta x$.

Hence, the change in intensity is $\Delta I = -\alpha I \Delta x$, or

$$-\frac{1}{I}\frac{\Delta I}{\Delta x} = \alpha(\nu) = \pi\frac{e^2}{mc}afg(\nu)N_0, \qquad (4.10)$$

where (4.1) has been used with the corrections for the three effects. By integrating α over ν, we may eliminate g and relate the area under the curve to the product of the unknowns a and f. Alternatively, one may guess a from a theory of Lorentz and assume that the product $\alpha_m H$ is proportional to the area under α, with a proportionality factor a_s introduced previously in Section 3. This leaves only one unknown, f. Traditionally, one uses the second alternative, which actually increases the number of assumptions, but does not affect the number of unknowns, since the product, af, is replaced by f. These assumptions are important only if one attempts to obtain f from the ϕ's or if one uses f in emission problems since here one must use the actual value of the oscillator strength.

To evaluate a, we recall that $I(\nu)$ is proportional to E^2 calculated at the center. This field differs from the vacuum E and two corrections must be made; one is the change in the velocity of light in the medium and the other arises because there is an inhomogeneity in the solid.

The Poynting vector of an electromagnetic wave gives the intensity

$$I = \frac{c}{4\pi}|\mathbf{E}\times\mathbf{H}| = \frac{cn}{4\pi}E^2 \qquad (4.11)$$

where n is the index of refraction, and c is the velocity of light.*

---

* For a plane electromagnetic wave in a medium with a dielectric constant κ and a magnetic permeability equal to unity, the ratio of $\mathbf{H}$, the magnetic vector, to $\mathbf{E}$, the electric vector, is $\sqrt{\kappa} = n$.

In (4.11), $\mathbf{E}$ is the electric field in the medium. Hence, for equal intensities, E^2 in a medium is $1/n$ times that of a vacuum. No allowance is made for local distortion about the F-center. A simple assumption made by Lorentz is that the local inhomogeneities give the following relation between $\mathbf{E}_L$ (local field), $\mathbf{E}$, and $\mathbf{P}$ (the polarization vector):

$$\mathbf{E}_L = \mathbf{E} + \frac{4\pi}{3}\mathbf{P} = \tfrac{1}{3}(2+n^2)\mathbf{E} \tag{4.12}$$

(see Born and Huang, p. 100 ff).

Combining (4.11) and (4.12) results in

$$a = \frac{1}{9n}(2+n^2)^2. \tag{4.13}$$

To evaluate Smakula's constant, one must assume a frequency dependence of g. Traditionally, one assumes that g is Lorentzian, so that a_s is given in Table 3.5. Theoretically, the arguments in atomic spectra (see Heitler) for selecting a Lorentzian curve may not apply to a trapped electron in an ionic crystal. Arguments exist for assuming a Gaussian shape, but they did not appear until the 1950's. Dexter (1956S; see also Dexter, 1958S) has suggested that such a shape should be used in Smakula's formula.* Experimentally, the absorption band associated with the F-center is only approximately Gaussian (Section 3). We shall use the Lorentzian shape for historic reasons since it gives the traditional form, Smakula's equation. Using (4.10), (4.12), and a_s from Table 3.5, we obtain

$$N_0 = \frac{9}{2}\frac{n}{(2+n^2)^2}\frac{mc}{e^2}\frac{1}{f}\alpha_m \Delta\nu.\dagger \tag{4.14}$$

In view of the many assumptions this f can hardly be regarded as the true oscillator strength. In the above form, $\Delta\nu$ is in frequency, not electron volts. Another form of this equation is

$$\alpha_m = \frac{2}{9}\frac{e^2}{mc}\frac{1}{\Delta\nu}\frac{(2+n^2)^2}{n}fN_0 \tag{4.14a}$$

$$= 7.75\frac{1}{H}\frac{(2+n^2)^2}{n} \times 10^{-18}fN_0. \tag{4.14b}$$

---

* This introduces a modification in the value of the oscillator strength. Since this correction involves the local field parameter a, which we know very little about, the modification of a_s does not really resolve any problem.

† In (4.14) $\Delta\nu$ corresponds to H (in frequency) and is not related to $\Delta\nu$ of (4.7).

Substituting the appropriate values for KCl results in

$$\alpha_m = \frac{9.26}{H} \times 10^{-17} f N_0 \qquad \text{for KCl} \qquad\qquad (4.14c)$$

$$= 2.65 \times 10^{-16} f N_0 \qquad \text{for KCl at } 300° \text{ K} \quad (H = 0.35 \text{ ev}) \quad (4.14d)$$

$$= 5.61 \times 10^{-16} f N_0 \qquad \text{for KCl at } 5° \text{ K} \qquad (H = 0.165 \text{ ev}) \quad (4.14e)$$

Similarly, for NaCl,

$$\alpha_m = \frac{9.64}{H} \times 10^{-17} f N_0 \qquad \text{for NaCl} \qquad\qquad (4.14f)$$

$$= 2.06 \times 10^{-16} f N_0 \qquad \text{for NaCl at } 300° \text{ K} \quad (H = 0.469 \text{ ev}) \quad (4.14g)$$

$$= 3.78 \times 10^{-16} f N_0 \qquad \text{for NaCl at } 5° \text{ K} \qquad (H = 0.255 \text{ ev}) \quad (4.14h)$$

Two means for testing (4.14) suggest themselves. First, we may keep N_0 constant and vary α_m and H by changing the temperature. Konitzer has carried through such tests. The product $\alpha_m H$ is essentially temperature independent (see Table 3.6). Further, using the area in place of $\alpha_m H$ does not lead to any improvement. This does not mean that (4.14) is correct but that $\alpha_m H$ is proportional to the "area"—that is, $\int \alpha(\nu) d\nu$— the proportionality factor being independent of the temperature. Actually, Table 3.6 indicates that the factor approaches the one given by the Gaussian curve. This indicates that Dexter's suggestion for the proportionality factor is superior to the one usually employed.

One may evaluate f empirically by using (4.14) where α_m and N_0 are measured. There are many ways to measure N_0 (some of which we shall discuss later). Some values are summarized in Table 4.1.

TABLE 4.1. f FOR KCl AT RT

Method	Value of f	Experimentalists
Electrical conductivity	0.9	Stasiw[a]
Chemical	0.81	Kleinschrod[b]
Chemical	0.91	Doyle[b]
Chemical	1.17	Scott and Hill[b]
$F \to F'$ conversion	0.81	Pick[b]
Paramagnetic resonance	0.85	Silsbee[b]
Magnetic properties	0.66	Rauch and Heer[b]

[a] This value was calculated by the author from data of Stasiw (S).
[b] See references under these names at the end of the section.

The table is remarkable in that it gives a fair consistency in the values of f; the variations, however, are larger than one would hope for. We shall associate special reliability to the values of Pick, although they involve a complex theoretical interpretation. His experiments require a "pure" F-band, while some of the other values may have been obtained on the B-structure. Ultimately, one would hope for a better agreement.

Heer and co-workers have used their magnetic technique to measure the F-center oscillator strength in various salts (Section 23). The H value reported by these workers indicates that the measurements may have included some B-centers. As we shall indicate, these centers have different magnetic properties (Section 24.4). Nevertheless, the data are of great value and are presented in Table 4.2.

TABLE 4.2. f FROM MAGNETIC PROPERTIES

Crystal	f
KCl	0.66[a]
KBr	0.71[a]; (0.85)[e]
KI	0.46[a]
NaCl	0.7[a]; (0.87)[c]
	(0.72)[d]; (0.86)[e]
LiF	0.82[b]
CsBr	0.38[a]

[a] Rauch and Heer (S).   [c] Silsbee (S).
[b] Bates and Heer (S).   [d] Pick (S).
         [e] Doyle (S).

We may conclude by stressing the fact that Smakula's formula has profound experimental importance since it gives us a means to determine the concentration of imperfections; f in (4.14) most probably is not simply related to the usual definition of oscillator strength but depends on a, a_s, and g. Further theoretical work is required to evaluate these quantities. This change will not modify (4.14) but only changes the relation between the experimental f values and the matrix component of (4.3).

To get an order of magnitude for the relation between α_m and N_0 we may substitute the constants into Eq. (4.14). [See Eqs. (4.14b) to (4.14h).] We shall assume that the crystal is colored uniformly and that its thickness is 1 mm, and the desired value of A_m is unity. Lower values make the measurements difficult because of the scattering from the surfaces.

Higher values create optical difficulties, since stray light enters the instrument. Generally, good measurements should be limited to the range between 0.8 and 1.4; this depends on the instrument. Some modern instruments may give reliable readings for considerably higher values. Then, N_0 is several times 10^{16} centers/cc, depending on the salt and the temperature of the measurement—that is, values of H and f.

APPENDIX

The Sum Rule and the Conservation of the Area

In atomic spectra it is known that f_{ij}, the oscillator strength which connects the levels i and j, obeys a simple rule, namely, $\sum_j f_{ij} = 1$ (see Slater, p. 503). An alternate rule is obtained when optical transitions between allowed energy bands in perfect solids are considered. In this case, the electrons are described by Bloch functions. For details see Seitz (1940, p. 650). One may not carry over these concepts to spectra associated with imperfection because of the various modifications we have introduced in arriving at Eq. (4.14). We would like to obtain two relations between the oscillator sum rule and the integrated "area" under an absorption curve, namely $\int \alpha(\nu)\,d\nu$ or $\int \alpha(\epsilon)\,d\epsilon$.

a. The Sum Rule for a Single Imperfection

We assume a series of excited states—1, 2, 3, etc., with excited eigenfunctions ϕ_1, ϕ_2, ϕ_3, etc. Associated with the transition from the ground state to these states are the shape factors, $g_1(\nu)$, $g_2(\nu)$, etc., all having the property (4.8). The net integrated absorption is

$$
\int \alpha(\nu)\,d\nu = \pi \frac{e^2}{mc} N_0 a \sum_{i>1} f_i \int g_i(\nu)\,d\nu
$$
$$
= \pi \frac{e^2}{mc} N_0 a \sum_{i>1} f_i, \tag{4.15}
$$

where the sum extends over all the excited states. To obtain $\int \alpha(\nu)\,d\nu$ we do not have to resolve the absorption into separate bands but we must be sure that $\alpha(\nu)$ does not involve two or more types of imperfections. f_i is simply the atomic oscillator strength whose sum equals unity. The net absorption is

$$
\int \alpha(\nu)\,d\nu = \pi \frac{e^2}{mc} a N_0. \tag{4.16}
$$

The author does not believe that (4.16) is obvious. A detailed proof would require the establishment of (4.8) for transitions to every excited level. This will be discussed briefly in Sections 30 and 31 when the adiabatic and the Condon approximations will be introduced. Equation (4.8) can indeed be established rigorously for the F-band. The reader will note that an unknown, namely, a, remains in (4.16) and the area does not equal $N_0 \pi e^2/mc$.

b. Conservation of Area during the Transformation of the Imperfections

During the exposure of an F-center to light (bleaching), some of the centers are transformed from one type to another. Equation (4.16) applies in the unbleached state, whereas in the bleached state

$$\int \alpha(\nu)\, d\nu = \frac{\pi e^2}{mc} \sum_{\beta} a_\beta N_\beta \sum_i f_{\beta i} \int g_{\beta i}(\nu)\, d\nu. \qquad (4.17)$$

Here β refers to the type of center the electron is attached to, while i refers to the excited states of these centers. N_β refers to the number of electrons; hence, $N_0 = \sum_\beta N_\beta$, where N_0 is the number of electrons before bleaching. Using the properties of the g's and the f's, the following result is obtained

$$\int \alpha(\nu)\, d\nu = \frac{\pi e^2}{mc} \sum_{\beta} a_\beta N_\beta. \qquad (4.18)$$

The area under the absorption curve is conserved *only if* a_β is really independent of the imperfection. [a_β is a of Eq. (4.13), not Smakula's constant.]

REFERENCES

R. T. Bates and C. V. Heer, *Phys. Chem. Solids* **7**, 14 (1958).
D. L. Dexter, *Phys. Rev.* **101**, 48 (1956).
D. L. Dexter, *Solid State Physics* **6**, 353 (1958).
W. T. Doyle, *Phys. Rev.* **111**, 1072 (1958).
F. G. Kleinschrod, *Ann. Physik* **27**, 97 (1936).
J. J. Markham, *Rev. Mod. Phys.* **31**, 956 (1959).
E. Mollwo and W. Roos, *Gött. Nachr.* p. 107 (1934).
H. Pick, *Ann. Physik* **31**, 365 (1938).
C. J. Rauch and C. V. Heer, *Phys. Rev.* **105**, 914 (1957).
A. B. Scott and M. E. Hill, *J. Chem. Phys.* **28**, 24 (1958).
R. H. Silsbee, *Phys. Rev.* **103**, 1675 (1956).
A. Smakula, *Z. Physik* **59**, 603 (1930).
O. Stasiw, *Gött. Nachr.* p. 261 (1932).

II. The Production of F-Centers

Quite a few methods exist for the production of F-centers. Our present knowledge of the experimental details is extremely incomplete in many cases; moreover the theory remains to be developed in most situations. The part of this field associated with the use of radiation provides a very interesting phase of the general field of radiation damage. In this chapter, the present state of our knowledge will be described in a general way. We shall not describe all the details of the theory of radiation damage since they lie outside our scope and are in a state of flux.

5. PRODUCTION OF F-CENTERS BY IRRADIATION

Coloration is produced when an alkali halide is exposed to light in the exciton region.* This also occurs when the radiation is harder—shorter wavelengths. Generally, the color arises from an F-band, although there are usually some small subsidiary bands lying to the violet and to the red. We shall ignore these additional complications in this section.

It is useful to distinguish between three types of radiation:

Exciton radiation: If the energy of a bombarding particle (photon or electron) is sufficient to create an electron–hole pair, but is not sufficient to completely dissociate the pair, the hole and electron are bound by their coulomb attraction and they wander together through the lattice. We may visualize such an exciton as a metal atom coupled to a halide atom. This structure is not stationary, for the extra electron on the metal ion can jump from ion to ion and is followed by the hole. This pair can react with

* An exciton is an imperfection where an electron in the conduction band is coupled to a hole (missing electron in the conduction band). The simplest coupling is a coulombic attraction between the two. Excitons are usually formed by irradiating the crystal in the edge of the fundamental band, that is, the region to the ultraviolet where the strong absorption starts (as one proceeds towards the shorter wavelengths) due to the excitation of electrons from the valence band to the conduction band. This will be referred to as the "exciton region of the spectra." These imperfections are quite complex and have been fully described by Knox (S).

37

other imperfections of the lattice, and the electron (or hole) may be captured and release the hole (or electron). Many alternate descriptions of the exciton exist, but these variations need not concern us here.

Conceptually, the stimulation of exciton radiation is extremely simple. The ultraviolet edge absorption is believed to be due to the generation of excitons. Martienssen (1959S) and co-workers have made several detailed studies of this absorption region. At high temperatures, the edge may be described simply in terms of a relation due to Urbach:

$$\text{absorption} = K_0 \exp\left\{-(\sigma/k\theta)(\epsilon_0 - \epsilon)\right\},$$

where k_0 and ϵ_0 are constants of the material. Studies at lower temperatures, for example, Etzel and Patterson (S), indicate that deviation from this rule occurs, and irregularities or bands in the absorption plots have been reported. These bands are due to small amounts of impurities. For example, in KBr, the absorption edge starts at about 6.2 ev at room temperature (6.6 ev at $20°$ K). The presence of the OH$^-$ ion causes an absorption which peaks at 5.75 ev (at $78°$ K). No simple way exists to separate completely the creation of excitons from the excitation of impurity ions imbedded in the host crystal. Some absorption, believed to be due to excitons, may actually be caused by excitation of impurity ions.

Soft and hard radiation: If one regards the crystal as a collection of isolated ions, the conservation of energy and momentum is required in the interaction between an ion and a fast particle. The masses of x-rays or electrons are so small that they can only transfer a small fraction of their energies to the heavy ions. Table 5.1 shows the energy a photon or electron must have to impart 25 ev to an ion in a head-on collision. This is approximately* the energy required to produce a direct ionic displacement.† We define *soft* radiation as that which imparts less than 25 ev to the ions, while *hard* radiation is that which may cause direct ionic displacements out of the lattice. Actually, the distinction between soft and hard radiation has not yet been observed experimentally, possibly because a detailed experimental study is not available. It is made here since it could be of profound theoretical importance. As we shall see in Section

---

* This figure is used in the literature; it is not known exactly for an alkali halide. It is of the order of electron volts, however.

† No such limitation exists in the production of free electrons, since this is a three-body problem, so that a photon can impart all its energy to a bound electron. The limitation of Table 5.1 would be removed if the crystal were not considered only as a collection of ions. Under these conditions, the knock-out process may be considered as a three-body collision problem. At present, however, there is no reason for making the assumption of a three-body process.

25, it is believed that the F-center is an electron trapped at a negative-ion vacancy. Hard radiation can produce these vacancies by a direct collision. Soft radiation usually has much more energy than a photon in the exciton range.

TABLE 5.1. ENERGY TO IMPART 25 ev TO A
Cl⁻ Ion[a]

| From a photon | 645 kev |
| From an electron | 400 kev |

[a] Head-on collision.

Coloration by irradiation tends to produce a nonuniform distribution of centers. For example, it has been estimated that unfiltered 50-kv x-rays color only a layer 0.07 mm thick in NaCl; filtered and harder x-rays color the crystal in a much more uniform manner. For cases like this, one must use A, defined in Section 3.

a. Coloration by Excitons

Figure 5.1 presents the data of Smakula (S) in KBr irradiated with light which produces excitons at RT and 90° K. The light source was an arc from which he could select discrete frequencies. The number of centers per unit area was calculated by Eq. (4.14) with $f=1$ and was plotted against the number of photons absorbed. The initial rapid coloration stage is followed by a stage which indicates some saturation (especially at 90° K). The density of centers is very small: 10^{15} cm⁻³. (We assume that the thickness of the colored region is of the order of 1 mm.)

Smakula reported the absorption coefficient of his crystal at 6.1, at 6.2, and at 6.4 ev to be 0.36, 4.1, and 10 mm⁻¹, respectively. If we assume that every photon absorbed generates one exciton, the number produced in the distance Δx from the exposed surface is proportional to $I_0(1 - e^{-\alpha\Delta x})$. Hence, the number generated in the first 0.1 mm at the three wavelengths is $(0.035)I_0$, $(0.336)I_0$, and $(0.632)I_0$, respectively. Thus, the 6.1-ev light produces excitons throughout the crystal, while the 6.4-ev light produces excitons only near the surface. If the production of coloration were a local effect—that is, the exciton travels only a few lattice distances—the saturation plateau would depend strongly on the wavelength of the excited light, since shorter wavelength light is absorbed very near the surface. This follows, because 6.1-ev light colors the crystal fairly uniformly, while the

6.4-ev light will only color the very surface. The "saturation" value is not as strongly wavelength dependent as the absorption coefficients, and one may conclude that the exciton travels, or that it may transmit its energy a large distance compared to the distance between ions.

Smakula's data show that initially every photon absorbed produces one F-center (actually, the f of the crystals used was unknown when these data were taken), and fewer centers are produced at 90° K. It has been assumed

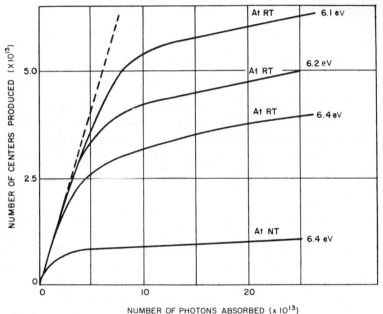

FIG. 5.1. Coloration of KBr by excitons. Energy of excitation indicated on curve. (after Smakula, S).

at various times that impurities affect the "growth rate curve," that is, curves of the type shown in Fig. 5.1. For this reason Smakula added Pb (0.003 per cent), but this had very little effect on the coloration.

Schröder (S) and Etzel (1955S) have also studied the production of F-centers by excitons. Their work suggests that the past history of the sample influences the uv colorability. One sample of NaCl could not be colored at room temperature; Schröder believes this crystal was exceptionally pure. Etzel studied the effect of pretreating the crystal with x-rays. The NaCl he used could be bleached by an exposure to light at RT after an irradiation with 40-kv x-rays at RT. The author's experience reveals this is not true for most samples of NaCl. Etzel found that this treatment greatly enhanced the effect of uv radiation; indeed, 20 times more *F*-centers could be formed. The "memory" of the crystal, that is, the effects of pretreatment, remained for a long time (at least 18 hr).

One is inclined to visualize the coloration by uv as a double process: (1) the formation of the exciton, and (2) its trapping at an imperfection to form the *F*-center. There must be some kind of a dissociation of the exciton, since the hole is not part of the center. The high initial quantum yield suggests that the imperfections are extremely efficient exciton traps. The actual process which occurs will of course not be known until we have a complete understanding of the process of coloration by ionizing radiation. Further, the work of Schröder and Etzel indicates that the number of traps present is influenced by impurities and x-radiation. (See Table 5.6, Section 5*a*.)

b. General Features of Coloration by X-Rays and γ-Rays

We now turn to the effects of the harder radiation. It is extremely difficult to compare results from different laboratories since the techniques vary even when the same maximum voltages are employed on the x-ray tube. To understand this problem we must consider certain experimental details. The x-ray output of a tube consists of two parts: (1) the characteristic radiation which results from the de-excitation of electrons in bound states (these electrons were originally excited by the electrons which bombard the anode), and (2) the continuous radiation which arises from the slowing down of the bombarding electrons by the nuclei in the anode (that is, the bremsstrahlung). The present experimental techniques use mainly the second type. One would like to describe the radiation output of a tube in terms of an effective wavelength so as to distinguish between hard and soft radiation and effective number of photons emitted. A statement as to the voltage and current is not sufficient. The voltage describes the maximum energy of the photon, but the crystal is affected mainly by the softer radiation which depends on the filtration between the anode and the crystal. Some x-ray tubes have beryllium windows and, if one uses cells with beryllium windows, the crystal is exposed to most of the soft x-rays produced. This technique has been used in the United States. In Germany, the beryllium windows are usually replaced by thin glass, and the crystals are not exposed to the softest rays. Tubes producing harder x-rays are usually better shielded so that the softest components, which can be the major output of the tube, are eliminated. In comparing results from different laboratories, this point must be kept in mind. Are the results different because of the use of purer samples, because harder rays are used, or because softer rays are employed?

Mador and co-workers (S) studied this effect by x-raying the crystal in one direction and measuring the optical absorption by passing the light beam at right angles to the direction of irradiation. Soft x-rays (30–50 kv)

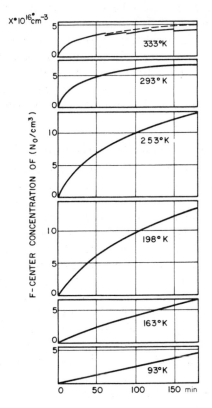

FIG. 5.2. Coloration of KCl by shielded x-rays at various temperatures. Output 10^{15} ev/cm² sec (after Harten, S).

from a Machlett tube were employed. Their spectrometer beam width was 0.04 cm, so that effects at the very surface could not be studied. Two results are of interest: (1) the initial coloration is proportional to the energy absorbed (within one's ability to estimate this quantity), while longer exposure shows saturation effects. For example, the coloration at a depth of about 0.05 cm (center of beam) remained practically unchanged after the first 16 min. The band formed at 0.09 cm had a much larger H

(0.61 ev at RT) than that formed at 0.5 cm (0.49 ev). This is a clear indication that additional bands were formed near the surface—perhaps it was exposed to light. (The effect of an exposure to light at RT is discussed in Section 14.2; see Table 3.4.)

Figure 5.2 gives the result of Harten (S), who used filtered 60-kv x-rays. X-raying at high temperature shows a definite saturation, while at low temperatures, the growth curve is a straight line. Figure 5.3 gives the energy it takes to create the initial *F*-center. It is many times the energy an exciton requires to produce an *F*-center. The initial increment of

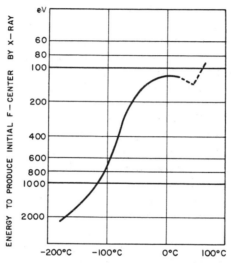

FIG. 5.3. Energy required to produce the initial *F*-center in KCl by x-rays at various temperatures by 60 kev shielded—10^{15} ev cm^{-2} sec^{-1}. It takes about 6.5 ev to produce the initial *F*-center by excitons in KBr at 90° K and RT (after Harten, S).

coloration on Harten's curves corresponds to a much greater color center density (about 10^{16} cm^{-3}) than Smakula's saturation value (about 5×10^{14} cm^{-3}); hence, the results should not be compared. The plateau at RT is influenced by the intensity of the irradiation. Growth rate curves have been obtained on KBr at 20° K using a glass filter (Martienssen, 1952S) and on NaCl at 5° K using a Machlett tube and a Be window (Duerig and Markham, 1952S). Both studies agree with Harten's low temperature curves—that is, the coloration seems to be a linear function of the time of exposure; thus, at low temperature, the energy required to produce a center is independent of the irradiation time. This quantity increases greatly with time at higher temperatures, however.

The ability of x-irradiation to form F-centers at extremely low temperatures came as a surprise to workers in the field, since we believed that ionic diffusion was required to form the F-centers. It has been established that an F-center is an electron trapped at a negative-ion vacancy (see Section 25) and one believes that these negative-ion vacancies must be produced at low temperature. These processes should be small at 78° K and should stop at 4° K. Dutton *et al.* (S) were the first to show that F-centers could be produced by irradiation at about 10° K. Subsequently, studies have shown that one may produce F-centers readily even at 2° K. If diffusion takes place, it must be activated in some manner by the irradiation.

The data from Göttingen (Harten, S; Martienssen, 1952S) indicate that it is harder to color crystals at low temperatures. On the other hand, work in this country indicates that it is just as easy (for NaCl, KCl, and KBr); this difference is either due to the purity of the crystal or the experimental technique.

In addition to NaCl, KCl, and KBr, one may readily form F-centers in LiF (at NT), NaF (at HT), and KF (at HT) at low temperatures. The induced F coloration at low temperatures is very small in KI (grown in Germany and in the USA), NaBr, and RbBr. At present, there is no explanation for these differences.

The growth rate curve seems to be a result of an extremely complex process. Harten found that the saturation value depends on the temperature of the crystal. If the number of F-centers was above the saturation value (this could be obtained by warming the crystal from $-20°$ C to $15°$ C), further irradiation *decreased* the concentration. Likewise, if the concentration were too low (this was obtained by allowing the crystal to bleach in the dark for 24 hr), the x-rays restored the original saturation value. Duerig (1954S) found a similar effect in KCl and KBr at NT.

Figure 5.4 shows Hummel's (S) data on the γ-irradiation (hard radiation) of KCl doped with Ca. The addition of Ca^{2+} increases the colorability of the crystal and changes the shape of the growth curve. The plateau disappears for higher concentrations. One is forced to assume that the influence of Ca^{2+} on the trapping of electrons by $\boxminus$ is indirect, since this ion creates *positive*, not negative-ion vacancies. Positive vacancies might trap holes, thus releasing more electrons to form F-centers. A substitution of Cd^{2+} for Ca^{2+} might produce similar effects, since the ions resemble each other. Etzel (1952S) has made a study of this and finds marked effects only with Ca^{2+}. A tentative explanation might be that the positive-ion vacancy is more closely associated to Cd^{2+} than to

Ca²⁺; thus, the vacancies in Ca²⁺ do not trap holes. The work of Rabin to be discussed in Section 5a, shows that the addition of Ca²⁺ creates a large number of *negative-ion* vacancies. This is undoubtedly the explanation for the increase in the growth rate. It is not at all clear at present why these ions produce negative vacancies or increase the *F*-center production.

The effect of impurities on the growth rate is not understood, and each additional one has to be considered separately.

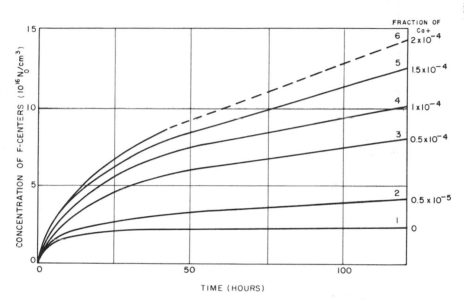

FIG. 5.4. γ-irradiation of KCl doped with Ca²⁺ (the x-rays range from 40 kev to 6,000 kev) (after Hummel, S).

The bleaching of a crystal without heating may or may not remove the *F*-band, depending on the crystal and source. It will not, however, remove all the effects of irradiation, as is shown by the exciton study of Etzel. For this, heat treatment at several hundred degrees above the radiation temperature is required. For example, if one irradiates at NT, one may remove the memory by warming at RT, while an irradiation at RT requires heat treatments at 350° or 400° C.

We may roughly describe the curves shown in Figs. 5.1, 5.2, and 5.4 by the differential equation,

$$dN_0/dt = A - kN_0,$$

(5.1)

where A is assumed to be proportional to the intensity of the irradiating source. The second term suggests that the irradiation destroys F-centers. One may integrate Eq. (5.1) to obtain

$$N_0(t) = N_\infty(1 - e^{-kt}),$$ (5.2)

where N_∞ is the final F-center concentration; it equals A/k. Equation (5.2) roughly describes the data and can be traced back to the color center school which worked at the University of Vienna under the leadership of Professor K. Przibram.

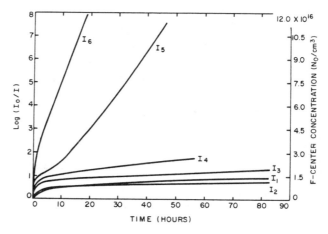

Fig. 5.5. Growth rate curves of F-center in KCl at RT using 140 kvp x-rays (after Mitchell *et al.*, S).

Run:	I_1	I_2	I_3	I_4	I_5	I_6
Intensity (R/hr):	300	1,200	2,700	4,800	14,700	30,000
Thickness (mm):	1.45	1.38	1.05	1.03	0.85	0.75

c. Further Details on Growth Rates by X-Rays

Seitz (1946) was the first to consider the density of the imperfection which traps an electron to form an F-center. Some vacancies are present in any crystal, as can be shown by the use of general thermodynamic arguments. Various estimates made by Seitz indicate that an uncolored crystal does not have a sufficient number of vacancies to produce 10^{17}- or 10^{18}-cm^{-3} F-centers. We shall not present Seitz's arguments but shall rely on the measurements of Rabin (see Section 5e), which give this number directly. Therefore, additional vacancies must be produced by the irradiating source. The coefficient A in Eq. (5.1) was assumed to be proportional to the intensity—that is, the number of free electrons produced. Since the irradiation produces both free electrons and vacancies, we should expect deviations from the behavior described by (5.2). Such behavior is not apparent in Figs. 5.2 and 5.4 but has been found in more recent studies. The first serious discussion of this deviation was made by Mador and co-workers (S). These considerations were extended by Gordon and Nowick (S). We shall, however, present the more recent and detailed study of the group working with Smoluchowski (see Mitchell *et al.*, S).

Two typical sets of growth rate curves are shown in Figs. 5.5 and 5.6. Figure 5.5 indicates that for more intense radiation, coloration occurs in

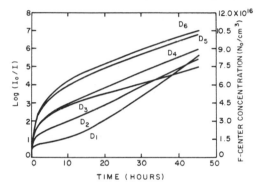

FIG. 5.6. Effect of plastic deformation on the growth rate of the *F*-center in KCl using 140-kvp x-rays (after Mitchell *et al.*, S). An x-ray intensity of 13,900 R/hr was used.

Sample	Deformation (%)	Sample	Deformation (%)
D_1	As cleaved	D_4	1.56
D_2	0.6	D_5	2.02
D_3	1.32	D_6	3.04

two stages. Filtered 140-kvp x-rays were used in these experiments. At low intensity, one obtains a saturation curve—that is, Eq. (5.2)—while, for higher intensity, one has a linear curve (approximately) imposed upon this saturation curve. The question which has never been resolved in a completely satisfactory manner is whether there is a true saturation. A comparison of the data presented in Figs. 5.1–5.5 indicate that there is true saturation for low intensity radiation. The author believes this is the case, although some experimental questions remain. The linear curve resembles Harten's low temperature data, Fig. 5.2. The data in Fig. 5.5 extend to measurements of $\log_{10}(I_0/I)$ as high as 8. Data for such large absorptions are extremely difficult to obtain and may be unreliable.

In Fig. 5.6, data on the effect of plastic deformation are shown; here the ionizing radiation is held constant. The linear part of the growth rate curve seems to be greatly affected. This is also true for various heat treatments that one can give the crystal.

The explanation of these data is far from understood at present. Two types of F-centers have been suggested; those that are formed

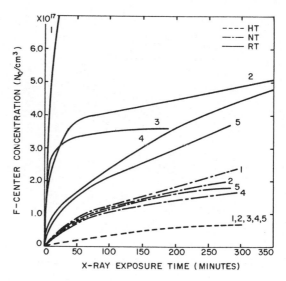

FIG. 5.7. Growth of the F-band in various NaCl crystals exposed to x-ray radiation (43 kvp) at room, liquid nitrogen, and liquid helium temperatures. The number represents various samples (after Rabin and Klick, S).

initially from vacancies which are present at RT and those formed from vacancies created by the irradiation. There is little doubt that negative-ion vacancies are generated by the irradiation during the straight line portion of the curve. One might hope to detect two types of F-centers. Since H is one of the most sensitive parameters associated with the F-center, searches for the variation in its value have been made; however, generally none have been detected. An exception occurs in the paper of Mador and co-workers, as mentioned before. Even heavily deformed crystals seem to produce the same type of F-centers, judging from the values of H and ϵ_m. Impurities can have many effects on the colorability of a crystal, yet the same type of *F*-center seems to be produced, judging from the measurement of these parameters. Measurements of Rabin and Klick (S) indicate that the past history of a sample influences the growth rate curve at high temperatures but not at low temperatures. This is a very striking effect shown in Fig. 5.7. In Table 5.2 we give the average

TABLE 5.2. AVERAGE ENERGY TO PRODUCE
AN *F*-CENTER AT HT[a]

Crystal	Energy (ev)
LiF	6.2×10^2
NaF	1.3×10^3
NaCl	1.4×10^4
NaBr	8.3×10^5
KCl	1.3×10^3
KBr:KH	1.4×10^3
KI	5.2×10^4

[a] After Rabin and Klick (S).

energy required to form an *F*-center; this should be compared to Fig. 5.3.

The problem of explaining the data of Smoluchowski and co-workers will not be dealt with here. It involves the problem of generating negative-ion vacancies by soft radiation. Two suggestions have been made so far by Seitz (S) and by Varley (S). Attempts have been made to combine both of these ideas.

d. Coloration by Electron Bombardment

One would assume that electron bombardment would produce coloration as do excitons, x-rays, and γ-rays, since free electrons (in conduction bands) are generated. A detailed study of the effect of electrons (5 kv) has been made by Fischer (S) and we shall base our discussion on his paper. It is confined to LiF, NaF, and NaCl, and all the optical measurements were made at $90° K$. Fischer (S) used single crystals, as well as a thin layer of alkali halides deposited on quartz at various temperatures (90–500° K). The amount of energy transferred to a fluoride or a chloride ion by a head-on collision with a 5-kv electron is extremely small. The values calculated from elementary mechanics, using the laws of the conservation of energy and momentum, are shown in Table 5.3. The coloration is confined to a very thin layer of the crystal, or the film. It is estimated that the layer is only 500 mμ for LiF; 450 mμ for NaF; and 580 mμ for NaCl. The F-center formed by the electron is not identical to the center formed by x-rays or by additive coloration (Section 6) or by the U-center

TABLE 5.3. MAXIMUM ENERGY
TRANSFERRED TO AN ION BY
A 5–kv ELECTRON

Ion	Energy (ev)
F	0.58
Cl	0.31

(Section 7d). The differences are given in Table 5.4. The conclusion one arrives at from these data is that electrons produce a slightly different F-center than do x-rays. Since a 50-kv x-ray may produce several 5-kv electrons, one would not expect a different type of imperfection. We place

TABLE 5.4. PARAMETERS OF THE F-CENTER IN NaCl

	ϵ_v (ev)	ϵ_m (ev)	ϵ_r (ev)	H (ev)
Produced by x-rays; Fischer; measured at 90° K[a]	2.90	2.76	2.62	0.28
Produced by x-rays; Markham and Konitzer; measured at 78° K[b]	2.907	2.758	2.632	0.275
Produced by electrons; measured at 90° K				
Film	2.94	2.82	2.71	0.23
Single crystal	2.95	2.82	2.71	0.24

[a] Fischer (S).
[b] Markham and Konitzer (S).

particular reliance on Fischer's values of H, since he made a detailed comparison of his measurements with data previously reported in the literature. An essential difference may be the density of centers. The electrons are absorbed in such a thin surface layer that the imperfection density is of the order of 5×10^{19} cm^{-3}, which is several orders of magnitude higher than the density usually employed (5×10^{16}–5×10^{17} cm^{-3}).

Fischer used 100-kv x-rays to obtain the first line in Table 5.3, while Markham and Konitzer (S) employed 140-kv x-rays.

Typical growth rate curves are shown in Fig. 5.8. The temperature of the crystal, or the layer, during the irradiation was 90° K. Figure 5.8 should be compared to Harten's curves taken at low temperature and not the data of Smoluchowski taken at RT. The density of centers at saturation has much higher values than those reported in Harten's curve.* The lower points on a single crystal curve in Fig. 5.8 show a rise to a maximum and subsequently a decrease with time.

The same effect occurs for the amorphous layer, although the maximum does not appear in the figure. Fischer points out that the growth curves in

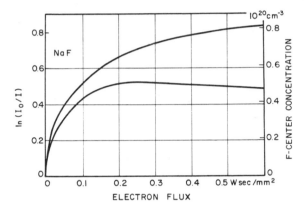

FIG. 5.8. Growth rate curve for electron bombardment of NaF (upper curve: condensed film; lower: single crystal) (after Fischer, S).

amorphous layers are extremely sensitive to the temperature of deposition. Layers deposited at 90° K actually do not color when exposed to electrons at the same temperature. The coloration is a function of the total energy falling on the crystal (see Fig. 5.9). The crystal coloration will therefore give an exact (not linear) measure of the energy which has fallen on it as long as we have not gone beyond the maximum on the coloration curve. The reader should note that a corresponding statement cannot be made for the growth rate curve produced by x-rays (see Fig. 5.5), and the coloration is not in general a measure of the total amount of x-ray energy falling on the face of the crystal.

* Harten used shielded x-rays. Duerig and Markham (S) estimated that unshielded 50-kv x-rays colored a crystal to a depth of 0.07 mm, which implies a penetration depth much larger than the values suggested by Fischer's measurements.

Fischer has found a simple analytic expression for the growth curve. It has the form

$$S = S_0 - \sum_i A_i e^{-\lambda_i W}, \tag{5.3}$$

where i is summed over two or three values, depending on the alkali halide, on the type of thin film (temperature of deposition), or on whether one uses thin films.

There are distinct differences between the coloration by x-ray and by electrons, although the results are similar superficially.

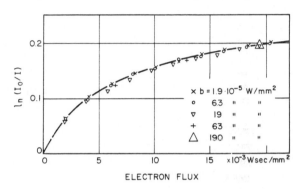

FIG. 5.9. Effect of electron beam intensity on the rates of coloration (after Fischer, S); b is the radiation intensity. Single crystals were used.

e. Expansion of a Crystal during the Irradiation

Seitz (1946) suggested that a crystal will expand on coloration. A series of most important papers has subsequently appeared. Estermann *et al.* (S) made the first successful attempt by measuring the density of a colored and uncolored crystal and checking Seitz's prediction. The centers were produced by soft x-rays (beryllium windows) in KCl at RT. At appropriate temperatures, each crystal could be suspended in a liquid (1,3-dibromopropane). From the temperature dependence of the density of the liquid, one calculates the change induced by the irradiation and the number of negative- and positive-ion vacancies produced. The data in Table 5.5 compare the number of F-centers obtained from Smakula's equation with $f = 0.81$ and the number of total vacancies produced.

Two alternate methods have been used to measure the expansion of a crystal. In the first method, the crystal is coupled mechanically to a condenser which is part of a tuned circuit. An expansion of the crystal causes a change in the capacity of the condenser, which can be measured by the circuit. Since the expansion due to the irradiation is very small, this technique requires very careful temperature control. The technique is due to Sakaguchi and Suita (S); it has been used by Lin (S) and most recently by Rabin (S). On the other hand, one may irradiate only part of a crystal and thus set up strains in the material. This in turn induces photoelastic effects which can be used to evaluate the expansion caused by the irradiation. This method is due to Primak *et al.* (S), and has been used by Wiegand and Smoluchowski (S).

TABLE 5.5. DATA ON THE *F*-CENTER OF KCl[a]

Irr. time (hr)	Number of *F*-centers	Number of vacancy pairs
17	6×10^{17}	12×10^{17}
8.5	6.5×10^{17}	9×10^{17}

[a] From Estermann *et al.* (S).

We shall present data taken from the paper of Rabin and the paper of Wiegand and Smoluchowski. A typical expansion curve is shown in Fig. 5.10 for LiF. The radiation source was 45-kv, 35-ma source. The x-rays had to penetrate a thin aluminium window. Since LiF has a small x-ray absorption coefficient (low density of electrons), the rays are not all absorbed at the surface as they are in material made of heavier ions. The striking feature of these data is that at high temperature, the growth rate shows a saturation very much like Harten's data (Fig. 5.2). This type of growth curve may be governed by the rates of production of negative vacancies and not due to the destruction of *F*-centers by the irradiation— that is, the second term in Eq. (5.1). At low temperatures, one obtains a straight line typical of a low-temperature growth rate curve. If one measures the number of *F*-centers formed in LiF by the same irradiation source, one obtains similar curves; however, these cannot be obtained over the same irradiation times due to the high optical density after a few hours of x-ray exposure. In Fig. 5.10, the curves cross at about 15 hours, while the absorption curves cross at 11 hours.

Figure 5.11 shows the data of Rabin taken at 34° C on NaCl. This temperature was used because of experimental details. The past history and the heat treatment affect the expansion just as they affect the growth rate curves (see Fig. 5.7). Rabin used a 43-kvp, 20-ma source with some shielding. A more meaningful curve is obtained (Fig. 5.12) by plotting the expansion against the F-center concentration. The concentration was obtained from Smakula's equation with $f = 0.7$. The long dashed line

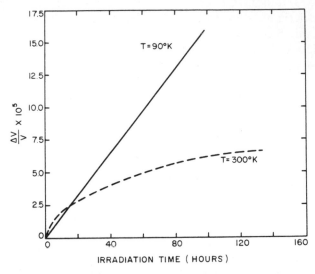

FIG. 5.10. Fractional volume expansion of LiF versus irradiation time. T is the temperature of irradiation (after Wiegand and Smoluchowski, S).

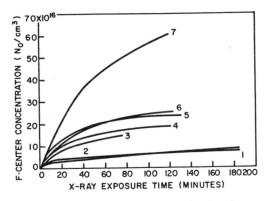

FIG. 5.11. Growth rate of F-band in NaCl crystals of various purities at $34°$C: 3, 0.1 $M\%$ CdCl$_2$; 4, 1.0 $M\%$ KCl; 7, 0.5 $M\%$ CaCl$_2$; other curves, "pure" crystals (after Rabin, S).

assumes that one F-center requires the production of one positive-ion vacancy and one negative-ion vacancy. The volume expansion per F-center is then $2a^3$, while the linear coefficient (the measured quantity) is one-third this number; a is the distance between nearest neighbors. If one actually computes this quantity for NaCl, one obtains the value

$$\frac{\Delta l}{l} = 14.8 \times 10^{-24} N_0, \qquad (5.4a)$$

where N_0 is the number of F-centers/cc. If the volume of the unit cell is replaced by the volume of a negative-ion, (Cl^-) the above expression becomes

$$\frac{\Delta l}{l} = 8.3 \times 10^{-24} N_0, \qquad (5.4b)$$

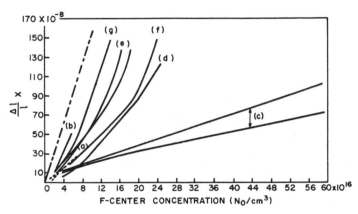

FIG. 5.12. Relative linear expansion as a function of F-center concentration. The long dashed line gives the locus of points for which there is a one-to-one relationship between vacancy pairs and F-centers. This line has slope of $2/3$ a^3, where a is the distance between ions (after Rabin, S). (a) Natural NaCl. (b) Harshaw NaCl. (c) NRL NaCl 0.5 Mole percent $CaCl_2$. (d) NRL NaCl 1.0 Mole percent KCl. (e) NRL NaCl. (f) NRL NaCl 0.1 Mole percent $CdCl_2$.

which would give an appreciably different slope from the line drawn in Fig. 5.12. The constant in Eq. (5.4b) was calculated from the Goldschmidt radius of the Cl^- ion (see Seitz, 1940). The figure indicates that there is a break in the growth rate curves. In the later stages of coloration, one F-center seems to be produced per vacancy pair generated. The crystals which are harder to color have a steeper initial slope in Fig. 5.11, and the break in the curve occurs for lower values of N_0. By extrapolating the later stage of the curves downward to the zero on the x-axis, one may estimate the number of vacancies originally in the crystal. Some values obtained by Rabin from Fig. 5.12 are given in Table 5.6. The first column gives the source of the crystal. Harshaw and Optovac are two companies which manufacture crystals. NRL stands for those grown at Rabin's laboratory, the Naval Research Laboratory. The impurity is measured in mole percent added to the melt. The crystal has a lower amount since the melt becomes more concentrated as the crystal grows.

TABLE 5.6. ESTIMATE OF INITIAL NEGATIVE VACANCIES IN VARIOUS NaCl CRYSTALS[a]

Harshaw		1×10^{16} cm^{-3}
NRL		14×10^{16}
Optovac		16×10^{16}
NRL	0.1 $M\%$ CdCl$_2$	4×10^{16}
NRL	0.5 $M\%$ CaCl$_2$	60×10^{16}

[a] After Rabin (S).

Rabin's study lends strong support to the concept emphasized several times by Nowick and co-workers that the growth process occurs in two steps. Figure 5.10 indicates that this concept cannot be carried through for the production of *F*-centers at low temperatures without modification. Further, some curves in this figure show that the second stage does not always occur. Perhaps the production of vacancies and *F*-centers is balanced by the bleaching of *F*-centers by the irradiation (second term in Eq. (5.2)).

Summary of Section 5

This section has emphasized primarily the irradiation by soft x-rays, by soft electrons, and by radiation which produces excitons. There have been studies of the effect of harder irradiation—that is, natural α- and β-irradiations, high-energy protons (350 Mev), high-energy electrons and neutrons. All these sources produce *F*-centers as well as other imperfections. Since it is not the object of this book to give an encyclopedic review of all the experimental data, we shall omit these effects. One should stress that the puzzle is how *F*-centers can be formed at low temperatures where most certainly knock-out atoms are not produced. Compton (S) has shown that the *F*-center formed by the irradiation with 2-Mev electrons at NT is identical to those formed by soft irradiation. The measured value of *H* is 0.196 ev, which is identical with the *H* obtained on additively colored and x-rayed crystals. (See Table 3.4.) For this case, knock-out ions exist.

F-centers may be formed by:

(a) Excitons;

(b) Soft x-rays;

(c) Hard x-rays and γ-rays;

(d) Electron bombardment;

(e) High-energy proton bombardment;

(f) α-rays.

The growth rate rises linearly at low temperatures, while at high temperature, it seems to reach a saturation value after an appropriate time for low intensity of irradiation. For high intensity irradiation, there is a second stage of coloration which arises from the creation of vacancies during the irradiation. The curves depend on the past thermal treatment of the sample as well as on the intensity of the irradiating source (see Harrison, S). Large variations in the growth rate curves exist, and any simple generalization has to be taken cautiously.

Some alkali halides color more easily at low temperatures than at high. This depends on the crystal, perhaps the source of the sample, and perhaps the nature of the irradiation source. Optical bleaching alone does not remove all the effects of radiation, although heat treatment seems to.

The creation of F-centers is accompanied by a decrease in density of the crystal. Crude estimates suggest that a pair of ion vacancies is produced per F-center in the later stages of coloration at RT. This probably is not true at low temperatures. This is a very important theoretical problem and deserves further careful theoretical and experimental study.

REFERENCES

W. D. Compton, private communication.

W. H. Duerig and J. J. Markham, *Phys. Rev.* **88**, 1043 (1952).

W. H. Duerig, *Phys. Rev.* **99**, 65 (1954).

D. Dutton, W. Heller and R. Maurer, *Phys. Rev.* **84**, 363 (1951).

I. Estermann, W. J. Leivo and O. Stern, *Phys. Rev.* **75**, 627 (1949).

H. W. Etzel, *Phys. Rev.* **87**, 906 (1952).

H. W. Etzel, *Phys. Rev.* **100**, 1643 (1955).

H. W. Etzel and D. A. Patterson, *Phys. Rev.* **112**, 1112 (1958).

F. Fischer, *Z. Physik* **154**, 534 (1959).

R. B. Gordon and A. S. Nowick, *Phys. Rev.* **101**, 977 (1956).

P. G. Harrison, *J. Chem. Phys.* **37**, 388 (1962).

H. U. Harten, *Z. Physik* **126**, 619 (1949).

H. Hummel, Dissertation, Göttingen, 1950; unpublished.

R. S. Knox, "Theory of Excitons," Academic Press, New York, 1963.

L. Lin, *Phys. Rev.* **102**, 968 (1956).

I. L. Mador, R. F. Wallis, M. C. Williams, and R. C. Herman, *Phys. Rev.* **96**, 617 (1954).

J. J. Markham and J. D. Konitzer, *J. Chem. Phys.* **34**, 1936 (1961).

W. Martienssen, *Phys. Chem. Solids* **8**, 294 (1959).

W. Martienssen, *Gött. Nachr.* p. 11 (1952).

P. V. Mitchell, D. A. Weigand, and R. Smoluchowski, *Phys. Rev.* **121**, 484 (1961).
W. Primak, C. J. Delbecq, and P. H. Yuster, *Phys. Rev.* **98**, 1708 (1955).
H. Rabin, *Phys. Rev.* **116**, 1381 (1959).
H. Rabin and C. C. Klick, *Phys. Rev.* **117**, 1005 (1960).
K. Sakaguchi and T. Suita, *Tech. Rept. Osaka Univ.* **2**, 177 (1952).
H. J. Schröder, *Z. Physik* **76**, 608 (1932).
F. Seitz, *Phys. Rev.* **80**, 239 (1950).
A. Smakula, *Z. Physik* **63**, 762 (1930).
J. H. O. Varley, *Nature* **174**, 886 (1954).
D. A. Wiegand and R. Smoluchowski, *Phys. Rev.* **116**, 1069 (1959).

6. ADDITIVE COLORATION

It is possible to dissolve a metal into an alkali halide and form F-centers. Two types of experiments have been done: (1) the crystal is in equilibrium with a metal vapor, or (2) it is in equilibrium with a colloid embedded in the lattice. The first experiment colors the crystal and the technique is known as additive coloration. Both these situations correspond to a thermodynamic equilibrium between two phases, one of which is a dilute solution of a metal in a crystal, while the other is a vapor or a solid metal. In discussing the experiments, several relations will be needed. These will now be developed.

The chemical potential of an ideal monatomic gas can be written in the form

$$\mu_i = g_i(p, \theta) + k\theta \ln c_i \qquad (6.1)$$

where c_i is the relative concentration (mole fraction) of the ith component, and g_i is the Gibbs free energy per particle at temperature θ and total pressure p. One may evaluate g_i by means of statistical mechanics; for a monatomic gas it is (see Fowler and Guggenheim)

$$g(p, \theta) = k\theta \ln p - k\theta \ln \frac{(2\pi M)^{3/2}(k\theta)^{5/2}}{h^3} \qquad (6.2a)$$

$$= k\theta \ln n_v - k\theta \ln \frac{(2\pi M)^{3/2}(k\theta)^{3/2}}{h^3} . \qquad (6.2b)$$

In Eq. (6.2b), n_v is the number of atoms per unit volume, and M is the mass of the atom.

We require a model of a crystal to show that an equation of the type (6.1) also applies to F-centers. We shall again assume that the center is an electron trapped at a negative-ion vacancy. Since the experiments described in Section 2 were done at high temperatures, there was an appreciable concentration of vacancies in the crystals. During the coloration process, the electron is not simply trapped at a negative vacancy, but must create its own vacancy or bring one in from outside. Otherwise, there would be an excess of negative charge. The original presence of the vacancies makes the diffusion of ions a relatively easy process. In the electron injection case, most probably positive-ion vacancies are initially emitted at the plate.

The entropy of the mixture or solution is required to obtain a relation between the number of F-centers in the crystal and the macroscopic variables of the vapor. One may ignore the very small concentrations of vacancies.* For this purpose, let there be $N+n$ positive ions, n F-centers† and N negative-ions. There are $N+n$ sites where one may place a negative-ion or an electron; hence, there are $(N+n)!/N!n!$ independent ways of arranging the crystal giving the following entropy term:

$$\Delta S = k \ln \frac{(N+n)!}{N!n!}$$

$$= -k \left[n \ln \left(\frac{n}{N+n} \right) + N \ln \left(\frac{N}{N+n} \right) \right]. \tag{6.3}$$

where use has been made of Stirling's formula. ΔS is only the entropy term for the mixing.

Explicit expressions for other entropy terms which arise due to other degrees of freedom—for example, the vibration of the solids—will not be required. We define ϵ_L as the lattice energy per particle—that is, the energy gained per particle when an equal number of positive and negative ions are brought together to form a crystal. Further, let μ_F be the energy gain when an electron is dissociated from a metal atom (in the vapor) and placed in a negative-ion vacancy. The dissociation energy must be included, since (6.1) applies to neutral atoms. The total energy of the system is approximately‡

$$U = (N+n)\epsilon_L + N\epsilon_L + n\mu_F. \tag{6.4}$$

---

* The number of vacancies is small compared to the number of ions but large compared to the number of F-centers. One may estimate this number to be of the order of 10^{18}/cc at the crystal temperature employed, using an equation obtained by Etzel and Maurer (S). These vacancies, however, are effectively inert since, as stated, every injected electron must carry with itself an additional negative-ion vacancy if neutrality is preserved.

† In this section, N_0 is replaced by n, except for notation in figures.

‡ Approximately because all the ions are not in perfect sites.

The total volume is

$$V = (N+n)v_+ + Nv_- + nv_F, \tag{6.5}$$

while the total entropy has the form

$$S = (N+n)s_+ + Ns_- + ns_F + \Delta S. \tag{6.6}$$

v is the volume associated with a positive or negative ion or with an F-center; s is the corresponding entropy term.

This results in the following expression for the total Gibb's free energy

$$G = U - \theta S + pV = (N+n)\mu_+ + N\mu_- + n\mu_F$$
$$= +k\theta\left[n\ln\frac{n}{N+n} + N\ln\frac{N}{N+n}\right] \tag{6.7}$$

where

$$\mu_+ = \epsilon_L - \theta s_+ + pv_+, \qquad \text{etc.} \tag{6.8}$$

The chemical potential of the trapped electron in the crystal given by $(\partial G/\partial n)_{\theta, P, N}$ is

$$\mu_c = \mu_+ + \mu_F + k\theta \ln c_F \tag{6.9}$$

where $\mu_+ + \mu_F$ essentially equals the energy to create an F-center from a neutral atom outside the crystal, and $c_F = n/(N+n) \approx n/N$.

We shall not write an explicit expression for the chemical potential of a small metal embedded in an alkali halide lattice, μ_M. Here we have only one component; hence, there is no mixing term. It will be further assumed that μ_M is independent of the size of the colloid (this neglects the effect of the surface tension), in spite of the fact that the particle is very small, less than 50 Å (see Scott *et al.*, 1953S).

First, we consider the equilibrium relation between the F-centers in the crystals and the metal vapor which surrounds them. The vapor is at a sufficiently high temperature that it is almost completely dissociated; hence, c in Eq. (6.1) is unity. Equating μ_i to μ_c and using (6.2b), it follows that

$$\frac{n}{N+n} \approx \frac{n}{N} = n_v\left(\frac{h^2}{2\pi Mk\theta}\right)^{3/2} \exp\left(-W_F/k\theta\right) \tag{6.10}$$

where

$$W_F = \mu_+ + \mu_F. \tag{6.10a}$$

Equation (6.10) was obtained by Mott and Gurney with a slight misprint. A more complete derivation has been given by Jost (S). We stress that it assumes that one atom in the metal vapor enters into the crystal to form one F-center, that is,

$$F\text{-center} \rightleftarrows \text{metal}.$$

Since N is constant, (6.10) relates n to the macroscopic variables p and θ.

Next, we investigate the equilibrium between the colloid and the F-centers; hence, μ_c is related to μ_m a function of p and θ.

$$\Delta G = W_F - \mu_M + k\theta \ln c_F. \tag{6.11}$$

Equation (6.11) states the relation between the F-center concentration and the change in the Gibbs' free energy as a function of temperature and pressure. The pressure enters in implicitly. At equilibrium $\Delta G = 0$. To obtain the heat of the reaction, we differentiate $\Delta G/k\theta$ with respect to the temperature. This is equivalent to assuming that the system goes through nonequilibrium states; thus,

$$\left[\frac{\partial}{\partial\theta}\left(\frac{\Delta G}{k\theta}\right)\right]_{p,n} = \frac{1}{k\theta}\left(\frac{\partial \Delta G}{\partial\theta}\right)_{p,n} + \Delta G\left[\frac{\partial}{\partial\theta}\left(\frac{1}{k\theta}\right)\right]_{p,n}$$
$$= -Q_{FC}/k\theta^2. \tag{6.12}$$

To define Q_{FC}, and obtain Eq. (6.12), use has been made of the thermodynamic relation

$$\left[\frac{\partial \Delta G}{\partial\theta}\right]_{p,c_F} = -\Delta S = \frac{-Q_{FC}}{\theta}. \tag{6.13}$$

Further we let $\Delta G = 0$ after the differentiation.

Q_{FC} is the heat of the reaction for making F-centers from colloids. Further, from (6.11) at equilibrium if W_F and μ_M do not depend on θ, it follows that

$$n = N \exp(-Q_{FC}/k\theta). \tag{6.14}$$

The following relation is obtained:

$$k\frac{\Delta\{\ln c_F\}}{\Delta\{1/\theta\}} = -Q_{FC}, \tag{6.15}$$

provided Q is temperature independent. Experimental measurements show that this is not actually the case in general; and variations of μ_M and W_F have to be taken into account; W_F and Q_{FC} have been measured by Rögener (S) and by Scott and Smith (1951S), respectively.

Rögener's technique is to enclose a crystal (at the top) and a liquid metal (at the bottom) in a tube. The temperature of the liquid is controlled by a lower furnace. This fixes the vapor pressure—that is, n_v. The crystal temperature is controlled by an upper furnace, which in turn gives θ of Eq. (6.10); n_v is calculated by assuming that the metal vapor obeys an ideal gas law and that we have an isobaric process in the tube.

Usually, the tube is of glass, which means that the crystal is cooled relatively slowly to room temperature. To obtain the pure F-center, that is, centers which give narrow bands (see Section 3), one must reheat the crystal to 600° C and then place it on a good conducting (copper) plate at room temperature. Alternately, one may use a metal bomb which can be opened within seconds after it is removed from the furnace. This permits rapid quenching in oil.*

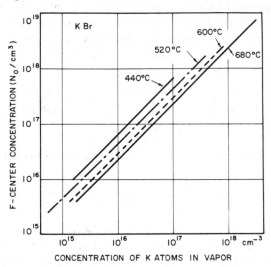

FIG. 6.1. Relation between the F-center concentration and the K atom concentration in additively colored KBr (f assumed to equal 1) (after Rögener, S).

Figure (6.1) shows Rögener's data on KBr: n was obtained from optical absorption data with $f=1$. Plots of $\ln(n/n_v)$ against $1/\theta$ give straight lines with

$$W_F = -0.25 \quad \text{ev} \quad \text{for KBr}$$
$$-0.10 \quad \text{ev} \quad \text{for KCl.}$$

There is no indication of a $\theta^{3/2}$ dependence as expected in Eq. (6.10). This is not too surprising in view of the size of W_F for KBr. The data for KCl are too meager, and hence, the value quoted is not reliable. In this case, a $\theta^{3/2}$ dependence would be expected. Mott and Gurney have estimated W_F theoretically by means of a cyclic process and obtained values in fair agreement with the data.

Scott and Smith (S) found that if one heats an additively colored

* It should be stressed that the production of "pure" F-centers by additive coloration is an art and not a science. There are, however, many advantages in using additively colored crystals, and it is worthwhile mastering.

crystal, a new band forms to the red. This band is believed to arise from metal atoms which precipitate out of the crystal. (See Section 2, Fig. 2.3.)

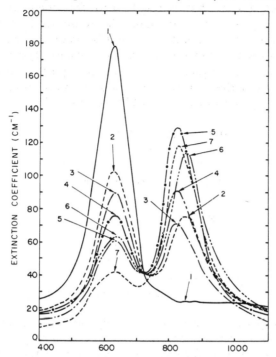

FIG. 6.2. Effects of the various heat treatments on the F-band in additively colored KBr. The crystal was quenched from the indicated temperature. x-Axis in mμ. (After Scott et al., S).

Curve:	1	2	3	4	5	6	7
Quenched from (°C):	400	350	340	325	318	309	283

A two-phase system is formed—that is, colloidal metal particles and alkali halides with F-centers. From the calculation of Savostianowa, one would expect that colloidal metal particles would produce absorption bands to the red of the F. The exact position will depend on the shape and size of the particles; hence, these bands should vary with the heat treatment. This is, indeed, what is observed, as Fig. 6.2 shows. One should note, in particular, that the shape of the band to the red varies a great deal, while the F-band does not. Using Smakula's equation and the height of the F-curve, one may calculate the number of F-centers in a crystal in equilibrium with a colloidal particle—that is, c_F of Eq. (6.14). From plots of c_F against $1/\theta$, one obtains Q_{FC} of that equation. Table 6.1 gives the results of the measurements of Scott *et al.* (S). Data by Scott and Smith (S) indicate that Q_{FC} is slightly temperature dependent. It is different from Rögener's W_F, even as to sign. The equilibrium number of F-centers increases with temperature when it is established with a colloid, but it decreases with temperature when it is established with a metal vapor. One heats the crystal near the melting point during additive coloration to avoid the formation of colloids and so that the inward diffusion of metal atoms take a reasonable length of time.

TABLE 6.1. Q_{FC} FOR VARIOUS ALKALI HALIDES[a]

Crystal	Q_{FC} (ev/particle)
KCl	0.35
KBr	0.5
KI	0.4
NaCl	0.4

[a] After Scott, Smith, and Thompson (S).

The Scott experiments are not completely satisfactory, for the band is broader than one might hope for. The expected value of H resulting from rapid quenching is 0.34 ev for KCl at RT, compared to the reported value of 0.36 ev. The width reflects the formation of secondary small bands, in which case the method of analysis is incomplete. We do not know what treatment will give only "pure" F-centers and colloidal bands.

Rögener does not report his value of H. One would, however, expect proper quenching, since it was known in Göttingen at the time the work was carried out that proper quenching was required (see Section 7).*

REFERENCES

H. W. Etzel and R. J. Maurer, *J. Chem. Phys.* **18**, 1003 (1950).
W. Jost, "Diffusion in Solids, Liquids, and Gases." Academic Press, New York, 1952.
R. Rögener, *Ann. Physik* **29**, 386 (1937).
A. B. Scott and W. A. Smith, *Phys. Rev.* **83**, 982 (1951).
A. B. Scott, W. A. Smith, and M. S. Thompson, *J. Phys. Chem.* **57**, 757 (1953).

* Some extremely interesting experiments have been done on thin film with excitons —see L. Apker and E. Taft, "On the Nature of Imperfections in Nearly Perfect Crystals" (W. Shockley, ed.) p. 246. Wiley, New York, 1952.

III. The Photoconductivity of the F-Center

7. INTRODUCTION

So far we have discussed the detection of F-centers by optical methods, a natural means since the coloration caused by these imperfections is quite spectacular. Other physical changes are induced by the presence of the F-centers, most of which will be described. A pure alkali halide crystal is diamagnetic and shows no photoconductivity for wavelengths longer than the intrinsic absorption (see Section 3). The center causes the crystal to be paramagnetic. It also has a photoelectric response and an emission spectrum for stimulation in the F-absorption region. In the next two chapters we shall describe most of the nonmagnetic properties, while in the latter part of the book the induced magnetism will be considered.

We owe our knowledge of photoconductivity of F-centers almost exclusively to the studies of the Göttingen School. This work was done mainly between the two wars and shows a remarkable consistency. Nevertheless, one would like other laboratories to do independent work so as to check the results. Some of this work is being done at the University of Illinois by Professor F. C. Brown. The material here is mainly drawn from papers published in the late thirties, since they are extensions of earlier studies. We start by developing some important concepts.

The field of photoconductivity is closely related to an important technology which employs some photoconductors that are a good deal more complex than the alkali halides doped with a metal. These complexities have given rise to the suggestion that the simple concepts so beautifully developed by the school under the leadership of Professor Pohl be abandoned (see Rose, S). The concepts, however, are extremely useful in this field and, if abandoned, would be a great loss to science. We are going to present these ideas and show their utility for the photoconductive properties of the F-center. We shall not attempt to generalize them for any other material.

a. Concepts of Photoconductivity—Hecht's Theory

We start by developing the theory of Hecht (S) (see also Mott and Gurney, p. 117). A more general case has been considered by van

Heyningen and Brown (S). Now consider a crystal with electron traps which have one bound state; every photon absorbed will produce one electron in the conduction band. These electrons will be free to move and hence will change the insulator into a conductor. If two bound levels exist, the absorption may still produce photoconductivity, provided the excited state is close to the conduction band. In this case, the second jump from the excited state to the conduction band occurs thermally and the photoconductivity is temperature dependent. The electron's life in the conduction band will be short, for it will be recaptured by some imperfection. This may be of the type from which it originated or it may be by a new one, depending on the state of the solid. Consider the situation illustrated in Fig. 7.1. We assume that an electron is liberated at X; if it is

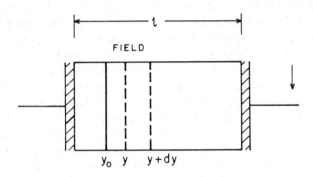

FIG. 7.1. A crystal exposed to light. The light comes from above, that is, perpendicular to the paper.

in thermal equilibrium with the lattice, its kinetic energy is $\frac{3}{2}(k\theta)$. During its mean free life of T seconds, the electron travels a distance $(3k\theta/m)^{1/2}T$. This is random motion which averages to zero and hence cannot be measured. The field imposes a much slower nonrandom drift, which is of interest to us. The nonrandom distance traveled is

$$w = \mu FT, \qquad (7.1)$$

where μ is the mobility, F is the field strength, and w is the mean electron range or, following the Göttingen term, the "Schubweg."

When one deals with a large crystal such that $w \ll l$ (see Fig. 7.1), every electron released by the light induces a charge of $e(w/l)$ on the plates. This follows, since the energy due to the displacement of the charge, that is, ewF, must equal the energy absorbed by the external circuit, qlF (q is the effective charge—that is, the charge induced on the plates); hence,

$$q = e(w/l) = (e/l)\mu TF. \tag{7.2}$$

The induced charge is proportional to the field. This comes about because we are interested in the nonrandom drift along l. If w is greater than l, the induced charge must equal q. By appropriate selection of the physical parameters, one may obtain cases where $w \approx (1/2)l$; hence, more exact relations between q, w, and l are required. The theory has further interest, since Rögener (S) has used it to study some basic properties of color centers.

For this purpose, let $n(y)$ electrons be set free by a narrow beam of light at y_0. In the interval from $y+dy$ to $y(y>y_0)$ dn electrons are absorbed—that is, they are trapped and no longer contribute to the current. From the definition of w, we have

$$dn = \frac{-n(y)}{w} dy \tag{7.3}$$

or

$$n(y) = n_0 \exp\{-(1/w)(y-y_0)\}. \tag{7.3a}$$

For a small w $(w \ll l)$, the effective mean free path is w, while, if $w \gg l$, the path is $l-y_0$. For the intermediate case,

$$\text{effective path} = \frac{1}{n_0}\left\{ \int_{y_0}^{l} (y-y_0)\left[-\frac{dn}{dy}\right] dy + (l-y_0)n_0 \exp[(1/w)(l-y_0)] \right\}. \tag{7.4}$$

The second term accounts for the electrons which go to the anode and travel a whole distance $l-y_0$. The first term is the contribution by those which get absorbed in the medium at y. An elementary integration results in

$$\text{effective path} = w\{1 - \exp[-(1/w)(l-y_0)]\}. \tag{7.4a}$$

If the crystal is illuminated uniformly, we must average (7.4a) over l; hence,

$$\langle w \rangle_{av} = \langle w \rangle = w\{1-(w/l)(1-e^{-(l/w)})\}. \tag{7.5}$$

As expected for $l \gg w$

$$\langle w \rangle_{av} = w. \tag{7.6a}$$

Hence, (7.2) applies and the charge accumulated depends on the field. The net charge induced on the plate is

$$Q = \frac{n_0 ew}{l} = \frac{n_0 e}{l}\mu FT. \tag{7.7a}$$

For $w \gg l$, however,

$$\langle w \rangle_{av} = \tfrac{1}{2} l \qquad\qquad (7.6b)$$

and

$$Q = \tfrac{1}{2} n_0 e. \qquad\qquad (7.7b)$$

n_0 is the net number of electrons liberated. Equation (7.5) will be employed to calculate $\langle w \rangle_{av}$ for cases where $w \approx l$.

There will be no polarization problems as long as the resistance at the contact between the crystal and the metal plates is ohmic. At low temperatures the ionic currents are very small and, if n_0 is also small, the major part of the potential drop occurs within the crystal. Hence, the drop across the boundaries is extremely minute and theoretically no rectification occurs at either junction.* As the crystal becomes a better conductor, there may be larger potential drops across the metal crystal boundary and rectification. This will lead to the accumulation of charges —that is, polarization effects. In any actual experiment one must be sure that one has eliminated all these effects.

Thus, Q will not be proportional to F if (1) $w \gg l$ (this occurs at high fields), and (2) if the contacts to the crystals are non-ohmic, which can occur for high currents. In the work we describe, special care has been taken to be certain that (7.7a) applies. The only exception is in the work of Rögener, where Eq. (7.5) is studied (see Section $7f$).

b. The Measurement Technique†

Before describing the equipment, let us consider the magnitude of the quantities involved, as reported by Glaser (S). Some typical values for KCl are:

Intensity of light absorbed by the crystal: 7.5–80×10^{12} ev/sec or 3.6–35×10^{12} photons/sec

Wavelength of light used: 555 mμ or 2.23 ev

---

* We do not know exactly what happens at alkali halide boundaries. The reason one suspects that it would be ohmic is that other junctions are. For an elementary treatment of a p–n junction, see Shockley (S). These types of junctions are ohmic for very small potential drops, the type of interest to this problem. Actually, however, the experimentalist in this field seems to always produce a blocking layer. For a detailed discussion of space charge effects see MacDonald and Brachman (S).

† Onuki (S) has recently made some photoconductivity measurements using direct current methods. As far as the author is able to see, his results are not in complete agreement with those reported by the workers at the Göttingen School. The reason for the discrepancy is not clear at present. The author feels that the basic photoconductivity concepts developed by Göttingen will stand the test of time; see von Gericke's (S) paper.

Voltage applied: 460 volts

Field: 1340 volts/cm (crystal thickness: 0.35 cm)

Density of F-centers: 4.3×10^{15} cm^{-3}*

Temperature of crystals: 100° K

Current produced: $0.6–7 \times 10^{-12}$ amp (currents can be 10^{-3}–10^4 times this value, depending on the experimental conditions).

The schematic diagram of the equipment is shown in Fig. 7.2. Our interest will be the effect of a square pulse of light; hence, the light

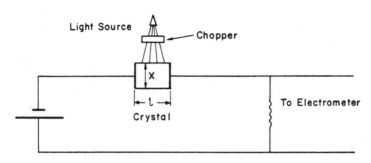

FIG. 7.2. Method of measuring photoconductivity.

chopper. The electrometer should have a fast response time since the rate of build-up and decay is of interest. Von Gericke (S) has developed equipment with response times of 10^{-6} sec. All the data presented here, however, were measured with equipment which had a much longer response time (about 10^{-1} sec). The difference between these results and those of von Gericke's is only of a qualitative nature, which means that one may rely on the older data. The crystal is in a cryostat during the measurement since its temperature is an important variable.

When the light in the F-band of intensity I_0 falls on the crystal (see Fig. 7.2), the number of electrons liberated per unit time is:

$$n_0 = \eta_c(I_0/\epsilon)\left\{1 - \exp\left[-\int_0^X \alpha(t, \epsilon, x)\, dx\right]\right\}$$

$$= \eta_c(\Delta I/\epsilon). \tag{7.8}$$

Where ϵ is the photon energy, X is the depth from the top surface and η_c is the quantum yield, an experimental parameter. The last quantity is

* The author assumes that this was calculated from Smakula's equation with f set equal to unity. Kleinschrod did his work in 1939.

the number of electrons released by the light to the conduction band per photon absorbed. It presumably ranges from 0 to 1. ΔI is the energy absorbed in the crystal per unit time.

In Eq. (7.8), α may be a function of time, wavelength, and depth of the crystal. If the crystal has been colored additively, it is independent of the depth. In lightly colored crystals (5×10^{15} cm^{-3}), it is as small as 0.5 cm^{-1}. (The radiation energy is rarely at ϵ_m.) Equation (7.8) then takes the simple form ($X \approx 0.2$ cm)

$$n_0 = (\eta_c/\epsilon) I_0 \alpha X. \tag{7.8a}$$

In one special case, α is independent of time—that is, when every ionized center retraps a conduction electron—since, in this case, n_0 remains constant. This is not true in general. For higher concentrations (about 10^{17} or even 10^{18}), Eq. (7.8) must be used with the development of van Heyningen and Brown, which take this into account.

Here, we shall employ the expression developed by the Göttingen School and write the following equation for the current measured by the electrometer

$$i = en_0 \frac{\langle w \rangle}{l} = e\eta_c \frac{\Delta I}{\epsilon} \frac{1}{l} \langle w \rangle. \tag{7.9}$$

If square pulses of light are used, one may measure the net charge produced; hence

$$Q = \int i(t)\, dt = \frac{e\eta_c}{\epsilon} \frac{\langle w \rangle}{l} \int \Delta I\, dt \tag{7.10a}$$

$$= \frac{\eta_c}{\epsilon} \frac{J}{l} \langle w \rangle e, \tag{7.10b}$$

where J is the total energy absorbed.

In (7.9) and (7.10), η_c and w are the unknowns; hence, the measurements determine

$$\frac{\eta_c}{F} \langle w \rangle = \frac{i}{\Delta I} \frac{l}{F} \frac{\epsilon}{e} \tag{7.11a}$$

and

$$\frac{\eta_c}{F} \langle w \rangle = \frac{Q}{J} \frac{l}{F} \frac{\epsilon}{e}. \tag{7.11b}$$

Where (7.6a) applies, we obtain with the help of (7.1)

$$\frac{\eta_c \langle w \rangle}{F} = \eta_c \mu T = \frac{i}{\Delta I} \frac{l\epsilon}{F e} \tag{7.12a}$$

or
$$\eta_c \frac{w}{F} = \eta_c \mu T = \frac{Q}{J} \frac{l}{F} \frac{\epsilon}{e}. \tag{7.12a}$$

In Eq. (7.9) i may be time dependent if n_0 varies because of changes in $\int_0^x \alpha(t,x)\,dx$. This effect occurs even if I is held constant. Equations (7.12a) and (7.12b) assume that $\langle w \rangle = w$, otherwise we could not have used (7.6a).

If we use (7.6b) in place of (7.6a) (that is, $l \ll w$), then

$$\eta_c = \frac{2i}{\Delta I} \frac{\epsilon}{e} \tag{7.13a}$$

or
$$\eta_c = \frac{2Q}{J} \frac{\epsilon}{e}. \tag{7.13b}$$

Under these conditions, one measures the quantum yield directly. This type of measurement has been made by Rögener (S).

In a sense, photoelectric data are a good deal more complex to interpret than an optical absorption measurement. A plot of $(i/\Delta I)$ against the temperature may or may not give one the dependence of $\eta_c w$ on θ. This is determined by the value of F. Likewise, a plot of $i\epsilon/I_0$ against ϵ may or may not give one a plot of α against ϵ, depending on the product $\alpha(t,\epsilon)X$. One obtains I (that is, $I_0 - \Delta I$) directly from an optical absorption measurement. A photoelectric measurement only gives a quantity which is proportional to ΔI. By the optical approach, one may readily calculate $\log_{10} I_0/I$. To compare the two types of measurements, one must plot ΔI against the photon energy or wavelength. One might expect that i and α will have the same wavelength dependence if η_c is independent of ϵ (as in the case of the F-center). This is only true, however, if

$$\frac{i\epsilon}{I_0 e} = \frac{\eta_c}{l} \langle w \rangle \alpha X. \tag{7.14a}$$

In general, αX is not small and we must use the relation:

$$\frac{i\epsilon}{I_0 e} = \frac{\eta_c}{l} \langle w \rangle \left\{ 1 - \exp\left[-\int_0^X \alpha(\epsilon)\,dx \right] \right\}. \tag{7.14b}$$

After considering the behavior of the mobility, we shall turn to the data on the photoconductivity of the F-centers. The temperature, the wavelength of the excitation light, the density of the F-centers, and of course, the medium it is in may be varied. The Göttingen School has studied the effects of all these parameters.

c. The Electron Mobility in an Alkali Halide

In the original work, the temperature dependence of the mobility was neglected since its variation was believed to be small over the range of interest. Workers at the University of Illinois (Redfield, S, as well as Brown and Inchauspé, S and Wild and Brown, S) were the first to

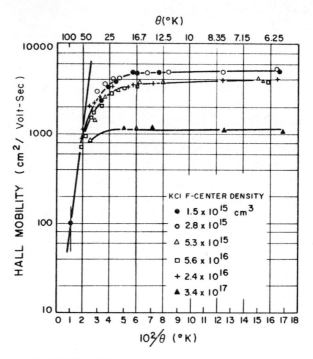

FIG. 7.3. Low-field Hall mobility as a function of temperature for electrons released by light in crystals with different *F*-center concentrations in KCl. The straight line is the function $\mu = 3.6 \exp(300/T)$ corresponding to optical phonon scattering (after Brown and Inchauspé, S).

measure this quantity. Here, we shall very briefly review the experimental facts. For a description of the elegant technique developed by Redfield to measure mobilities in insulators, the reader is referred to the original article.

Figure 7.3 presents the measurements of Brown and Inchauspé (S) on KCl. The source of the electron is an *F*-center which is exposed to light. The mobility of an electron is not small, as one might expect offhand, since an alkali halide is a polar material. For example, the mobility in copper at room temperature is about 30 cm²/volt sec. The values in Fig. 7.3 compare reasonably with some semiconductors. The plateau in the figure depends on the F-center concentration, indicating that the mobility at low temperature is limited by the electron F-center scatterings. Above 50°K, the mobility is given by a simple equation of the form

$$\mu = Ae^{b/\theta}. \tag{7.15}$$

The values of A and b for NaCl, KBr, and KCl are presented in Table 7.1.

TABLE 7.1. VALUES OF A AND b FOR VARIOUS ALKALI HALIDES

	NaCl[a]	KCl[b]	KBr[c]
b	370	300	240° K
	0.032	0.026	0.021 ev
A (cm²/volt sec)	3.9	3.6	15

[a] Redfield (S).
[b] Brown and Inchauspé (S).
[c] Onuki (S), calculated by the author.

The value of b in KCl indicates that the modes which scatter the electron in the conduction band are most probably the longitudinal optical modes.* This follows since the angular frequency associated with b of 300° K is 4×10^{13} sec⁻¹ and compares favorably with the maximum frequency calculated (see Fig. 29.9, Section 29). A similar argument can be made using the data and calculation on NaCl. Onuki has suggested that an equation of the type

$$\mu = A(e^{b/\theta} - 1), \tag{7.15a}$$

fits his data better than (7.15). The author questions this conclusion. Onuki's data do not agree with Redfield's values at 84°K.

Table 7.2, taken from Redfield's measurements, indicates the variation of μ with the salt.

---

* In this mode, the ions vibrate out of phase and the wavelength has a pure longitudinal character (Born and Huang, Chapter II). This mode has the highest frequency in an alkali halide. This frequency should be (bk/h).

TABLE 7.2. VARIATION OF MOBILITY[a]

NaCl	250
KCl	100 (90° K)
KBr	110
KI	150

[a] After Redfield (S); measured at about 85° K in cm²/volt sec.

As we shall see, our interest in the variation of μ is limited to the range from 300°K to 40°K and Fig. 7.3 indicates a variation of μ of a factor of ten. The photocurrent varies by a factor of 10^4 over this range and the

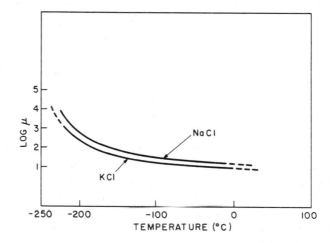

FIG. 7.4. Plot of the mobility of KCl and NaCl against temperature (data from Table 7.1).

major temperature-dependent factor is η_c, not μ. To orient the reader, we have plotted in Fig. 7.4 the variation of μ on the "standard photoconductivity plot."* The variation seems smaller than that in Fig. 7.3; of course, it is actually the same.

* These types of plots have been used for many years in this field. They are useful and will be employed here. A comparison between these types of plots and those used in mobility measurements is difficult without new graphs.

d. The Effect of Temperature on the Photoconductivity

General Features*

Figure 7.5a and b presents Gudden and Pohl's (S) measurement of the photocurrent as a function of time. The crystal used was rock salt† (natural NaCl) which had been colored by x-rays; hence, α was not a constant. The excitation light was a mercury arc and the 405- and 436-mμ lines were used (λ_m for NaCl at RT is 465 mμ). The figure shows that the current is not independent of time. This is particularly striking when strong illumination is employed. This is due to polarization and some other nonlinear effects which will be discussed later.

Equation (7.8) indicates that from measurements of i as a function of λ one may obtain plots of α versus λ using Eq. (7.8) as one does from optical measurements, provided η_c is independent of wavelength. Gyulai (S) has made such a study again using x-rayed rock salt. His data are shown in Fig. 7.6. A few points were obtained on the ultraviolet side of the band which show the same relation.‡ We conclude from these measurements that the photocurrent response and α have the same wavelength dependence, that is, η_c is independent of λ, at least for NaCl at RT.

The data in Figs. 7.5 and 7.6 are of a qualitative nature. Some 10 years later, Glaser and Lehfeldt (S) presented some elegant quantitative data (see Fig. 7.7). The crystal was again rock salt which had been additively colored (uniform α at $t=0$). These experimenters were aware that to obtain a simple result, which could be easily interpreted, the crystal had to be handled with extreme care. Before the measurement, the sample was heated to about 700° C (about 100° below the melting point) and then rapidly quenched by placing it on a metal at RT. From recent work (Section 3), we know that this process produces the pure F-center.§

---

* Onuki and Ohkura (S) have studied space charge effects due to the photocurrent in additively colored KBr using alternating current methods.

† Much of the early data on the F-center were obtained with rock salt. Generally speaking, synthetic crystals behave similarly to the crystals found in nature. Some differences, however, exist.

‡ In these data, no corrections were made for the wavelength dependence of ϵ.

§ Glaser and Lehfeldt (S) knew that they had to have quenched crystals, but they did not know why. Mollwo's (Section 3) famous measurements were done two years earlier and, from the reported values of H, one suspects that the crystals were not handled by the same technique. Work coming out of Göttingen since 1935 is mainly on the pure F-center because the technique used by Glaser and Lehfeldt was employed. Unfortunately, the same technique was not always used outside the Göttingen School and quite often the B-band (the broad F-band) has been studied instead of the pure F-band.

Four types of behavior were obtained, depending on θ. At 30° C, the current is constant with time; it is known as type I. We note that the current in Fig. 7.5a is smaller than in Fig. 7.7, yet it decreases with time.

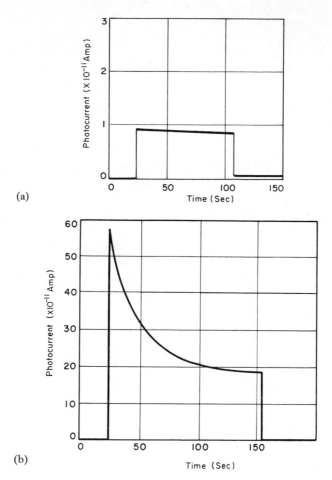

(a)

(b)

FIG. 7.5. Photoconductivity of the F-center in natural NaCl; coloration by x-rays; irradiation in the F-band (after Gudden and Pohl, S). (a) Weak illumination; (b) strong illumination.

Three reasons for this discrepancy suggest themselves: (1) the irradiation time in the earlier work is much longer (80 sec compared to 5 sec); (2) α in the earlier work is nonuniform; (3) Gudden and Pohl used x-rayed crystals. Items 1 and 3 must be of primary importance in the explanation. At any rate, Fig. 7.7 shows that in region I, the current produced by F-light (light in the F-band) is constant, showing a very rapid rise and fall time. As stated, von Gericke (S) has more recently studied the rise and fall times with superior equipment. He has concluded that at RT these times are less than 5×10^{-6} sec for NaCl. In these experiments (Fig. 7.7), the fraction of ionized F-centers must be very small since, as we shall see, every absorbed photon produces one ionized F-center; the fraction (based on the first three curves of Fig. 7.7) is 0.017.

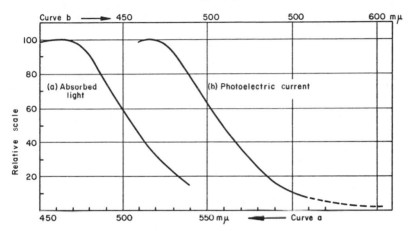

FIG. 7.6. A comparison of the photoconductivity and the absorbed light from the F-center in natural NaCl at RT; coloration by x-rays (after Gyulai, S). Curve a, absorbed light; curve b, photoelectric current.

After the irradiation in the F-band, photoconductivity can be produced by an irradiation in the infrared ($\lambda > 700$ mμ). We shall not concern ourselves with the details of this effect until the next section.

Lowering the temperature will only cause a decrease in the magnitude of the current. Raising the temperature produces an increase in the current as well as a change in the pulse's shape. This second effect must be related to the infrared response, as is evident from the right-hand side of the figures. At 80° C (type II), one may separate the current into two parts, A and B. Part A is caused directly from the motion of electrons released from the F-centers, as in case I, while part B (shaded area) results from a secondary effect which depends on θ. At 125° C (III), current B is much larger, although one may still attempt to resolve it from A. At 235° C (IV), this no longer is possible. We see that the type of current is

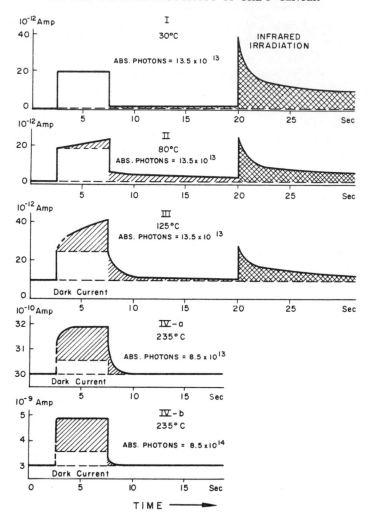

FIG. 7.7. Photoconductivity from the *F*-center in natural NaCl, additively colored. $N_0 = 8 \times 10^{15}$; field strength: 1,070 volts/cm; violet irradiation at 2.64 ev (after Glaser and Lehfeldt, S).

temperature independent below 30° C for NaCl, whereas above that level there is a marked dependence on θ.

Glaser and Lehfeldt (S) have obtained similar curves for KCl and KBr. Similar regions occur in these crystals but the temperatures are quite different (see Table 7.3).

For these experiments, Eq. (7.12) applies; Eq. (7.12a) can be used in regions I, II, and III, while Eq. (7.12b) is useful in regions II, III, and IV. Using the first equation, one may obtain $\eta_c(w/F)$ for current A and using the second equation, one obtains this quantity for the sum of the two currents. Of course, one can use (7.12b) throughout by integrating the current.

TABLE 7.3. RANGE OF PHOTOCONDUCTIVITY TYPES[a]

Current type	Temp. (°K)		
	NaCl	KCl	KBr
I	300	140	90
II	350	210	110
III	400	230	190
IV	500	300	220

[a] The data are qualitative. Most probably, KCl is of type I, even at 170° K.

Using the data of the type presented in Fig. 7.7, Glaser and Lehfeldt, as well as Glaser (S), have measured $\eta_c(w/F)$ as a function of 0 for NaCl, KCl, KBr, KI, RbCl, and RbBr. Figure 7.8 presents the data for KCl. The solid line is for the *total* current, *while the dashed line is for the A current*. The general nature of the curve in region I is independent of the way the crystal is colored. Glaser has studied the product for F-centers in KCl produced by four techniques: (1) by additively coloring with K; (2) by x-raying; (3) by injecting electrons; and (4) by dissolving H_2.* The shape of the curves is the same in region I. The absolute values of $\eta_c(w/F)$, however, depend on the means of coloration being four times larger in an additively colored crystal than in an x-rayed one. The current of the type B depends critically on the means of F-center production. The value at RT is 300 times larger in an additively colored crystal than in an x-rayed one. The shape of the curve also varies. The current B is believed to be due to an extension of w at high temperature. It is hence referred to

* We have not described this technique. It is possible to make a mixed crystal of KCl and KH. This crystal has an absorption band at 5.79 ev (214 mμ) known by the letter U. When these crystals are exposed to ultraviolet light at temperatures above NT, the F-band forms.

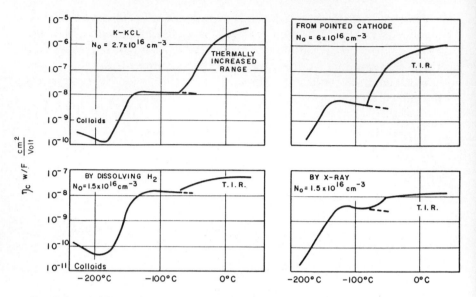

FIG. 7.8. $\eta_c(w/F)$ as a function of θ, irradiated with 2.23-ev photons (after Glaser, S).

as "the current due to the thermally extended range" or "extended range current."

Figure 7.8 assumes that η_c is independent of the wavelength; ϵ_m for KCl at RT is 2.23 ev; hence, Glaser was irradiating at the peak at RT. However, at 77° K, ϵ_m is 2.30 ev and the irradiation was on the red side of ϵ_m. To test the above assumption, Rögener measured the product as a function of temperature for additively colored KCl using two frequencies, 2.43 and 2.18 ev. The quantity was independent of the wavelength; hence η_c does not seem to be a function of ϵ at any temperature. Rögener has presented similar data for NaCl, exciting with 3.06- and 2.53-ev light. Here, ϵ_m is 2.68 ev at RT and 2.76 ev at NT.

The Low Temperature Region

What is the meaning of the knee at about $-150°$ C in Fig. 7.8? We do not expect μ or T to account for this variation. T is determined by the thermal motion and should be proportional to $\theta^{-1/2}$. The measurement of Redfield shows that μ increases as the temperature is lowered. The variation in μ most probably explains the decrease on the high temperature side of the knee but we must ascribe the sharp drop in the product to a decrease in η_c.

One may explain the curve by assuming that the $\bar{F}$-center has two bound levels. When the center absorbs a photon, it becomes excited (not ionized). At high temperature, there is sufficient vibrational energy around the center so that it is ionized. Below a critical temperature, θ_c, an excited center cannot dissociate and hence a conduction electron is not produced. The electron returns to the ground state either by emitting one photon or many phonons.

The first successful search for the emitted photon—that is, the luminescence—was made by Botden, van Doorn, and Haven (S). As expected, the emission is to the red of the absorption. This emission is discussed in detail in Section 8. In this section, we shall only require the emission probability as given by Einstein's A coefficient (modified for the crystalline medium; see Appendix of Chapter X). The equation which is obtained there has the form

$$A = \left\{ \frac{n}{9}(n^2+2)^2 \right\} \frac{8\pi^2}{mc^3} e^2 \nu^2 f$$

$$= \{2.9\}\{4.3 \times 10^7\} \epsilon_e^2 f \quad \text{sec}^{-1} \qquad \text{for KCl} \qquad (7.16a)$$

$$= 1.2 \times 10^8 \epsilon_e^2 f \quad \text{sec}^{-1}. \tag{7.16b}$$

The expression in the first curly bracket is the correction for the medium, f is the oscillator strength, and ϵ_e is the peak of the emission curve in electron volts. In view of Section 4, f can be assumed to be equal to unity (f for absorption is assumed to equal f for emission). We shall see that $\epsilon_e \approx 1$ ev. Equation (7.16) actually gives a lifetime much shorter than the one measured (see Section 8). The reason for the difference is not understood at present. The measurements will be given in Section 8. We assume that the probability of ionizing a center after excitation is given by the expression $se^{-\epsilon_t(1)/k\theta}$ which means that the center absorbed phonons to release the electron. $\epsilon_t(1)$ is the thermal activation energy for raising an electron from the excited state of the F-center to the conduction band, and s is a frequency factor. One must distinguish between thermal and optical activation energies; they may be quite different for transitions between identical levels. We shall return to this problem shortly (Section 12) when an energy diagram for the F-center is presented.

Hence, the probability of an electron escaping to the conduction band after a photon absorption is given by

$$\eta_c = \frac{se^{-\epsilon_t(1)/k\theta}}{A + se^{-\epsilon_t(1)/k\theta}}. \tag{7.17}$$

η_c approaches unity at high temperatures if s is much greater than A. Assuming that $f=1$, and $\epsilon_e = 1$, Eq. (7.16) gives 10^8 for A. If s is of the order of the thermal vibration, it equals 10^{12} sec^{-1}. One may also obtain a value of s from thermoluminescent experiments. In this case, a much smaller value, that is, 10^{10} (see Garlick, S) is obtained. (Actually, A seems to be of the order of 10^6 sec^{-1}; f for absorption probably does not equal f for emission. Nevertheless, s is much larger than A and η_c approaches unity at high temperature.) We may test Eq. (7.17), using photoconductivity data to establish its validity. This may be done by ignoring the temperature dependence of the mobility and the small dependence of T on θ. To justify this procedure, we have made Fig. 7.4, which indicates that the variation in μ is much smaller than that of the triple product and in the wrong direction. Later, we shall be able to evaluate η_c by an alternate procedure and obtain T from the known values of the mobility.

If one assumes that η_c equals unity at the knee of Fig. 7.8, one can evaluate s and $\epsilon_t(1)$ from plots of $\ln[(1/\eta_c)=1]$ against $1/\theta$ since

$$\ln\left\{\frac{(\eta_c\mu T)_m}{(\eta_c\mu T)} - 1\right\} = \epsilon_t(1)\frac{1}{k\theta} + \ln\frac{A}{s}. \tag{7.18}$$

$(\eta_c\mu T)_m$ is the value at the knee. Actually, plots of

$$\ln\left\{\frac{(\eta_c\mu T)_m}{(\eta_c\mu T)} - 1\right\}$$

against $1/\theta$ give straight lines from which the $\epsilon_t(1)$'s may be evaluated. The values of ϵ_t obtained from all available photoconductivity data are given in Table 7.4. The actual values in the table were obtained for

TABLE 7.4. VALUES OF THE THERMAL ACTIVATION ENERGY

Crystal	Means of production:	$\epsilon_t(1)$ (ev)	$\epsilon_t(1)$ (ev) (corrected)
NaCl	Additively colored	0.11	0.08
KCl	Additively colored	0.08	0.05
	X-rayed	0.14	0.09
KBr	Additively colored	0.15	0.13
KI	Produced from U-centers	0.10	
RbCl	Electrolytic coloration	0.18	
RbBr	Electrolytic coloration	0.16	

temperatures well below the knee. We shall develop a more exact theory of the temperature variation of $\eta_c \mu T$ in Section 13. It will indicate that points around the knee should not be used in evaluating ϵ_t and that the values of ϵ_t in Table 7.4 have to be corrected. This was done for NaCl, KCl, and KBr, since the electron mobility data are available for these crystals (see Section 13a).

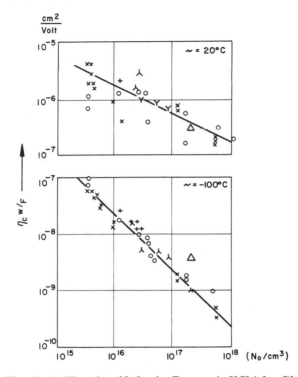

FIG. 7.9. Plot of $\eta_c(w/F)$ against N_0 for the F-center in KCl (after Glaser, S).

e. Effect of Concentration on the Photoconductivity

To understand fully the photoconductivity data, we need to change some of the parameters which enter into the process. One such variable is the F-center concentration. Glaser (S) has measured $\eta_c(w/F)$ as a function of the F-center concentration, Fig. 7.9. The lower curve is for type I conductivity, while the upper is for type II.* At the lower temperature, the product depends inversely on the F-center concentration

* The measurements were done on additively colored crystals.

and the spread in the data is small. Similar data have been obtained on additively colored KCl at $300°$ C (again type I conductivity); KCl at $173°$ K, and NaCl at RT (by Glaser, S, and by Glaser and Lehfeldt, S). These points are well below the knee of the curve on a $\eta_c(w/F)$ temperature plot.

The dependence on the concentration in KCl is quite different at $293°$ K, where the conductivity is of type IV. The product $(\eta_c\mu T)$, corresponds to the net current since one may not resolve the two types. Here the product depends on the -0.5 power of the concentration. As is evident from the figure, the points scatter a great deal. Glaser and Lehfeldt measured the dependence of this product in additively colored KCl at $30°$ C and obtained essentially the same results. The properties of μ and η_c seem to be concentration independent at high temperature. We may reach this conclusion regarding μ by examining the data of Brown and Inchauspe in Fig. 7.3. We shall describe shortly how to measure η_c by an alternate method and shall find that it is independent of concentration; hence, we must conclude that the mean free path depends on the concentration of F-centers. These data can be explained if one assumes that the electron is released from an F-center and is captured by another center to form a new type of imperfection. If an F-center is an electron captured at a negative-ion vacancy, then the new type of center would be two electrons captured at a negative-ion vacancy. It will shortly be indicated why we believe this to be the case (Section 9).

No equivalent simple explanation has been given of the data for type II conductivity. The spread in the data suggests that there are important variables in addition to the concentration.

f. High-Field Photoconductivity

A very important extension of the photoconductivity measurements just described has been made by Rögener (S) using high electric fields. Under these conditions, the relation $l \gg w$ no longer holds and Eq. (7.6a) does not apply. The charge collected for the low-field case is given in (7.7a), while the maximum Q_m charge that can be collected at high fields is obtained from (7.7b). The ratio of these quantities is

$$\frac{Q}{Q_m} = \frac{2w}{l}, \tag{7.19}$$

which, because of w, is directly proportional to the field. In general, when the crystal thickness l is not much larger or much smaller than the electronic range, one obtains the relation

$$\frac{Q}{2Q_m} = \frac{\psi(F)}{\eta_c} = \frac{w}{l}\left[1 - \frac{w}{l}(1 - e^{-l/w})\right] \qquad (7.20)$$

by the use of (7.2), (7.5), and (7.7b). This defines $\psi(F)$. η_c appears in Eq. (7.20) since our calculations were related to electrons *released* to the conduction band. The presence of η_c relates the released electron to the light absorbed. Using data on K-KCl shown in Fig. 7.8 we may calculate the field when $w = l$. Assume that $l = 10^{-2}$ cm and let $\theta = 300°$ K. Then, $\eta_c(w/F) = 2.5 \times 10^{-6}$ cm²/volt. The upper left-hand plot is employed. Thus, $w = 10^{-2}$ cm and $F = 4 \times 10^3$ volts/cm. The potential difference required across the crystal is just 40 volts. Similar calculations for NaCl show that 5000 volts are required.

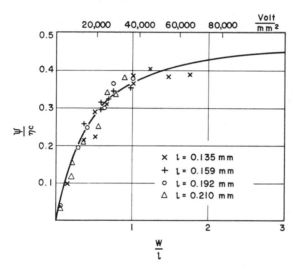

FIG. 7.10. Plot of ψ/η_c against w/l for rock salt. Plot of Rögener (S), using the data of Flechsig (S).

Flechsig's (S) early measurements of the photoconductivity in x-rayed natural NaCl at RT show a saturation in the photocurrent for a potential drop of the order of 4000 volts. Since μT depends only on the F-center concentration, it does not vary with the voltage. Therefore, w is proportional to the field, and we have the relation

$$\frac{w}{l} = c\,\frac{\text{potential}}{(\text{thickness})^2}, \qquad (7.21)$$

where c is a constant. Hence, if c is known, plots of $Q/2Q_m$ against potential(thickness)$^{-2}$ should have the analytical form of (7.20). By adjusting the scale, that is, c, Rögener obtained plots of $Q/2Q_m$ against potential(thickness)$^{-2}$, agreeing with the theoretical curve. These are shown in Fig. 7.10. This evaluates c and determines w/l. For NaCl, he used Flechsig's data. Rögener used his own measurements on additively colored KCl at RT. Combining these values with low-field measurements (that is, $\eta_c w/F$), he evaluated η_c. Some typical data are shown in Table 7.5. Rögener's average η_c is 1.8. From (7.17) and our elementary concept,

TABLE 7.5. DIRECT MEASUREMENTS OF η_c ADDITIVELY
COLORED KCl AT RT[a]

w/F (cm^2/volt)	$\eta_c (w/F)$ (cm^2/volt)	η_c
3.2×10^{-7}	3.7×10^{-7}	1.2
2.4×10^{-7}	7×10^{-7}	2.95
7.1×10^{-7}	5.8×10^{-7}	0.8

[a] After Rögener (S).

one would expect that η_c would be slightly less than unity at these temperatures. Although the results are not completely satisfactory, it is remarkable that one may measure η_c by this means and obtain results which are of the right order of magnitude. The data support Hecht's theory very well. We attribute the difference to experimental difficulties and accept (7.17) as correct with two empirical constants, $\epsilon_t(1)$ and A/s. While one would like additional studies of Rögener's type and a better understanding of the ratio of A/s, one must admit that the data presented in this section make a remarkably consistent story.

REFERENCES

Th. P. J. Botden, C. Z. van Doorn, and Y. Haven, *Philips Res. Rept.* **9**, 469 (1954).
F. C. Brown and N. Inchauspé, *Phys. Rev.* **121**, 1303 (1961).
W. Flechsig, *Z. Physik* **46**, 788 (1927).
G. F. J. Garlick, "Luminescent Materials." Oxford Univ. Press, London and New York, 1949.
G. Glaser, *Gött. Nachr.* **3**, 31 (1937).
G. Glaser and W. Lehfeldt, *Gött. Nachr.* **2**, 91 (1936).

B. Gudden and R. Pohl, *Z. Physik* **31**, 651 (1925).

Z. Gyulai, *Z. Physik* **32**, 103 (1925).

K. Hecht, *Z. Physik* **77**, 235 (1932).

J. R. MacDonald and M. K. Brachman, *J. Chem. Phys.* **22**, 1314 (1954) and reference therein.

M. Onuki, *J. Phys. Soc. Japan* **16**, 981 (1961).

M. Onuki and H. Ohkura, *J. Phys. Soc. Japan* **15**, 1862 (1960).

H. G. Redfield, *Phys. Rev.* **94**, 537 (1954).

H. Rögener, *Gött. Nachr.* **3**, 219 (1941).

A. Rose, *Photoconduct. Conf.*, *Atlantic City* (1954) p. 3. Wiley, New York, 1956.

W. Shockley, "Electrons and Holes in Semiconductors." Van Nostrand, New York, 1950.

R. S. van Heyningen and F. C. Brown, *Phys. Rev.* **111**, 462 (1958).

O. von Gericke, *Gött. Nachr.* 1 (1950).

R. L. Wild and F. C. Brown, *Phys. Rev.* **121**, 1296 (1961).

IV. Other Optical Properties of *F*-Centers

In the next few sections we shall discuss various other properties of the
F-center. Based on these properties we shall be able to build an energy
level diagram of this imperfection. As far as the author knows, no one has
attempted to draw an energy level diagram for an imperfection where
there are strong interactions between the trapped electron or electrons
and the lattice. Hence, this diagram will have some novel features. Very
recently, Wood and Joy (S) have also drawn such a diagram. The
diagram will be discussed in Section 12.

8. THE LUMINESCENCE

When discussing the properties of η_c at low temperature, we assumed
that there is a probability of a downward transition with the emission of a
photon (luminescence), this being given by A of Eq. (7.16b). Since the
time when Mott and Gurney suggested the existence of this emission,
considerable effort has been expended in attempts to find it. The first
successful one was the result of the work of Botden, van Doorn, and
Haven (S). Subsequently, the situation has been clarified due to work in
Holland and Stuttgart, and we now have a preliminary understanding of
the luminescence associated with the *F*-center.

In Fig. 8.1, we show the *F*-center emission in KCl at several temperatures taken from the data of Lüty and Gebhardt (S). In Fig. 8.2 the
variation of the width $H(e)$ and the peak of the band $\epsilon_m(e)$ are plotted as a
function of temperature. For comparison, the data in Fig. 3.7a are shown.
Like the absorption band, the emission is nonsymmetric and can be
described by a double Gaussian curve. The difference in the coefficients,
however, is smaller. As will be shown later, these data are of extreme
theoretical importance, and will be discussed in Sections 30 and 31. In
Table 8.1, we have summarized the data taken from the original paper of
Botden, van Doorn, and Haven. The reader will note a slight disagree-
ment in the value of $H(e)$ reported in Table 8.1 and in Fig. 8.1.

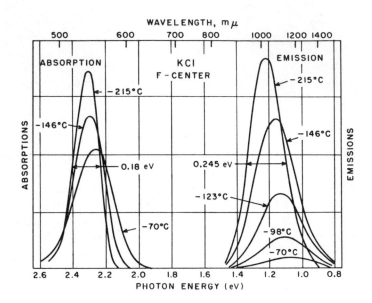

FIG. 8.1. Emission and absorption curves on the F-center in KCl at various temperatures (after Lüty, S).

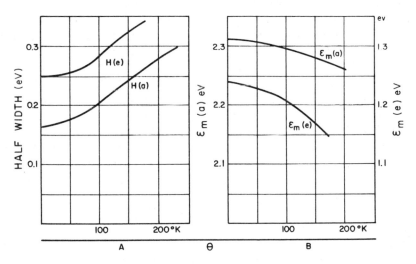

FIG. 8.2. Variation of H versus θ for absorption and emission in KCl (after Lüty and Gebhardt, S, and Konitzer and Markham, S).

The emission is greatly affected by the treatment of the crystal. We must, therefore, briefly consider what happens to an F-center when it is exposed to light at room temperature. The situation is illustrated in Fig. 8.3. Curve A shows a typical absorption curve of a heavily colored crystal (additive). The peak of the F-band is off the scale of the figure and our interest is in the small absorption bands to the red. Curve A' gives the emission data corresponding to the figure on the left A. Here the emission curve peaks at 1.2 ev and has a $H(e)$ value of approximately 0.28 ev.

TABLE 8.1. THE PEAK AND HALF-WIDTH OF THE EMISSION BAND
OF THE F-CENTER AT $20°\,\mathrm{K}$[a]

Alkali halide	$\epsilon_m(e)$ (ev)	λ_e (mμ)	$H(e)$ (ev)
KCl	1.26	980	0.26
KBr	0.97	1280	0.19
KI	0.85	1450	0.15
RbCl	1.1	1120	0.22
NaCl	1.1	1120[b]	

[a] After Botden, van Doorn, and Haven (S).
[b] At $77°\,\mathrm{K}$.

As the F-band is exposed to light, absorption bands appear to the red (see Section 14b), and this induces changes in the luminescence, as is evident from the emission curves on the right-hand side of the figure. The final emission is a band which peaks at about 1 ev. The small band which appears in curves A and B to the right of the F is the M-band. Measurements of van Doorn (S) indicate that the quantum efficiency decreases as the ratio of the M-band to the F-band increases. We define the quantum efficiency for luminescence as η_l

$$\eta_l = \frac{\text{quantum emitted}}{\text{quantum absorbed}}. \tag{8.1}$$

Some typical measurements are shown in Table 8.2. We have reproduced one part of van Doorn's data, and perhaps we have not done him full justice, since Table 8.2 does not completely establish the conclusion that the presence of M-centers (centers associated with the M-band) quenches the F-luminescence. Apparently, there is a complex relation between the two, but its exact nature does not seem to have been established at present. We shall return to this question in Section 14, where the relations between the F-center and the centers responsible for the bands which form on bleaching at high temperatures (approximately RT) will be discussed in greater detail. Pick (S) has given the quantum efficiency as a

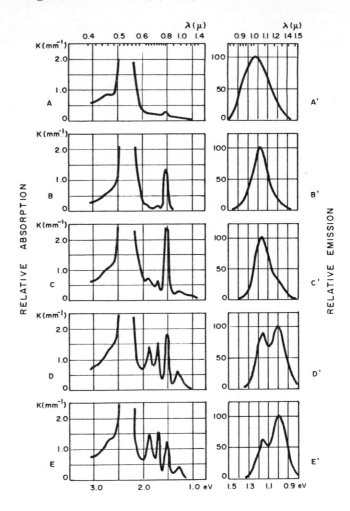

FIG. 8.3. Absorption and luminescence of the F-center in KCl at 77° K (after van Doorn and Haven, S). Curves A, A′: immediately after quenching from 610°C; B, B′: after a 10-min bleach at RT; C, C′: after a 25-min bleach at RT; D, D′: after a 165-min bleach at RT; E. E′: after an 18-hr bleach at RT.

TABLE 8.2. LUMINESCENCE EFFICIENCY OF THE F-CENTER
IN KCl AT 77° K

Concentrations of F-centers per cm^{-3}	Ratio[a] of $\alpha_m(M)$ to $\alpha_m(F)$	Quantum efficiency (%)
6×10^{15}	0	63
5×10^{16}	0	77
5×10^{16}	6.0	71
6×10^{17}	1.8	36

[a] $\alpha_m(F)$ is the maximum absorption for the F-band; $\alpha_m(M)$ is the corresponding quantity for the M [after van Doorn (S)].

function of concentration (Fig. 8.4) at approximately the same temperature, 73° K. These data do not agree with those of van Doorn as shown in Table 8.2. The table refers to smaller values of concentration than does the figure. We do not know if one may produce pure F-centers at a

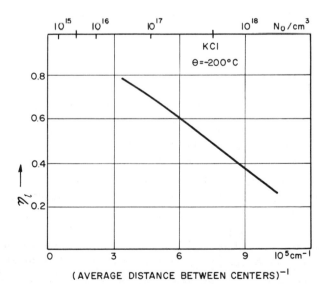

FIG. 8.4. Quantum efficiency of luminescence as a function of F-center concentration; N_0 concentration of F-centers (after Pick, S).

concentration of $10^{18}/cm^3$ (from electron paramagnetic resonance studies; one suspects, however, that it is possible—see Section 24).

The first reliable measurements of the quantum efficiency of η_l as a function of the temperature were obtained by Becker and Pick (S) (see Fig. 8.5). As might have been expected, η_l does increase rapidly at low temperatures below the photoconductivity knee (see Fig. 7.8), since in Eq. (7.17) A is greater than $se^{-\epsilon_t(1)/k\theta}$. The work of Becker and Pick

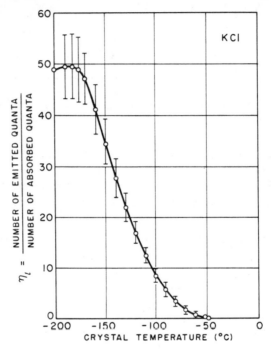

FIG. 8.5. Temperature dependence of η_e y-axis is in percent (after Becker and Pick, S).

strongly suggests that the low temperature drop in η_c is due to the luminescence, that is, the electron does not escape into the conduction band from the excited level. This is, therefore, a justification for the arguments leading to Eq. (7.17).

The reciprocal of A in Eq. (7.16) is the lifetime of the F-center in the excited state. This can be measured directly and indirectly. Such measurements have been done by Swank and Brown (S) and by Watts and Noble (S). Some are shown in Table 8.3. First we note that the lifetimes are of the order of 10^{-6} sec, not 10^{-8} or 10^{-9} sec as expected from Eq.

(7.16). In the author's opinion, this large difference has not been resolved. Since Watts and Noble used entirely different equipment, there can be no question regarding the correctness of the measurements of Swank and Brown.

TABLE 8.3. LIFETIME IN THE EXCITED STATE[a]

Alkali halide	Lifetime (10^{-6} sec)	$\epsilon_t(1)$ (ev)	
		Göttingen	Swank and Brown
NaCl	1.00	0.11	0.074
KCl	0.571	0.08–0.14	0.154
KBr	1.11	0.15	0.135
KI	2.22	0.10	0.110

[a] After Swank and Brown (S).

The recent measurements of $\epsilon_t(1)$ agree approximately with the results of the Göttingen measurements (Table 7.4). The reader will note that large variations exist for KCl in Table 7.4. We shall not attempt to explain the factor of 100 between the theory and the experiment here, but shall return to this question briefly when we discuss models of the F-center.

The information given in this section is slightly sketchy, reflecting the unsatisfactory knowledge of the F-center luminescence, in spite of the fact that it is one of the most important properties of the F-center. We shall return to this problem later, in Sections 13 and 33, after some of the bleaching properties of the F-center at low temperature, NT, have been discussed.

One should note, however, that the point of initial emission to the violet of $\epsilon_m(e)$ is temperature independent, not ϵ_v as in F-absorption bands.

REFERENCES

K. H. Becker and H. Pick, *Gött. Nachr.* 167 (1956).
Th. P. J. Botden, C. Z. van Doorn, and Y. Haven, *Philips Res. Rept.* 9, 469 (1954).
J. D. Konitzer and J. J. Markham, *J. Chem. Phys.* 32, 843 (1960).
F. Lüty and W. Gebhardt, *Z. Physik* 169, 475 (1962).
F. Lüty, "Elektronenubergange an Farbzentren," *Halbleiterprobleme* 6, 238 (1961).
H. Pick, *Nuovo Cimento Suppl.* 7, 2, 498 (1958).

C. Z. van Doorn, *Philips Res. Rept.* **13**, 296 (1958).
C. Z. van Doorn and Y. Haven, *Philips Res. Rept.* **11**, 479 (1956).
R. K. Swank and F. C. Brown, *Phys. Rev.* **130**, 34 (1963).
H. Watts and G. A. Noble, *J. Chem. Phys.* **40**, 2051 (1964).
R. F. Wood and H. W. Joy, *Phys. Rev.* **136**, A451 (1964).

9. The Bleaching of the *F*-Center at Low Temperature

A host of phenomena occur when one exposes a crystal with pure *F*-centers to light. The effects depend on the temperature and the length of exposure. First, we may examine the effect of ionizing the *F*-center at

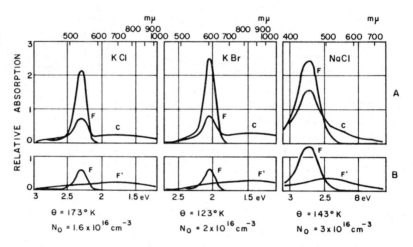

FIG. 9.1. Effect of bleaching KCl, KBr, and NaCl at the indicated temperatures. The absorption measurements were taken at lower temperatures. The lower diagram is the resolution of curve C shown in the diagram above; N_0 equals the concentration of *F*-centers (after Pick, 1938S).

low θ by studying the new bands which form. One may release electrons by irradiating the *F*-center with light at not too low a temperature (above HT); this process will be referred to as optical bleaching. Of course, some bleaching occurs during the photoconductivity measurements; however, the number of destroyed centers is kept to a minimum. Prolonged optical bleaching affects the photoconductivity as is evidenced from Fig. 7.5b.

This type of study was also started in about 1925 in Göttingen. An understanding of the low-temperature phenomena, however, was not obtained until 1938 and 1940, when Pick (S) made some very important studies of these effects. The problem of high-temperature bleaching was studied independently by Molnar (S) in 1940 at MIT and by Petroff (S) during the war at Göttingen. The high-temperature phenomena are not completely understood at present. The present data indicate that high-temperature bleaching causes effects which modify the *F*-center; this topic is outside the scope of this book, and is dealt with only briefly (in Section 14).

Figure 9.1 shows the effect of bleaching additively colored KCl, KBr, and NaCl. The values given in the figure denote the temperature of the crystal during bleaching. The absorption measurements were made at a lower θ; the spectra range of the bleaching light is in the *F*-absorption band. The crystals were handled with care, having been rapidly quenched from a high temperature (300°–600° C) after the additive coloration. The excitation produces another band, known as the *F'*, which is very broad and peaks to the red of the *F*. Actually, the breadths are so large that one may not ascribe a meaningful value of ϵ_m and H. Some very rough estimates are given in Table 9.1.

TABLE 9.1. PROPERTIES OF THE *F'*-BAND[a]

Crystal	$\epsilon_m(F')$ (ev)	$H(F')$ (ev)
NaCl	2.4	2
KCl	2.3	2
KBr	1.3	2

[a] From Fig. 9.1.

On bleaching the *F'*-band, one re-forms the *F*-centers and the crystal returns to its original state. One may define two types of quantum yields for these processes, namely*

$$\eta(2F \to F') = \eta(F') = \frac{\text{number of } F\text{-centers destroyed}}{\text{number of quanta absorbed by } F\text{-centers}},$$

$$(9.1)$$

* The reason for the notation will become clear after we examine the data. The definitions (9.1) and (9.2) do not agree with those found in Pick's paper but reflect a more recent interpretation (Seitz, 1946).

which occurs when F-centers are exposed to light, and

$$\eta(F' \to 2F) = \eta(F) = \frac{\text{number of } F\text{-centers created}}{\text{number of quanta absorbed by } F'\text{-centers}}$$

(9.2)

corresponding to the situation when F'-centers are destroyed optically. If the bands were well separated, the numerators could be measured directly with the use of Kleinschrod's f (for K-KCl). Since the bands overlap, one measures ΔK, the change of absorption at the peak of the F-band. ΔK results from a *decrease* in the F absorption and an *increase* in the F' absorption, or vice versa, and $\Delta K = \Delta K_F - \Delta K_{F'}$; hence

$$a = \frac{\Delta K_F}{\Delta K} = \frac{\Delta K + \Delta K_{F'}}{\Delta K},$$

(9.3)

$\Delta K_{F'}$ is the change in the F' absorption at the peak of the F-band. By resolving the actual absorption into two bands (see Fig. 9.1), one may estimate a, provided the ratio of $\Delta K_F / \Delta K_{F'}$ is independent of the concentration—a fact we shall establish. Since the shape of the F-band varies with θ, a should be slightly temperature dependent. Our definition of η makes it dependent on the concentration of imperfections: F-centers; F'-centers; and, as we shall see, the negative-ion vacancies.

Pick first studied the effect of θ and time of irradiation on $\eta(2F \to F')$. These data for KCl are given in Fig. 9.2. $\eta(F')$ is the slope of the curve, and it changes with time of irradiation. The initial value, $\eta_0(F')$, is 2 for temperatures between $-100°$ C and $-130°$ C. This means that for every absorbed photon, we destroy *two* (not one) F-centers. At low temperatures, $\eta_0(F')$ decreases markedly as shown. A plot of $\eta_0(F')$ as a function of θ appears on the right-hand side of Fig. 9.3. We note a similarity between the knees in Figs. 7.7 and 9.3. The knees, however, do not fall exactly at the same temperature.

Pick's data for $\eta(F)$ are given in Fig. 9.4* and a plot of $\eta_0(F)$ against θ is found in Fig. 9.3. The latter graph resembles the luminescent curve (Fig. 8.5), especially around $-100°$ C. The scatter in the data is large at $-200°$ C in both curves, so that one is not able to draw any conclusions regarding their similarity in that region.

---

* Actually, Pick does not report his data in the fashion shown but plots the number of F'-centers destroyed. He determines this by assuming that one F'-center is destroyed per F created. We have used this assumption in Fig. 9.3 and plotted the actual measured quantity.

We may resolve the problem of a quantum yield equal to two by assuming that every electron released from one F-center is trapped by a second F-center; thus, two centers are destroyed per photon absorbed. Likewise, if an electron is released from an F'-center, it creates two

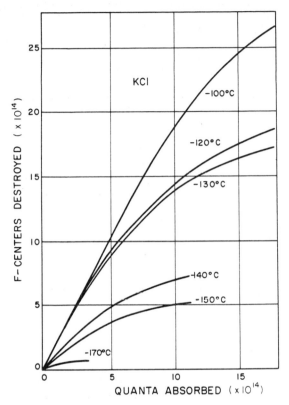

Fig. 9.2. Effects of bleaching the F-band at various temperatures. Number of F-centers destroyed as a function of the quanta absorbed in the F-band (after Pick, 1938S).

F-centers, one by the ionization and the other by a trapping process at another imperfection. We may, indeed, write a "chemical reaction equation" as follows

$$2F \rightleftarrows F'. \tag{9.4}$$

This is the reason for the nomenclature in Eqs. (9.1) and (9.2).

We would like to stress two points (see Markham, S). Consider briefly an electron wandering through the conduction band. Let there be n_-

traps per unit volume which can capture an electron and form an F-center. The argument only requires an electron trap. For convenience, we assume that it is a negative-ion vacancy (see Section 25). Let n_F be the concentration of F-centers (it replaces N_0 of Section 3). The probability that an electron in the conduction band ends up at a negative-ion vacancy is

$$P(F) = \frac{n_- \sigma_-}{n_- \sigma_- + n_F \sigma_F},\qquad(9.5)$$

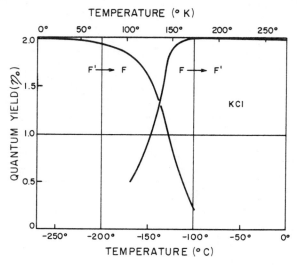

FIG. 9.3. $\eta_0(2F \to F')$ and $\eta_0(F' \to 2F)$ as a function of temperature (after Pick, 1940S).

where σ_- is the cross section for a vacancy to capture an electron and form an F-center;* σ_F is the cross section for an F-center to capture an electron and form an F'-center; and n_- equals the concentration of negative vacancies. Likewise, we define the probability of an electron forming an F'-center by

$$P(F') = \frac{n_F \sigma_F}{n_- \sigma_- + n_F \sigma_F}.\qquad(9.6)$$

Since $P(F) + P(F') = 1$, we are assuming that the electron in additively colored crystals has only two choices. This assumption underlies Pick's work and seems to hold for well-quenched crystals at low θ.†

---

* That is the probability of an electron ending up in the *ground state* of the trap.

† The situation might be different at *extremely* low temperatures ($10°$ K).

$\eta(F')$ is the product of the probability for releasing an electron to the conduction band, that is, η_c of Eq. (7.17), times $P(F')$; hence

$$\eta(2F \rightarrow F') = \frac{2n_F \sigma_F}{n_F \sigma_F + n_- \sigma_-} \frac{1}{1+(A/s)\exp[\epsilon_t(1)/k\theta]} . \qquad (9.7)$$

The factor 2 appears because one F-center is ionized while another is transformed.

Initially, in Pick's experiments, n_- is either a very small value or zero since the experiments are done at low temperatures; hence, $P(F') \rightarrow 1$

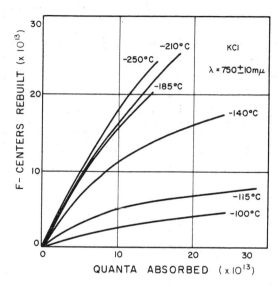

FIG. 9.4. Number of rebuilt F-centers as a function of the quanta absorbed in the F'-band at various temperatures (after Pick, 1940S).

and $\eta_0(F')$ is given by the second factor of (9.7). In the experiment, one has to irradiate in both the F- and F'-bands. Hence, as the concentration of F' increases, one starts to rebuild the F-centers.* The drop in the slope $\eta(F')$ (Fig. 9.2) with time of irradiation results from two causes—(1) an increase in n_- and (2) the photoionization of some F'-centers. At low temperatures, $\eta_0(F')$ decreases because only a fraction of the excited

* Actually, the number of negative-ion vacancies measured by Rabin (see Table 5.6) is comparable to the F-center concentration. The vacancies which are initially present in the crystal do not seem to take part in the experiments of Pick. The reason for this is not completely clear.

F-centers release electrons to the conduction band. This qualitatively explains the behavior observed by Pick. The fraction of *F*-centers which can be converted to F' depends on the temperature. Pick has measured this fraction as a function of θ; these data are given in Fig. 9.5(D, E, and F).

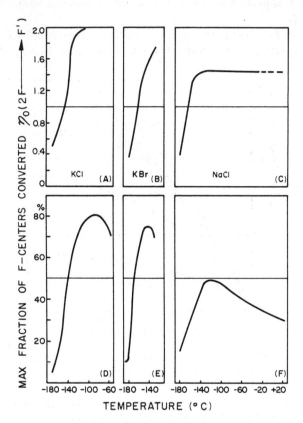

FIG. 9.5A, B, and C. $\eta_0(F')$ as a function of θ for KCl, KBr, and NaCl. For KBr and NaCl, the oscillator strength f of Section 4 was unknown and it was not included in the data. Parts D, E, and F show the maximum fraction of *F*-center one can convert to F'-centers in KCl, KBr, and NaCl at various temperatures (after Pick, 1938S).

On the top of this figure (A, B, C), $\eta_0(F')$ is plotted as a function of temperature. The curve for KCl goes to two at high temperatures. The reason for this is that these data include Kleinschrod's f factor (see Table 4.1). This factor had not been measured for NaCl and KBr. Using

Fig. 9.3, we may evaluate f for NaCl ($f = 1.45/2 = 0.72$). This value agrees with the data of Heer and co-worker reported in Table 4.2.

One may make two assumptions regarding $\eta(F' \to 2F)$. First, we might assume that negative-ion vacancies trap electrons in their ground state. As the measurement of Smakula shows (Section 11), the F is stable at these temperatures and

$$\eta(F' \to 2F) = \frac{2n_- \sigma_-}{n_F \sigma_F + n_- \sigma_-}. \tag{9.8a}$$

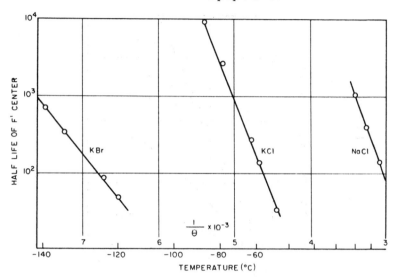

FIG. 9.6. Half-life of F'-centers at various temperatures for KCl, KBr, and NaCl (after Pick, 1938S).

On the other hand, the electron might be captured in the excited state and, hence, there is a probability that the center will be ionized, as given by η_c of Eq. (7.17). Using this second assumption, we obtain:*

$$\eta(F' \to 2F) = \frac{2n_- \sigma_-}{n_F \sigma_F + n_- \sigma_-} \left\{ 1 - \frac{1}{1 + (A/s)\, e^{\epsilon_t(1)/k\theta}} \right\}. \tag{9.8b}$$

* Our arguments are only qualitative since we ignore the following more complex process: An electron is released from the F'; then it is captured to form an F-center in an excited state. It could be released to the conduction band, only to be retrapped by a negative-ion vacancy, etc. Every time the electron is in the conduction band, it could form an F'-center. This type process must be important at some temperatures. Since we are only attempting to develop a semiquantitative picture, we ignore these complications.

Equation (9.8a) cannot explain the temperature behavior of $\eta_0(F)$; Eq. (9.8b), however, does. We may hence assume that the electron is captured in the excited state of the negative-ion vacancy.

The F' is thermally unstable at higher temperatures. Pick has measured the decay rate and found that it is not given by an equation of the type $e^{-\lambda t}$. Nevertheless, he reports the initial half life as a function of θ. His data are shown in Fig. 9.6. When the F' is unstable, bleaching produces another series of bands. These will be discussed in Section 14.

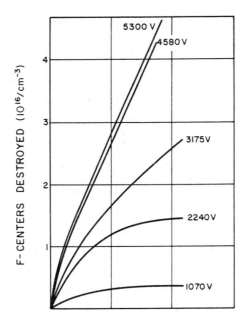

QUANTA ABSORBED

FIG. 9.7. Plot of the number of F-centers destroyed in KCl as a function of photons absorbed in the F-band at NT for various voltages. Crystal thickness 0.2 mm (after Lüty, S).

If the electron can only be trapped to form an F- or an F'-center, then ΔK_F and $\Delta K_{F'}$ are related, since these quantities are proportional to the changes in F- and F'-concentration, i.e., $\Delta K_F + \alpha \Delta K_{F'} = 0$ where α is some appropriate constant depending on the overlap of the two bands. This is the justification of the constancy of a in Eq. (9.3).

Lüty (S) has made an important contribution to our knowledge of the first excited state of the F-center. He used Pick's technique, but applied a strong electric field to assist the electrons to escape from the excited state into the conduction band. The experimental techniques are simple in principle; they are the same as Pick's except that an electric field is applied. His basic data are shown in Fig. 9.7. The curve resembles those

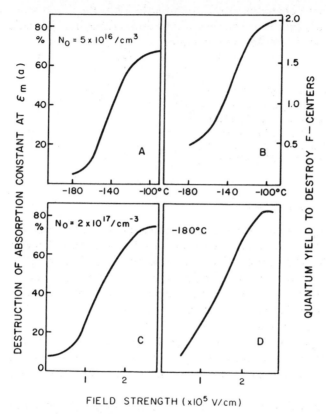

FIG. 9.8. Plot of the quantum efficiency of destroying an F-center in KCl as a function of temperature (B) and of field strength (D). Plots of the maximum number of F-centers that are destroyed are also shown (A and B). N_0 is the concentration of F-centers (after Lüty, S).

shown in Fig. 9.2 except that the temperature was kept constant at $93°$ K and is not a parameter associated with the individual curve. The applied voltage was altered so that the field used on the crystal varied from 53,500 volts/cm to 265,000 volts/cm. In Fig. 9.8, Lüty compares the situations when the temperature is changed (Pick's case) and when the field was changed.

The explanation of Lüty's results must be in a Zener-type tunneling from the trapped excited state to the conduction band. Since our knowledge of how to calculate the ionization energy is extremely limited, one can only make very preliminary estimates of the effects of the field. Some of these have been done by Lüty himself. The effect he discovered is, of course, very important and should be studied further theoretically. We, however, shall not do so in this book.

REFERENCES

F. Lüty, *Z. Physik* **153**, 247 (1958).
J. J. Markham, *Phys. Rev.* **88**, 500 (1952).
J. P. Molnar, Thesis, MIT (1940).
S. Petroff, *Z. Physik* **127**, 443 (1950).
H. Pick, *Ann. Physik* **31**, 365 (1938).
H. Pick, *Ann. Physik* **37**, 421 (1940).

10. THE α- AND β-BANDS

Associated with the F- and F'-centers are two other bands, known as the α- and the β-bands. They appear to the violet and ultraviolet near or in the edge absorption. They were discovered by Delbecq, Pringsheim, and Yuster (S) in a series of remarkable experiments. Their properties were studied further at Göttingen by Martienssen (Sa, b). The edge absorption in KI at RT and NT is shown in Fig. 10.1. Actually, the edge is more complex than is indicated in this figure, since small bands appear at the point where the edge absorption starts when the measurements are taken at lower temperatures (5° K). The small additional "bands" are most probably due to impurities, since they vary with the sample.

Upon x-raying the crystal at RT, the spectra shown in Fig. 10.2 appear (the measurements were made at NT). The band to the right is the F-band which we have been describing. Before bleaching, a single band appears at 226 mμ (5.48 ev). In actual measurement, the β-band appears as a perturbation of the fundamental band edge, and it is only after the subtraction of the intrinsic absorption that one can obtain the nice narrow structure shown in Fig. 10.2. Since the intrinsic absorption is large, there is always an element of uncertainty regarding the shape of this band— that is, its peak value, ϵ_β, and its width, H_β.* The β-band can be measured at RT and ϵ_β in KI is 5.27 ev (235 mμ).

---

* In this section, we shall replace α_m by α_F, etc., to simplify the notation.

Upon bleaching the *F*-band at low temperatures, a second narrow band, the α, appears to the right of the β-band, as is also shown in the figure. The band appears only after bleaching at low temperatures. The results of some experiments on additively colored KI are shown in Fig. 10.3, again taken from the study of Delbecq, Pringsheim, and Yuster (S). The *F*- and

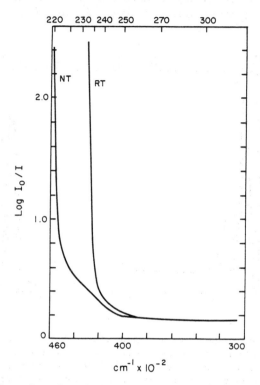

FIG. 10.1. Absorption edge of KI at room temperature and at liquid nitrogen temperatures (after Delbecq, Pringsheim, and Yuster, 1951S).

β-bands are large before bleaching and become small after bleaching; the exposure to light produces the α-band as shown.

The discoverers of the α- and β-band postulated that the imperfection responsible for the *F*-band perturbs the fundamental absorption of the crystal, thus creating these new bands. The β-band is due to the perturbation of the fundamental absorption by the *F*-center itself; the α-band is due to the perturbation of an ionized *F*-center. On the deBoer model (see Section 25), the β-band is due to the perturbation of the fundamental absorption caused by a negative-ion vacancy which has trapped an electron, while the α-band is just due to the perturbation of the negative-ion vacancy alone.

This hypothesis has two experimental consequences:

(1) The ratios of the area under the *F*- and β-bands should be the same. If the temperature does not change, H_F and H_β are constant; then

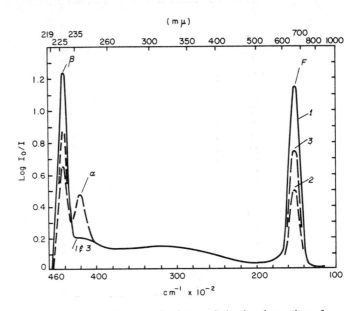

Fig. 10.2. Changes (edge absorption subtracted) in the absorption of a potassium iodide crystal due to treatment as indicated (all measurements made at liquid nitrogen temperature) (after Delbecq, Pringshein, and Yuster, S). *Curve* 1, 20-min exposure to soft x-rays at room temperature; *curve* 3, 75 hr in dark at room temperature; *curve* 2, additional 35-min bleach with *F*-light at liquid nitrogen temperature.

the values of α_F and α_β can be compared. Careful measurements of Martienssen (Sb) indicate that the ratio of α_β/α_F is constant under a large variety of conditions.* (See Fig. 10.4.)

(2) If one assumes that in an x-rayed crystal there are hole centers (that is, imperfections which have trapped holes in the valence band), and that every electron released from an *F*-center (by bleaching) ends up at

---

* This is a strong argument to indicate a relation between the two bands. However, such a relation can be obtained when the bands are not associated with a single imperfection; see, for example, Duerig (S).

such a trap, then the above hypothesis requires that one α-center be produced for *every* F-center destroyed. In an additively colored crystal this would not be true since, as we have seen in Section 9, F'-centers are produced. The production of an F'-center destroys an F-center but does not produce an α-band, although it might perturb the intrinsic absorption of the crystal and produce bands similar to the α and β. (No

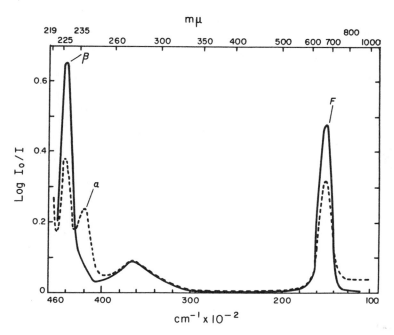

FIG. 10.3. Changes in the absorption of a KI crystal due to treatment as indicated (all measurements made at liquid nitrogen temperature) (after Delbecq, Pringsheim, and Yuster, S). *Curve* —, additively colored in sodium vapor; *curve* ---, bleached with F-light at liquid nitrogen temperature.

such band has been observed.) In this case, the change in α_α should be proportional to half the change in α_F. The proportionality factor can be established in x-rayed crystals and then compared to the one found in additively colored ones. Delbecq, Pringsheim, and Yuster have bleached additively colored and x-rayed crystals and established that the above arguments hold only approximately, as expected, since F'-centers are also formed in x-rayed crystals—although a large fraction of the released electrons end up at hole centers.

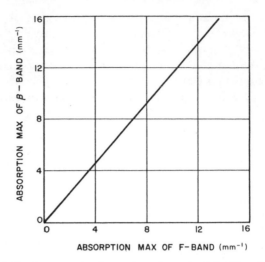

ABSORPTION MAX OF F−BAND (mm⁻¹)

F_IG. 10.4. Relation between the absorption of a peak of the *F*- and β-band in KBr (after Martienssen, Sa).

Martienssen extended the work done at the Argonne Laboratory and obtained the position of the α- and β-bands in several of the alkali halides. These are given in Table 10.1. These data agree with the values of the Argonne group.

T_ABLE 10.1. P_OSITION OF THE α- AND β-B_ANDS[a]

Alkali halide	NaF[b]	NaCl[b]	NaBr[b]	KCl[b]	KBr[c]	KI[c]	RbBr[c]	RbI[c]
α-Band:	9.43	7.16	6.23	6.95	6.15	5.21	6.04	5.16
β-Band:	9.75	7.38		7.31	6.44	5.48	6.31	5.40

[a] Data are in electron volts, measured at about 90° K.
[b] Onaka and Fujita (S).
[c] Martienssen (Sb).

The importance of the α-band is that it gives us information regarding the presence of negative-ion vacancies. Since no α-band appears in untreated crystals, we may conclude that there are no single negative-ion vacancies present. This conclusion leads to several problems. Etzel and Maurer (S) have shown from ionic conductivity measurements that the number of positive-ion vacancies in NaCl is approximately 10^{17} cm^{-3} at room temperature or below. We have seen that the number of negative-ion vacancies is of the order of 10^{17} (see Section 5.5). The positive-ion vacancy should be dissociated, since it produces a conductivity. This would lead us to suspect that the negative-ion vacancies are also dissociated and one should always be able to observe an α-band, which is not the case. Evidently, the negative-ion vacancy reported by Rabin must be in some associated form if our interpretation of this work on the α- and β-bands is correct.

A very strange phenomenon occurs during x-irradiation at low temperature. This is illustrated in Fig. 10.5, taken from Martienssen (Sb).

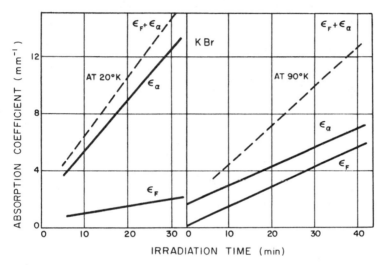

FIG. 10.5. Growth rate curves of the α and F produced by x-irradiation of KBr at 20° K and at 90° K. The dashed line is the sum of the growth curves (60 kev x-rayed at 6×10^{-3} amp were employed). (After Martienssen, Sb.)

On the left are shown growth rate curves for the α- and F-bands when a crystal of KBr is exposed to 60-kev x-rays at 20° K. The α-band grows rapidly while the F-band has a much slower growth rate. At 90° K, the situation is not nearly so extreme. We know from other studies that the α-band (negative-ion vacancy) will form even at higher temperatures. Figure 10.5 indicates that the production of negative-ion vacancies is not the only requirement for the formation of F-centers. Indeed, at very low temperatures, the production rate does not seem to be governed by the presence or absence of negative-ion vacancies. Perhaps the trapping of an electron at a negative-ion vacancy requires an activation energy, or there may be many holes in the valance band which destroy the F-centers or, finally, there may be an imperfection at low temperatures which competes for the free electrons formed by the ionizing radiation.*

The α-band does not always form but seems to require crystals of considerable purity. Hersh (S) tried to produce the α-band in KI at HT and NT in a crystal grown by the Harshaw Chemical Company. At HT, the phenomenon reported by Delbecq, Pringsheim, and Yuster did not

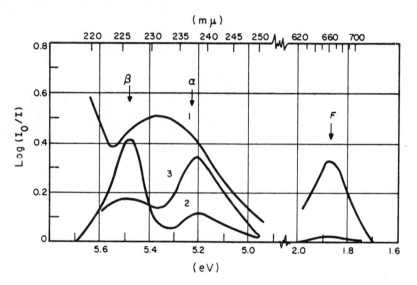

FIG. 10.6. Effect of the sample on the production of the α- and β-bands in KI. *Curve* 1 (x-rayed) at HT; *curves* 2 (x-rayed) and 3 (bleached) at NT. On bleaching, the F-band rises (not shown) (after Hersh, S).

occur; instead, a very broad band was produced in the α–β spectra region. At a subsequent date, Hersh was able to obtain KI which he believes were purer (again from the Harshaw Chemical Company) and, in this case, the α- and β-bands appeared as in the case when one irradiates KI at NT. His results are shown in Fig. 10.6. Similar results were obtained on crystals grown at Argonne National Laboratory by Delbecq and Yuster.

Dexter (S) and Fuchs (S) have attempted to calculate the properties of these new bands. We shall not present these calculations but only indicate

* The author believed that the third situation applied (See Markham, S). Since then, the presence of the V_k-center has been established (see Section 14c). This imperfection probably is the responsible electron trap.

the general principles involved. We believe that the transition at the absorption edge of the band in a perfect alkali halide lattice is due to a transition of an electron from a Cl^- ion to a Na^+ ion.* (For a simple picture, see the paper of Slater and Shockley, S.) If this occurs next to a negative-ion vacancy, the electron goes to a positive ion adjacent to the vacancy. This situation will be unstable and the electron will be pulled into the vacancy to form an *F*-center. The hole may or may not attach itself to the *F*-center by polarizing it. Most probably, the hole is free; otherwise, it would distort *F*-centers. Hence, the α-band is due to a transition of an electron from a next-nearest neighbor ion to a negative-ion vacancy. This forms an *F*-center. In the case of the β-band, the transition is again from a Cl^- ion but the resulting imperfection is now a negative-ion vacancy with two electrons, that is, an F'-center. These concepts are the basis of Dexter's calculation. Naturally, various relaxation effects have to be taken into account which we have not considered here.

Rüchardt (S) has measured the energy it takes to produce an α-band. The most detailed study is in KBr; this is related to the energy needed to produce an *F*-center.

REFERENCES

C. J. Delbecq, P. Pringsheim, and P. Yuster, *J. Chem. Phys.* **19**, 574 (1951).
W. H. Duerig, *Phys. Rev.* **94**, 65 (1954).
D. L. Dexter, *Phys. Rev.* **83**, 1044 (1951).
H. W. Etzel and R. J. Maurer, *J. Chem. Phys.* **18**, 1003 (1950).
R. Fuchs, *Phys. Rev.* **111**, 387 (1958).
H. N. Hersh, *Phys. Rev.* **105**, 1158 (1957).
J. J. Markham, *Phys. Rev.* **88**, 500 (1952).
W. Martienssen, *Z. Physik* **131**, 488 (1952a).
W. Martienssen, *Gött. Nachr.* p. 111 (1952b).
R. Onaka and I. Fujita, *Phys. Rev.* **119**, 1597 (1960).
H. Rüchardt, *Z. Physik* **140**, 547 (1955).
J. C. Slater and W. Shockley, *Phys. Rev.* **50**, 705 (1936).

11. THE THERMAL IONIZATION OF AN *F*-CENTER

Perhaps the two most picturesque experiments in the field of color centers are those done some time ago by Stasiw (1933S) and by Smakula (S). They approached a very fundamental problem in a simple although

---

* We shall not consider the many refinements associated with this very simple picture. The transitions within an alkali halide are of a complex nature and this problem dates back many years.

elegant manner. Their results are of profound importance. The phase of their work of interest to us here is a by-product that at present seems much more important than the original goal of the experiments. Indeed, their goal could not be achieved by the method employed.

The object was to measure the mobility of an electron in an alkali halide. Little was known about its value since the work predates the famous calculations of Fröhlich and of Mott and Fröhlich (see Mott and Gurney). The concept of the experiment follows directly from the definition of conductivity, namely,

$$I = exv = ex\mu F, \tag{11.1}$$

where

e is the electron charge,

x the number of free electrons per unit volume,

v the electron drift velocity,

μ the electron mobility,*

F the electric field strength, and

I the current density due to the electrons.

If I, e, F, and x are known, one has a measurement of v or μ. The beauty of this work is that the Göttingen workers found some extremely simple means to measure these quantities. Stasiw proceeded to obtain v directly by measuring the velocity of the colored cloud which enters into a crystal from a pointed cathode (Section 2). He used the very simplest means of optical observation, his own eye. Stasiw envisaged other means of obtaining the mobility, one of which was a steady-state method. This was subsequently developed in full by Smakula.

As we stressed in Section 2, one cannot simply inject electrons into a crystal, but must simultaneously produce imperfections which trap these electrons.† This is the disadvantage of the Stasiw method, since his experiments require a colored and uncolored region between which there may be fields. Hence, we turn to the study of Smakula, which is of a more extensive nature.

At Göttingen, several detailed studies have been made since the work of Smakula, which determined in more detail the whole process of electrolytic coloration. The latter, an involved kinetic problem, does not belong

---

* μ without a subscript is the electron mobility, while μ with a subscript is the Gibbs free energies associated with various imperfections.

† If 10^{13} electrons were injected into a crystal from a flat cathode (this is actually impossible), the field build-up would be approximately 2×10^7 volts/cm. This is much larger than that applied to the crystal. This means that an excess of electrons must induce an excess of negative-ion vacancies (we assume the deBoer model; see Section 25).

in this treatment; we have, however, given some important references at the end of the section (see Mollwo, S; Karabascheff, S; Heiland, S).

We wish to understand the steady-state situation. A great deal of confusion exists in the literature regarding the meaning of these measurements (see Pekar, S, and Stasiw, 1959S). Some elementary arguments by Mott and Gurney (p. 140) will be most helpful here. These are brief and will hence be reproduced for completeness. We hope that this analysis will remove some of the confusion. Once again, the assumption is made that the F-center is an electron trapped in a negative-ion vacancy.

Let there be:

(1) N ion pairs in volume V;
(2) n F-centers, and we shall assume that x of them are dissociated;
(3) X positive- and negative-ion vacancies; μ_v is the required Gibbs free energy to form a pair of these vacancies; and
(4) μ_F is the change of Gibbs free energy to just dissociate an F-center (it ignores the energy associated with the motion of electrons in the conduction band; μ_+, μ_-, and μ_F have the same meaning as in Section 6).

We proceed to calculate the total Gibbs free energy and require that

$$\left(\frac{\partial G}{\partial x}\right)_{p,\theta} = \left(\frac{\partial G}{\partial X}\right)_{p,\theta} = 0 \tag{11.2}$$

since we are dealing with an equilibrium state. In the analysis we shall use the Gibbs free energy as in Section 6. Later the free energy will be replaced by the potential energy. This makes the thermodynamic arguments more rigorous although the calculations are so crude that there is no real difference. The number of F-centers is determined by the temperature of injection and the voltage across the crystal. Once the process starts it will be assumed that n does not change, and hence is not a "macroscopic" variable.* We now proceed as before although here there are several ΔS. We note that there are:

$N+X+n$	lattice sites
N	negative ions
$N+n$	positive ions, and
n	F-centers (previously, N_0)

---

* It varies with the run but our interest is in I/n, hence, variations in n need not be considered.

Therefore, the mixing probabilities are:

(1) for the positive-ions

$$P_1 = \frac{(N+X+n)!}{(N+n)!\,X!} ;$$ (11.3)

(2) for the negative-ions

$$P_2 = \frac{(N+X+n)!}{N!\,(X+n)!} ; \quad \text{and}$$ (11.4)

(3) for the *F*-center

$$P_3 = \frac{(X+n)!}{(X+x)!\,(n-x)!}.$$ (11.5)

The total mixing entropy is

$$\Delta S = k \ln \frac{[(N+X+n)!]^2}{(N+n)!\,N!\,X!\,(X+x)!\,(n-x)!}.$$ (11.6)

The Gibbs free energy for an electron in the conduction band has the form (Wilson, S, p. 114)*

$$xk\theta \ln \left\{ \frac{P_e}{(k\theta)^{5/2}} \frac{h^3}{2(2\pi m)^{3/2}} \right\}$$ (11.7)

where

m is the effective mass of the electron and
P_e the "electronic pressure," that is, $xk\theta/V$.

Using the same argument we employed to obtain Eq. (6.7) with the definition given by Eq. (6.8) results in

$$G = (N+n)\mu_+ + N\mu_- + X\mu_v + n\mu_F' + x\mu_F$$

$$+ xk\theta \ln \left\{ \frac{P_e}{(k\theta)^{5/2}} \frac{h^3}{2(2\pi m)^{3/2}} \right\} - k\theta\{2(N+X+n)\ln(N+X+n)$$

$$- (N+n)\ln(N+n) - N\ln N$$

$$- X\ln X - (X+x)\ln(X+x) - (n-x)\ln(n-x)\}.$$ (11.8)

The μ's are the Gibbs free energy and, of course, Stirling's equation has been used. μ_F' is the free energy associated with the formation of an *F*-center in the ground state, while μ_F is the Gibbs free energy associated with the releasing of an electron from a negative-ion vacancy to the conduction band. The zero levels for the ions and electrons are in the

* The additional factor of 2 arises from the spin degeneracy.

dissociated vapor phase (ionized). μ_v is the free energy to form a vacancy pair. One may assume that

$$\frac{\partial}{\partial z}(z \ln z) = \ln z. \tag{11.9}$$

The condition

$$\left(\frac{\partial G}{\partial X}\right) = 0$$

gives

$$\mu_v - k\theta \ln (N + X + n)^2 + k\theta \ln X + k\theta \ln (X + x) = 0. \tag{11.10}$$

This results in the equation

$$\frac{X(X+x)}{N^2} = \exp(-\mu_v/k\theta) \tag{11.11}$$

since $N \gg X$ or n. The second equilibrium condition gives

$$\left[\ln \frac{X+x}{n-x}\right] - \ln\left[\frac{2(2\pi mk\theta)^{3/2}}{h^3}\right] - \ln \frac{V}{x} + \mu_F/k\theta = 0. \tag{11.12}$$

The reader will note that P_e is kept constant during the differentiation. Mott and Gurney obtained expressions (11.11) and (11.12) using the Helmholtz free energy and our μ's are replaced by the energy. It is, of course, somewhat artificial to hold the "electronic pressure" constant as we did and there is no essential difference in the derivations. We shall not differentiate between μ and ϵ (the energy) in the rest of this section. It follows that

$$\frac{x(X+x)}{n-x} = 2\left(\frac{2\pi mk\theta}{h^2}\right)^{3/2} V \exp(-\mu_F/k\theta) = AV\theta^{3/2}\exp(-\mu_F/k\theta) \tag{11.13}$$

where

$$A = 2\left(\frac{2\pi mk}{h^2}\right)^{3/2}. \tag{11.13a}$$

If we assume

$$(1) \quad X \gg x, \quad \text{and} \tag{11.14a}$$
$$(2) \quad n \gg x; \tag{11.14b}$$

the equations of Mott and Gurney result:

$$X = N\exp(-\tfrac{1}{2}\mu_v/k\theta) \tag{11.15a}$$

and

$$x = \frac{n}{X}AV\theta^{3/2}\exp(-\mu_F/k\theta) = \frac{n}{N}V2\left(\frac{2\pi mk\theta}{h^2}\right)^{3/2}\exp[-(\mu_F - \tfrac{1}{2}\mu_v)/k\theta]. \tag{11.15b}$$

One may calculate X from an empirical equation given by Etzel and Maurer(S); namely,

$$X = 1.2 \times 10^{23} \exp\{-11,700/\theta\}. \qquad (11.16)$$

Some typical values are shown in Table 11.1. The values of ϵ_v, that is, μ_v,

TABLE 11.1. NUMBER OF VACANCIES
IN NaCl

θ° C	X
600	1.8×10^{17}
650	4.5×10^{17}
700	7.1×10^{17}
750	1.3×10^{18}

can be obtained from detailed calculations as described by Mott and Gurney or from actual measurements. Some values are given in Table 11.2.

TABLE 11.2. VALUES OF ϵ_v FOR NaCl AND KCl

Crystal	Calculated[a] (ev)	Measured (ev)
NaCl	1.9	2.0[b]
KCl	2.1	2.1[c]

[a] Mott and Littleton, S. The values given in Mott and Gurney, p. 143, do not quite agree with the values reported here, and in the paper of Mott and Littleton.
[b] Etzel and Maurer, S.
[c] Wagner and Hantelman, S.

In Eq. (11.1) both μ and x depend exponentially on $1/\theta$. The dependence of μ is small, however, as we indicated in Section 7c, and can be ignored. The temperature dependence of the electronic current is due to x and hence proportional to $\exp -[(\epsilon_t(0) - \frac{1}{2}\epsilon_v)/k\theta]$ where n is determined by the injection techniques and is independent of θ. Here $\mu_F \approx \epsilon_t(0)$, the thermal binding energy of the ground state.

We now turn to the experiment itself, which is extremely simple; n was measured after quenching by means of Smakula's formula (assuming that $f = 1$). The voltage and the current are measured directly.

There are several problems of an experimental nature. First, one would suspect that a pointed probe would produce an extremely nonuniform field, so that it would be difficult to measure F and x in (11.1). Fortunately, near the anode, which is a flat plate, this is not the case and the distribution leads to no difficulties.

TABLE 11.3. DATA ON KCl: "SMAKULA'S MOBILITY"—$\mu(x/n)$

Temp. (°C)	Electrolytic current[a] (10^{-3} amp)	Electronic current (10^{-3} amp)	n ($\times 10^{16}$)	"Mobility" (cm/sec per volt/cm) ($\times 10^{-3}$)	Stasiw's "mobility" ($\times 10^{-3}$)	Field (volts/cm)
610	0.12	0.50	5.6	0.57		136
650	0.12	0.26	4.1	0.57	0.47	83
685	0.36	0.37	5.3	0.74	0.57	77
720	0.40	0.43	11.1	0.87	0.83	33
740	0.67	0.93	18.3	1.34	1.03	31
755	0.90	0.70	14.0	1.50		25

[a] Before the electron injection. Data taken from Smakula (S).

The one remaining problem is that I of Eq. (11.1) is not the total current density, but represents only the *electronic* part. As stated in Section 2, the injection of electrons is usually done at high temperatures, where the ionic current cannot be neglected. We assume, with Smakula, that both currents can be added and that one may subtract the ionic current (obtained without electron injection) from the total current to find that part associated with the electrons. We shall return to this problem at the end of this section. It will be useful at this point to present some data given by Smakula. The "Smakula mobility" is given by Table 11.3.

$$\frac{I}{enF} = \mu \frac{x}{n}. \tag{11.17}$$

The confusion in the literature mentioned before regarding Smakula's data can be traced to the position of the Fermi level of the electrons. Equations (11.3) to (11.7) assumed classical statistics. In an attempt to better understand what is happening, consider a simple calculation. The F-center is again assumed to be an electron bound to a negative-ion vacancy with a single bound state and we apply elementary statistical arguments.* Let the binding energy associated with an F-center be $\epsilon_t(0) = \mu_F > 0$, which is the energy it takes to place a trapped electron into the conduction band. We assume that a steady state exists and that the fraction of free electrons is determined by the temperature; hence,

$$p = \frac{x}{n} = \frac{AV\theta^{3/2} e^{-\epsilon_t(0)/k\theta}}{2(X+n) + AV\theta^{3/2} e^{-\epsilon_t(0)/k\theta}}. \qquad (11.18)\dagger$$

If the effective mass equals the free electron mass, then for unit volume

$$A\theta^{3/2} = 4.8 \times 10^{15}\,\theta^{3/2}\,\text{cm}^{-3}; \quad A\theta^{3/2} = 1.4 \times 10^{20}\,\text{cm}^{-3} \quad \text{at } \theta = 1000^\circ\,\text{K}$$

X must be large compared to the number of F-centers (associated plus unassociated). The author believes this from the empirical equations given by Etzel and Maurer (S), Wagner and Hantelmann (S), and from Table 11.3; hence $p \ll 1$.

The equations for p assume that Boltzmann's statistics apply to the ground state of the F-center, that is, this level is above the Fermi level. The energy gap between the valence and the conduction bands is larger than 6 volts, while the ground state of the F-center is at most 2.8 ev (in NaCl, KCl, and KBr) below the conduction band; hence, this is reasonable.

As stated, this problem is a very fundamental one for the study of the F-center. Pekar (S) assumed that Fermi-Dirac statistics applied and that Smakula measured $\frac{1}{2}\epsilon_t(0)$, not the value given by Eq. (11.15b). This would be true if the Fermi level at ϵ_F is between the conduction band and ground state—see Seitz, 1940, p. 186—and Boltzmann's statistics would not apply to this level. Twice Smakula's value happens to agree very well with Pekar's calculations for the thermal ionization energy and is a point that has been used as an argument in support of Pekar's theory.

To establish the fact that Boltzmann's statistics may be used, we write down the expression for the number of electrons in the conduction band

---

* The assumption of a single bound state is certainly untrue, but gives a reasonably simple analysis of Smakula's data. The author does not believe that the addition of one or several bound states will have a major effect on this analysis.

† The reason for using $2(X+n)$ in place of $X+n$ is explained in Wilson (S, p. 326). We shall employ this factor, which did not appear in our previous equation, from now on.

and for the number of electrons in the ground state of the F-center. This gives the following equation:

$$AV\theta^{3/2}\exp\left(\epsilon_F/kT\right)+X\left\{\frac{1}{\frac{1}{2}\exp\left[\epsilon_t'(0)-\epsilon_F\right]/k\theta+1}\right\} = n. \qquad (11.19)$$

The zero level is at the bottom of the conduction band and $X\gg n$. Here we have assumed Fermi-Dirac statistics for the electrons in the ground state of the center. From the measurements of Smakula and of Etzel and Maurer, we may assume that $X\approx 10^{18}$ and that $n\approx 10^{17}$; hence, the term in the curly brackets must be of the order of 10^{-1} or smaller. This assures us that $\exp[(\epsilon_t'(0)-\epsilon_F)/k\theta]$ is large compared to unity and, therefore, ϵ_F is more *negative* than $\epsilon_t'(0)$; that is, the Fermi level is below the ground state of the F-center. Boltzmann's statistics apply, and we are completely justified in using Eqs. (11.15b) and (11.18). Pekar's argument is not correct for another reason; he makes no allowance for the temperature variation of X. $\epsilon_t'(0)$ was introduced for simplicity.

Returning to Eq. (11.18), we see that the additional current density ($V=1$) has the form:

$$I = en(\mu+\mu')F\frac{A\theta^{3/2}\exp\left[-\epsilon_t(0)/k\theta\right]}{2X+A\theta^{3/2}\exp\left[-\epsilon_t(0)/k\theta\right]} \qquad (11.20)$$

where μ' is the mobility associated with the negative-ion vacancy or with the ionized lattice imperfection which traps the electron. The first term in (11.20) is the contribution to the current due to the free electrons while the second is due to the additional negative-ion vacancies which are produced when the center dissociates. $A\theta^{3/2}\exp[-\epsilon_t(0)/k\theta]$ will always be much smaller compared to $X\approx 10^{18}$. Equation (11.20) reduces to

$$I = \frac{en}{2X}\mu FA\theta^{3/2}\exp\left[-\epsilon_t(0)/k\theta\right] \qquad (11.20a)$$

$$= \frac{en}{2N}\mu FA\theta^{3/2}\exp\left\{-[\epsilon_t(0)-\tfrac{1}{2}\epsilon_v]/k\theta\right\} \qquad (11.20b)$$

where Eq. (11.15a) has been used. We have also assumed that $\mu'\ll\mu$. This must be so, since we know that $\mu'\ll\mu''$ where μ'' is associated with the positive-ion vacancy.* Further, if $\mu'\approx\mu$, then the electronic current would be much smaller than the ionic current, since the number of free electrons is much smaller than the number of negative-ion or positive-ion

---

* We assume that Tubandt's data (Seitz, 1946, Fig. 17) applies also to the intrinsic range of conductivity where the number of positive and negative ions must be equal.

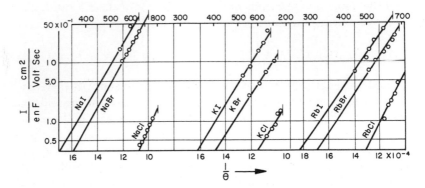

FIG. 11.1. Plot of I/enF against $1/\theta$ for various alkali halides (after Smakula, S).

vacancies. Since $\epsilon_t(0) > 0$ and $\epsilon_v > 0$, the quantity in the exponent is a difference of two values. Equation (11.20a) does not give the mobility directly, even at $\theta \to \infty$, unless one can measure A/X. Smakula attempted to extrapolate this expression to high temperatures and find an electron's mobility. We see that the problem is very complex and that the creation of vacancies must be considered.

In actual crystals at temperatures below the melting point, (11.20) applies and one may obtain $\epsilon_t(0)$ by neglecting the small temperature dependence part of μ and $A\theta^{3/2}$ provided ϵ_v is known. This means that plots of $\log I$ against $1/\theta$ are of interest if we are to determine $\epsilon_t(0)$. Smakula has obtained such plots for many of the alkali halides; they are shown in Fig. 11.1. From the slope of these plots, he obtained $(\epsilon_t(0) - \tfrac{1}{2}\epsilon_v)$. His values are given in Table 11.4.

TABLE 11.4. $\epsilon_t(0) - \tfrac{1}{2}\epsilon_v$ FOR VARIOUS
ALKALI HALIDES

Crystal	$\epsilon_t(0) - \tfrac{1}{2}\epsilon_v$ (ev)
NaCl	0.94
NaBr	0.80
NaI	0.76
KCl	1.00
KBr	0.84
KI	0.83
RbCl	0.84
RbBr	0.68
RbI	0.63

The author has attempted to check Smakula's values but the agreement is only approximate. Smakula claims that his values are only reliable to 20%, which must be the reason for the poor agreement.

In Table 11.5 we have used Eq. (11.20b) to calculate $\epsilon_t(0)$ using known values of ϵ_v (Table 11.2). Since $\frac{1}{2}\epsilon_v$ equals approximately $\epsilon_t(0)$, Pekar's values obtained from Table 11.4 are approximately the same as ours. This should not be generally true, however.

TABLE 11.5. VALUES OF $\epsilon_t(0)$

Crystal	$\epsilon_t(0) - \frac{1}{2}\epsilon_v$ (ev)	$\epsilon_t(0)$ (ev)	ϵ_v (ev)
NaCl	0.94	1.94	2.0[a]
KCl	1.00	2.05	2.1
KBr	0.84	1.80	1.92[b]

[a] From Table 11.2.
[b] Calculated by Mott and Gurney, p. 61.

There are some very interesting questions to be asked regarding the set of values of $\epsilon_t(0)$. First, "Do they obey a Mollwo-Ivey type of equation?" "Is there a constant ratio between ϵ_m for absorption or for emission with $\epsilon_t(0)$?" At present, the data are not sufficiently self-consistent to give us answers to these fundamental questions; hence, we may best not pursue them here.

Stasiw measured a nonequilibrium situation where the colored cloud moved through the crystal. If our present picture of the F-center is correct, the electron must carry negative-ion vacancies with it; otherwise, large charges will build up. This effect creates a drag on the electron and his measured mobility will naturally have a smaller value. Table 11.3 shows that this is indeed the case.

From Eq. (11.8) we may see why one can neglect the vacancies in Section 6. Since the dissociation of the electron was neglected, terms such as $(X+x)\ln(X+x)$ do not appear, and the number of F-centers is not influenced by the number of vacancies. This follows from (11.8) if we put $X \gg x$ and $n \gg x$. We recall that the chemical potential arises from $\partial G/\partial n$.

REFERENCES

H. W. Etzel and R. W. Maurer, *J. Chem. Phys.* **18**, 1003 (1950).
G. Heiland, *Z. Physik* **128**, 144 (1950).
N. Karabascheff, *Z. Physik* **118**, 718 (1942).
E. Mollwo, *Gött. Nachr.* p. 89 (1943).
N. F. Mott and M. J. Littleton, *Trans. Faraday Soc.* **34**, 485 (1938).
S. I. Pekar, "Untersuchungen über die Electronentheorie der Kristalle." Akademie Verlag, Berlin, 1954.
A. Smakula, *Gött. Nachr.* p. 55 (1934).
O. Stasiw, "Elektronen und Ionenprozesse in Ionenkristallen." Springer-Verlag, Berlin, 1959.
O. Stasiw, *Gött. Nachr.* p. 387 (1933).
C. Wagner and P. Hantelmann, *J. Chem. Phys.* **18**, 72 (1950).
A. H. Wilson, "The Theory of Metals." Cambridge Univ. Press, London and New York, 1953.

12. AN ENERGY LEVEL DIAGRAM FOR THE F-CENTER

One is tempted to draw an energy diagram for the F-center. Such diagrams have been drawn for atoms, for diatomic molecules, and for simple solids. For a diatomic molecule, one plots the total energy of the system along one axis, usually the y-axis, and the separation between the atoms along the other. In a system with many degrees of freedom, this is impossible. An elaborate and interesting attempt in this direction has been done by Wagner (S). Here, we shall draw a simpler diagram containing two types of transitions, thermal and optical.

As will be stressed in Section 30, the ions surrounding a trapped electron have an average force exerted on them due to the electronic charge distribution, $e|\psi(x)|^2$, where ψ is the wave function of the trapped electron. This force is different when the electron is in the ground and the excited state. This effect is completely absent in the ionized state.

Three kinds of potential wells exist: one associated with the electron in the ground state, denoted by a; another associated with the electron in the excited state, e; and the third, due to the ionized negative-ion vacancy i. Here we are making use of the Franck-Condon principle.

Turning to Fig. 12.1, we see that the absorption energy peak determines $E_1(a) - E_0(a)$. The width of the absorption band is associated with a broadening of the excited level, $E_1(a)$. It is due to an increase or decrease of the thermal vibrations of the ions surrounding the center after the

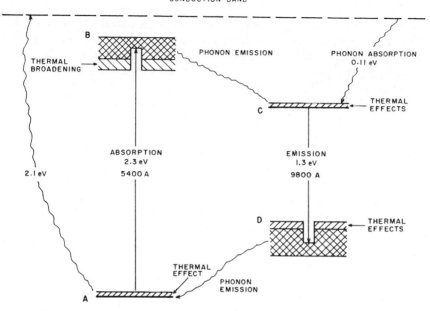

FIG. 12.1. Energy level diagram for the F-center in KCl. Note that we are plotting the system's energy, not the electronic energy; the latter would give a completely different type of diagram. $A \to E_0(a)$; $B \to E_1(a)$; $C \to E_1(e)$; and $D \to E_0(e)$.

photon absorption, that is, effect b in Section 4 (for detail see Section 31). This hypothesis is supported by Mollwo's observations (Section 3b). Thus, if one center is excited by a photon of energy, ϵ', and another with the energy, ϵ'', the energy difference appears as the vibrational energy of the surrounding ions. At low temperatures, there can only be phonon emission, and after a photon absorption or emission, the number of phonons can only increase from the thermodynamically expected value of the initial state which approaches zero as $\theta \to 0$. For high θ, there can be both phonon emission and absorption, and some modes may actually have less energy after an optical absorption or emission. The reader will note that the thermal broadening of $E_1(a)$ occurs only on the lower side. This is due to the fact that ϵ_v is essentially temperature independent. This is an observed fact which has not been explained so far. Also, the thermal broadening is on the upper side of $E_0(e)$ since the data of Lüty and Gebhardt indicated that the violet edge [initial point of absorption to the violet of $\epsilon_m(e)$] is independent of temperature.

In the diagram, the broadening of the emission is associated with a width of $E_0(e)$, since the induced transitions are known to cause transitions to various excited vibrational states associated with the ground level. We have no knowledge of the relative positions of the levels in the ground and excited wells. Crude calculations would make the distance between $E_1(a) - E_1(e)$ equal to $E_0(e) - E_0(a)$, but this is very approximate. The position of the bottom of the conduction band, $\epsilon_t(0)$, relative to $E_0(a)$, was obtained from Smakula's measurements (Section 11), while $\epsilon_t(1)$ was determined from the photoconductivity measurements of Glaser (Section 7). One should stress that $\epsilon_t(1)$ and $\epsilon_t(0)$ are of a different type of transition, and that the scale on the y-axis does not apply to them.*

The diagram suggests that the $E_1(e)$ is approximately a discrete level;† further, that the photoionization of the F-center is a two-step process. Theoretically, this has some very important implications. Rögener's experiments on NaCl (Section 13) show that the transition from $E_1(a)$ to the conduction band is independent of the wavelength of the exciting light. In one case, the system was excited to the bottom of $E_1(a)$, while in the other it was excited to the top. The difference in energy, 0.54 ev, must have gone into the vibrational energy of the surrounding ions, before the thermal ionization, since it did not affect the transition to the conduction band. If one associates a temperature with the vibrational energy, one may assume that when the shorter wavelength light was used, the instantaneous local temperature is $0.65 \times 10^4/n$, where n is the number of local modes. If there are 200 local modes involved, the difference in the local temperature is about 30° C. When Rögener used the higher frequency photons, the system was at least 30° warmer than when the low frequency photons were used. This would have readily been observed unless (1) an extremely large number of modes is involved, or (2) the transition is a two-step process. We adopt the second point of view.

Actually, the concept of modes for such large concentrations of energy is a difficult one. We may be sure that with such a large "thermal" vibration about the imperfection which traps the electron, the electron would readily be able to absorb 0.1 ev to escape to the conduction band, unless there is a very rapid way to dissipate this energy so that the system

---

* The reason for this distinction will appear later when the problem of the electron-phonon interaction will be considered.

† We may measure the frequency of vibration of the phonons closely associated with the negative-ion vacancy by a method to be described in Section 33. From the frequency and the temperature, the expected statistical distribution can be determined. Such a calculation indicates that the broadening of the levels, and $F_0(a)$ and $E_1(e)$, is always small.

goes to $E_1(e)$. We must conclude that such a method exists, and that $E_1(e)$ is a narrow level; another reason in support of this view is that $\epsilon_t(1)$ has a definite value.

While Fig. 12.1 gives only a small fraction of the parameters associated with the F-center, it illustrates some of the facts and indicates the difficulties of drawing energy level diagrams for point imperfections in ionic solids.

REFERENCE

M. Wagner, *Z. Naturforsch.* **15a**, 889 (1960).

13. FURTHER CONSIDERATIONS OF BLEACHING AND PHOTOCONDUCTIVITY

The energy level diagram shown in Fig. 12.1 is supported by the photoconductivity, bleaching, and fluorescence measurements: η_c, $1 - \eta_l$, $\frac{1}{2}\eta_0(F')$, and $[1 - \frac{1}{2}\eta_0(F)]$ all decrease as the temperature is lowered. A quantitative examination, however, shows that discrepancies exist. KCl's η_c reaches a maximum between $-140°$ C and $-120°$ C, depending on the way the centers are formed; $\eta_0(F')$, however, reaches a maximum at $-100°$ C. Further, the temperature dependence of the quantum yields are different (see Figs. 7.8 and 8.5; note, in particular, the difference in the scale along the y-axis—Fig. 7.8 plots $\log \eta_0$). These differences suggest a refinement in the theory which we now present. Dr. Lüty has also noticed discrepancies and has suggested that they can be accounted for in part by taking all the measurements on a single sample. The author believes that a more refined theory is needed as well. Included in this section is the effect of quenching on $\eta_c \mu T$.

a. Refined Theory of Photoconductivity

The experimentalist measures $\eta_c \mu T$, not η_c; hence, we must develop an equation for this quantity without assuming that μ and T are temperature independent. At the time the measurements were made, little was known regarding the behavior of μ and T, and it was natural to assume that the major temperature dependence came through η_c; the thermal dependence of T and μ was hence neglected. This assumption is, of course, only partly correct.

Consider the experiments where we have I, II, or III types of conductivity. The average distance the electron travels, from the excited

F-center to a second F-center, is fixed for small bleaching.* T is the mean distance divided by the thermal velocity $(3k\theta/m)^{1/2}$; hence, T is proportional to $\theta^{-1/2}$. The temperature dependence of the μ's and η_c's are given by Eqs. (7.15) and (7.17). Thus:

$$\eta_c \mu T = B' \frac{\theta^{-1/2} s \exp\{-\epsilon_t(1)/k\theta + b/\theta\}}{A + s \exp\{-\epsilon_t(1)/k\theta\}} \qquad (13.1)\dagger$$

or

$$\eta_c \mu T = B \frac{\exp\{b/\theta\}}{a \exp[\epsilon_t(1)/k\theta] + 1} \qquad (13.1a)$$

where

$$B = B' \theta^{-1/2}$$

and

$$a = A/s.$$

B' includes A of Eq. (7.15) as well as the mean free path divided by $(3k/m)^{1/2}$; hence, it is inversely proportional to the cube root of the concentration of F-centers.

In (13.1a), we ignore the temperature dependence of B. The activation energy associated with the mobility is about 0.03 ev or of the order of one-tenth of $\epsilon_t(1)$ (see Tables 7.1 and 7.4). The assumption made in Section 7 that $\epsilon_t(1) \gg b$ was partly justified. Here, we hope for better results. We see from (13.1a) that at low temperatures, the triple product decreases as $(B/a) \exp[(-1/\theta)\{\epsilon_t(1)/k - b\}]$ with *decreasing* values of θ. At high temperatures, the product decreases as $B \exp\{b/\theta\}$ with *increasing* values of θ. The maximum occurs at:

$$\frac{1}{\theta} = -\frac{k}{\epsilon_t(1)} \ln \left\{ \frac{1}{kb} \epsilon_t(1) - \frac{1}{a} \right\} \left[a \left\{ \frac{1}{kb} \epsilon_t(1) - 1 \right\} \right]. \qquad (13.2)$$

In Fig. 13.1, we have plotted $\eta_c \mu T$ against θ for $b = 372°$ K (0.032 ev) and $\epsilon_t(1) = 0.11$ ev, which are typical values for NaCl. The parameter which varies in the curve is $a = A/s$. We also show a plot of η_c given by Eq. (7.17). The figure indicates why the difference between η_c and $\eta_c \mu T$ occurs. Well below the knee of the curve, $\eta_c \mu T$ has the form

$$\left\{ \frac{B}{a} \exp \frac{1}{\theta} \left(b - \frac{\epsilon_t(1)}{k} \right) \right\};$$

---

* This assumes that the microscopic cross section for an F-center to capture an electron is temperature independent. This probably is not strictly correct, but seems to be a reasonable assumption at this time.

† In Eq. (13.1), s could have a temperature dependence. It is really remarkable how little we know about its properties. They could be obtained from theories of chemical reactions. There are two A's in (13.1), one from (7.17) and the other from (7.15). One of them, however, is included in B'.

hence, Table 7.4 actually reports $\epsilon_t(1) - kb$, instead of $\epsilon_t(1)$, as stated, bk, however, is small and would not greatly affect the values. Using the value of b in Table 7.1, we have made corrections to ϵ_t of Table 7.4. These are

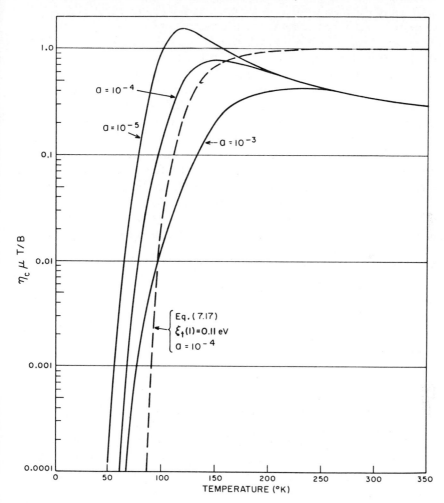

FIG. 13.1. Graph of Eq. (7.17) for various values of a; $b = 370°\,\text{K} \rightarrow 0.032$ ev $\epsilon_t(1) = 0.11$ ev. These values are for NaCl.

shown in the third column of the latter table. One may go one step further and attempt to measure b from Glaser-Lehfeldt's high temperature measurements. The scatter in the data would make the values meaningless. Figure 13.1, however, indicates that at the high temperature the drop is of the right order of magnitude.

These refinements in the theory remove the major difference between $\eta_0(F')$ and η_c.* One would not expect that $\eta_0(F')$ and $\eta_0(F) - 2$ to be the same since $\eta_0(F')$ corresponds to the case where $n_F \gg n_-$, while $\eta_0(F)$ is determined for the condition where $n_F \ll n_-$. Recently, Lüty (S) studied the initial luminescence when the number of negative-ion vacancies is small and when this number is large. When the conditions were such that the F'-center was easily formed, there was less luminescence. When F-centers reformed after bleaching, by the ionization of the F'-center, the luminescence increased. This supports the assumption that the imperfection which combines with the electron to form the F-center traps the electron in the excited state and then emits a photon. This idea was originally suggested in 1952 (Markham, S) from an analysis of the measurements of the production of F'-centers and the photoconductivity data taken at Göttingen. Lüty also employed this idea.

The refinements in the theory, however, do not remove the necessity of making all the measurements on one sample, as suggested by Lüty.

b. Effect of Quenching on Photoconductivity

While we have not stressed the fact, all the photoconductivity data reported so far were taken on crystals which had been rapidly quenched after the additive coloration process. We should like to describe what happened when crystals have not been treated in this manner. Several studies have been made.

(1) Glaser and Lehfeldt (S) studied the effect of omitting the quenching process. The data were taken on KCl at 30° C. They found a marked decrease of $\eta_c \mu T$. Further, the product $n_F \eta_c \mu T$ ($n_F = N_0$ is the number of F-centers) was not independent of n_F, as in well-quenched crystals.

(2) Glaser (S) has studied the temperature dependence of $\eta_c \mu T$ for *slightly bleached crystals*. (These data are again on KCl.) Here, from the absorption curve, one may detect the presence of R- and M-bands (see Section 14b).† Again, $\eta_c \mu T$ as a function of θ shows a different character. As more bands form to the red of the F-band, the knee in the curve (see Section 7) disappears and an unusual frequency dependence occurs.

(3) Geiger (S) has attempted to repeat Pick's experiment on the

---

* While there is a definite improvement in the use of Eq. (13.1a), it does not remove all the problems. Below the knee, $\eta_0(F)$ seems much less steep than the $\eta_c \mu T$ curve.

† The existence of M- and R-bands was unknown at the time Glaser did his work; yet these bands can be observed from the reported absorption data.

$F \to F'$ conversion with crystals which have bands of the Molnar-Petroff type (see Section 14b). His results are extremely erratic, which indicates that one requires "pure" F-centers to obtain reproducible results of the type reported by Pick.

The quenching technique is of fundamental importance in preparing colored crystals for photoconductivity measurements. Unusual effects are to be expected from poorly treated crystals. We shall return to this problem in Section 24.

c. Some Quantities Associated with F- and F'-Centers

In this section, we present some quantities pertaining to the F- and F'-centers obtained mainly from measurements at Göttingen. The mobility measurements of Redfield allow one to calculate the capture cross section for the negative-ion vacancy and for the F-center.* In this section, we shall also calculate the thermal dissociation energy for the F'-center.

Since the product, $\eta_c \mu T$ is known from the photoconductivity data of Glaser and Lehfeldt (see Section 7), one may calculate the mean free time of the electron T, and the cross section for an electron to be captured by an F-center. This forms an F'-center. At not too low temperatures, η_c is essentially unity; μ is known from Redfield's measurements (see Section 7). From Section 7d we know that $1/T$ depends on the F-center concentration, n_F, hence Tn_F should be independent of the imperfection density. The result of a calculation is given in Table 13.1. To obtain the last line we have used the relation $\sigma = (1/Tn_F)(1/v_{th})$ where v_{th} is the thermal velocity of the electron. The cross section should not depend critically on the temperature as it does when an electron is captured to form an F-center.

To obtain the capture cross section of a negative-ion vacancy, we may employ the data of Domanic (S), who measured the photoconductivity from the F'-center in KCl at very low temperatures, between 150° K and 20° K. There is a minimum at 73° K, and below this temperature other imperfections may act as traps (see Fig. 7.3). Before making a set of measurements, Domanic converted as many F-centers into F'-centers as possible by bleaching the crystal with light in the F-band at the appropriate temperatures according to the measurements of Pick (see Section 9). This means that at moderately low temperatures, the electron released from the F'-center is captured by a negative-ion vacancy, emits luminescence, and forms a stable F-center. We assume that the capture cross

---

* Here, the F-center is assumed to be an electron captured at a negative-ion vacancy.

TABLE 13.1. CAPTURE PROBABILITY AND CROSS SECTION OF AN *F*-CENTER[a]

Alkali halide	NaCl	KCl	KBr
Temp (°K)	200	200	150
μ (cm^2/volt sec)	25	15	15
n_F (cm^{-3})	10^{16}	2×10^{17}	1.6×10^{16}
$\eta_c \mu T$ (cm^2/volt)	5×10^{-8}	10^{-9}	7×10^{-9}
η_c (assumed)	1	1	1
$(Tn_F)^{-1} = \mu/\mu Tn_F$ (cm^3/sec)	5×10^{-8}	7.5×10^{-8}	1.3×10^{-8}
v_{th} (cm/sec)	0.95×10^7	0.95×10^7	0.84×10^7
σ (cm^2)	5×10^{-15}	7.5×10^{-15}	1.5×10^{-15}

[a] Data taken from Redfield (S) and Glaser and Lehfeldt (S)

section for a vacancy is larger[*] than for an *F*-center, and that there are many more negative-ion vacancies than *F*-centers. The calculations support the first assumption and the experimental conditions assure one that the second situation applies.

Domanic's data are $\eta_c \mu T = 3.2 \times 10^{-9}$ cm^2 (volt)$^{-1}$ at $\theta = 113°$ K with an *F*-center concentration of 3×10^{16} cm^{-3} before bleaching (that is, about 1.5×10^{16} cm^{-3} after bleaching). Since $\eta_c = 1$ for the *F'*-center, we may calculate μ from the parameters in Table 7.1. T has the value of 6.3×10^{-11} sec and

$$\sigma = 1.5 \times 10^{-13} \qquad \text{cm}^2 \text{ at } 113° \text{ K.}$$

The author believes this value is for the electron to be captured in the excited state. It should be independent of temperature to the first approximation. The probability for capture into the ground state is strongly temperature dependent and decreases rapidly above 78° K. Combining the above data with that in Table 13.1, we obtain

$$\sigma_F/\sigma_- = 0.05. \tag{13.3}$$

One should note that σ_F was obtained at 200° K. This should not be too important since to first order these quantities must be temperature independent *provided* the electron does not escape from the excited state (as in Domanic's experiments—this occurs at temperatures above 150° K). Costikas and Grossweiner (S) have measured this ratio at 80° K by a study

[*] The capturing occurs in the excited state.

of the kinetics of the process of photoionization. They had to assume a value of the quantum efficiency. Their ratio is 0.016 ± 0.005. Lüty (S) has also reported this ratio by means of a curve. His approach is similar to the one used here but with his own data. Costikas and Grossweiner have extrapolated Lüty's values to low temperatures and obtained a ratio of 0.05. Thus

Costikas and Grossweiner	0.02 at 80° K
Lüty (extrapolated by Costikas and Grossweiner, S)	0.05 at 80° K
Present calculations	0.05

Finally, we shall calculate the thermal ionization energy of the F'-center, using Pick's data (Fig. 9.6). We shall assume that the half-life has the form

$$A \exp[-\epsilon_{F'}/kT].$$

Actually, the F'-center does not decay exponentially and care in the definition of a half-life is necessary. Using Pick's data, we obtain the following values (Table 13.2):

TABLE 13.2. THERMAL IONIZATION ENERGY
FOR THE F'-CENTER

NaCl	0.51 ev
KCl	0.47 ev
KBr	0.22 ev

REFERENCES

A. Costikas and L. I. Grossweiner, *Phys. Rev.* **126**, 1410 (1962).
F. Domanic, *Ann. Physik* **43**, 187 (1943).
F. E. Geiger, *Phys. Rev.* **99**, 1075 (1955).
G. Glaser, *Gött. Nachr.* **2**, 109 (1936).
G. Glaser and W. Lehfeldt, *Gött. Nachr.* **2**, 91 (1956).
F. Lüty, *Halbleiterprobleme* **6**, 238 (1961).
J. J. Markham, *Phys. Rev.* **88**, 500 (1952).
A. G. Redfield, *Phys. Rev.* **94**, 537 (1954).

V. Some Optical Effects Related to the *F*-Band

14. INTRODUCTION

The optical and electrical properties of the *F*-band have been discussed in some detail. One is tempted to stop at this point since we have limited our interest; however, several additional effects are extremely closely related to the imperfection which causes the *F*-band and these should be considered at least briefly.

The first is a series of four bands that form to the violet of the *F*-band and seem to be related to it; the second is the effect of optical bleaching at higher temperatures (RT or above). The latter process forms a series of imperfections which are related to the *F*-center but must be due to additional imperfections which form mainly during high-temperature bleaching. Research in the area of optical bleaching at high temperatures has expanded rapidly in recent years. The bleaching has an extremely complex character which has not yet been resolved. This field is therefore treated only very briefly, and many of the interesting phenomena that are being discussed in the literature are not dealt with here.

Finally, there is the problem of the hole (a missing electron in the conduction band). If an electron is produced by x-irradiation, so must a hole. It also must be trapped at an imperfection; otherwise, it would wander in the lattice and eventually get trapped by the electron in the *F*-center, thus destroying the color. Early attempts were made to build hole centers (imperfections that trap holes) by analogy with electron centers. This approach has not been productive since holes attached themselves to halide ions and halide ions have a very unusual chemistry and form "molecules" within the crystal. Some progress has been made in our understanding of these problems as a result of the electron paramagnetic resonance (EPR) work of Kanzig and co-workers, and of some extremely original optical work by Hersh. These problems lead us again into a large field that is only indirectly related to the *F*-center. The author has therefore again decided to discuss the hole center problem (*V*-centers or *V*-bands) only in an extremely limited manner. Even the EPR techniques are considerably different from those used on the *F*-band (see

Sections 15–24). The molecules formed within an ionic crystal involve concepts of chemistry and physics which are not well understood at present, and are only indirectly related to the main topic of this book.

a. The K- and L-Bands

A question of interest is the number of bound electron states an imperfection can have. The problem was discussed theoretically by Peierls.

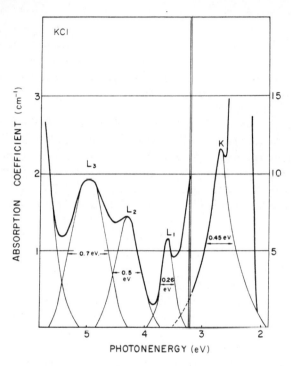

Fig. 14.1. The L- and K-bands in additively colored KCl at 93° K. Note two different scales for the K- and the L-bands, $N_0 = 6.5 \times 10^{17}$ cm^{-3} (after Lüty, 1960S).

Experimentally, additional levels will give bands to the violet of the F-bands. Such have been found by Kleinschrod (S) and by Lüty (1960S).

The Kleinschrod band—the K-band—is shown in Fig. 3.4 (see inset) and the absorption due to it has to be subtracted before one may obtain the true shape of the F-band. This band always forms with the F-band and the ratio of the maximum absorption in the K-band to the maximum absorption in the F-band in KCl at NT is 0.047 for x-rayed (see Seitz,

1954, p. 9) and 0.046 in additively colored crystals. This suggests that the *K*-band is due to a transition to the next higher excited state of the *F*-center. These ideas date back to a suggestion of Mott and Gurney, who thought it might be a transition to the conduction band.

Quite recently, Lüty discovered three additional bands to the violet of the *K*, known as the L_1-, L_2-, and L_3-bands. These are very small bands, and are observed only in extremely thick crystals or in samples which have been very densely colored. Good optical absorption work on the *F*-center (in KCl at NT) is usually limited to a density range 2–5 × 10^{16} centers/cm^3. Lüty's samples had 6 × 10^{17} centers/cm^3. While good *F*-band measurements cannot be obtained under these conditions, the *K*-band and *L*-band could be measured. Some of these data are shown in Fig. 14.1. The peak position of these bands can be established from these data, but the detailed shape and the width at half height cannot. One must regard the values of the width at half height and area under the absorption band reported by Lüty as somewhat uncertain. In Table 14.1, we list ϵ_m at NT

TABLE 14.1. ϵ_m OF *K*- AND *L*-BANDS AT NT FOR SEVERAL ALKALI HALIDES[a]

Alkali halide	F (ev)	K (ev)	L_1 (ev)	L_2 (ev)	L_3 (ev)
KCl	2.3	2.7	3.6	4.3	5.0
KBr	2.1	2.4	3.3	3.9	4.5
KI	1.9	2.1	2.8	3.2	3.8
RbCl	2.0	2.4	3.1	3.7	4.6
RbBr	1.9	2.1	2.8	3.4	4.1
RbI	1.7	1.9	2.4	3.0	3.7

[a] After Lüty (1960S).

associated with these bands. The fundamental questions are: "Are the *K*- and *L*-bands really associated with the *F*-center?" and "What is the true nature of the excited states?" Lüty's arguments for this association are:

(1) The ratio of the maximum absorption, α_m for any violet band (*K* or *L*) to α_m for the *F*-band is constant. Lüty was able to vary $\alpha_m(F)$ over a factor of 40.

(2) The *L*- and *K*-bands always appear in any alkali halide, even in a mixed crystal of KBr (60 percent) and KCl (40 percent). In a mixed crystal, the *L*-bands are characterized by the mixture and seem to have no

relation to those found in either KBr or KCl. The ϵ_m of these bands seems to obey a Mollwo-Ivey type of relation (Section 3).

(3) During an $F \to F'$ conversion, the K- and L-bands should decrease if they are indeed related to the F-center. Since the F'-band overlaps the K- and L-bands, this is difficult to observe, with one very important exception—the L_3 band. The latter does decrease during the conversion of F-centers to F'-centers in both KCl and KI.

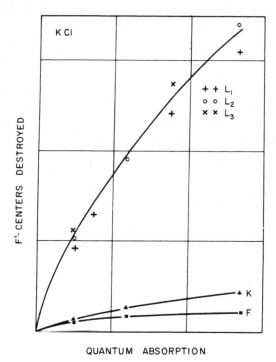

FIG. 14.2. The formation of the F'-band by irradiating in the F-, K-, and L-bands of KCl at low temperature. $N_0 = 5.3 \times 10^{16}$ cm^{-3} and $\theta = 93°$K (after Lüty, 1960S).

(4) From Section 9, we know that the F to F' conversion stops at low temperature and $\eta_0(2F \to F')$ approaches zero. In a preliminary study at 93° K, Lüty has indicated that $\eta(2F \to F')$, $\eta(K \to F')$ are much smaller than $\eta(L_i \to F')$ for $i = 1$, 2, and 3. The difference is very striking (see Fig. 14.2).

(5) Lüty, using some data of Inchauspé (S), found a one-to-one correspondence between the L-bands and some structure in the photoconductivity curve at low temperatures (80° K).

Lüty has presented strong arguments to prove his point that the K- and L-bands are transitions to higher states of the F-center. If Lüty is correct, and he well may be, he has made a major contribution to our knowledge regarding imperfections in alkali halides. Regarding the K- and L-bands, one must say that at a high density of F-centers, small bands appear to the red, as well. These will be described in Section 14b.* Judging from the EPR measurements of Noble (see Section 24), one may conclude that the density of F-centers can be as high as 5×10^{18} centers/cm^3 without causing a major change on the magnetic properties of the center.† This is probably true for the optical and the photoelectric properties. Nevertheless, small optical bands of an unknown nature often appear in crystals with more than 10^{17} centers/cm^3.‡ The L-bands may be associated with these additional centers and have nothing to do with the F-center. This statement cannot apply to the K-band since it appears at all concentrations.

The consistency of the ratio of the area under the bands ignores the scatter of the data.§ It is most difficult to make such measurements; hence, until detailed data are given, there will be an element of doubt. Unfortunately, Lüty has not presented such data. Some data regarding this point have been obtained by Inchauspé (S), who measured the photoelectric response in six samples and got six different types of plots. In only *one* case did the photoelectric response resemble Lüty's optical data. On the other hand, Wild and Brown (S) reproduced the L_1- and L_2-bands moderately well, also by means of photoelectric measurements taken on additively colored KCl at temperatures near $10°$ K.

Stungis, Markham, and Noble (S) measured the ratio at the point of maximum absorption in the K- and F-bands in RbCl. In unpurified samples, the ratio was 0.056 ± 0.072 from 20 random crystals. The large uncertainty indicates that the ratio has a very large scatter and the average

* Dr. Lüty has claimed that this is not the case, but the author has never seen carefully taken optical spectra on densely colored crystals which do not show at least a small M-band.

† This is not true at $4°$ K; see G. A. Noble, *Phys. Rev.* **118**, 1028 (1960).

‡ The R-, M-, and N-bands discussed in Section 14b may appear when the F-center concentration is above 10^{17}/cm^3. It is known that on bleaching, when one produces the bands on the red side of the F, one also produces bands to the violet. Perhaps the L-bands are formed in densely colored crystals because there are always some R- and M-bands.

§ The value of $\alpha_m(K)$ to $\alpha_m(F)$ in x-rayed crystals quoted above has considerable scatter. This may be due to experimental problems or to the fact that the bands to not originate from the same imperfection. Recent data indicate that the scatter in the ratio is less than in the first set of measurements.

has little meaning. Measurements on a purified sample of RbCl gave the ratio 0.032 ± 0.002, showing only a small scatter. This ratio indicated only a small variation in KCl. The data on purified RbCl and on KCl support Lüty's views.

Wild and Brown (S) measured η_c for the F-, K-, and L-bands at very low temperatures. Their values are given in Table 14.2; η_c for the L-band is much larger than the corresponding value for the F- and K-bands. It is very much smaller than the value for a transition from a bound state to a state in the conduction band (unity). This value of η_c for the L_1-band leads to some extremely difficult theoretical problems. If we are to associate the L_1-band with the F-center, the band must correspond to a transition to a state 3.6 ev above the ground state which, from our present

TABLE 14.2. η_c AT $10°$ K ON ADDITIVELY COLORED KCl

F-band	0.00027 ± 0.00005
K-band	0.0046 ± 0.0005
L_1-band	
(3.6 ev)	0.04 ± 0.01

knowledge of the band scheme associated with the F-center, would probably lie in the conduction band (see Fig. 12.1). This is certainly true for the L_2- and L_3-bands. Under these conditions, η_c must equal unity and cannot be of the order of 10^{-2}. Further, the structure and thermal behavior of the new bands suggests that the transition is between bound states and not to the conduction band. The reader will note the difference in the F'-band shape, which we know is due to a transition from a bound state to the conduction band. It is a very broad one and seems to be insensitive to temperature changes.

b. Bleaching of the F-center at Higher Temperatures

The presence of other electron bands (besides the F, F' and the colloidal) has been known for some time. Upon exposure of NaCl containing F-centers to light at room temperature, a broad band with little structure forms on the long wavelength side of the F. Early workers at Göttingen related this band to the F'; this broad band, however, shows structure at lower temperatures, which indicates that it is not the F'-band (for detail, see Platt and Markham, S). Many additional absorption bands form after various treatments of the crystal; usually, these treatments occur after the crystal has been colored by the presence of F-centers.

The most common treatment is to expose a colored crystal to white light or light in the F-band spectral region (F-light) at RT. This produces a series of bands to the red of the F-band which we shall refer to as the Molnar-Petroff series. This effect or series of effects was first studied independently by Molnar (S) and by Petroff (S). Other treatments which produce different bands are known [see, for example, Scott and Bupp (S) and Yagi (S)]. We shall very briefly discuss the Molnar-Petroff series here since it plays an important role in color center research. These bands do not seem to be related to the F-center as is the F'-band—that is, arising from the same point imperfection. Their presence, however, modifies many of the properties of the F-centers. No attempt at a complete study of these modifications is made here since this field is in a state of flux at present, and the complex properties of the Molnar-Petroff series are still far from understood. The absorption bands have strong dichroic characteristics which are being employed to resolve some of their interesting properties.

On the irradiation of K–KCl (additively colored KCl) at RT with F-light, a series of absorption bands appear. Unfortunately, two sets of notations exist; we shall employ the one used at present, although the older Göttingen notation is more logical (see Table 14.3).

For very short irradiation, two bands appear right next to the F, which are known as the A- and B-bands (see Figs. 14.3 and 14.4). The A-band seems to be due to an impurity in the crystal. Some of the other bands may also be due to impurities. There is a great deal of evidence that a second band appears which is covered up by the F-band. We shall ascribe it to the B-band originally observed by Petroff. Table 3.4 shows an increase in H with bleaching; this has been ascribed to the appearance of one or more bands in the vicinity of the F-band. While the term B-band will be used for the broader absorption structure, we do not suggest that it is a single band or that it occurs on a particular side of the F.*

Longer irradiations produce a band which appears at 1.57 ev (measured at NT); it is known as the M-band (in honor of Molnar). This band was first observed by Ottmer (S). It appears for most alkali halides with the F on longer x-irradiations at RT. Then, on still longer exposures, two bands appear between the F and M, at 1.7 and 1.9 ev in KCl at NT. These two are known as the R_1- and R_2-bands (because they appear to the red

---

* The term B-band can be identified with a particular absorption structure which can be resolved by dichroic measurements, or it can be used for the general broadening observed about the F-band. We shall use it in the second sense. This is not a universally accepted usage.

of the F). With these bands, a complex structure usually appears at about 1.25 ev. Burstein and Oberly (S) of the Naval Research Laboratory first called attention to this structure; they called it the N-band. Actually, it was first observed by Molnar in NaCl and by Petroff in KCl. The N-structure is a composite of several bands, probably three. There are bands to the red of the N-cluster which could be called the O-band.*

TABLE 14.3. THE MOLNAR-PETROFF BAND IN VARIOUS ALKALI HALIDES

Nomenclature				
American	Petroff's	NaCl[a]	KCl	KBr
A	A		2.1 (NT)[b]	
B	B		Broadens the F[b]	Broadens the F[c]
M	C	1.73 (NT)	1.57 (NT)[c]	1.38 (NT)[a]
R_1	E	2.27 (NT)	1.9 (NT)[c]	1.69 (NT)[a]
R_2	D	2.08 (NT)	1.7 (NT)[c]	1.56 (NT)[a]
N	G	1.50 (NT)	1.25 (NT)[c]	1.12 (RT)[e]
O			0.89 (NT)[d]	
		LiF[h]	RbBr[a]	KI[g]
M		2.77 (RT)[f]	1.3 (NT)	1.23 (HT)
R_1		3.87 (RT)[f]	1.5 (NT)	1.53 (HT)
R_2		3.28 (RT)[f]	1.44 (NT)	1.37 (HT)
N		2.25 (RT)[f]		

[a] Molnar (S).
[b] Petroff (S).
[c] Konitzer and Markham (S).
[d] Okamoto (S).
[e] Burstein and Oberly (S).
[f] Okuda (S).
[g] Hersh (a, S).
[h] See also Penneman (S).

The bands have been named in a completely haphazard manner. The historic reasons have been stated in the hope that they will help the reader remember the nomenclature. Petroff named the bands in order of their appearance on bleaching KCl.

* The structure was studied in KCl by Okamoto (S).

In Table 14.3, we show the relation between Petroff's nomenclature and the one used herein. The peak positions of the bands in various alkali halides are also given. The letters HT and NT refer to the temperature at which the optical absorption was measured. We retain the notation A and $B*$ of Petroff. Ottmer (S) reports structures to the red of the F-band in NaF and KF. It is impossible to know the bands in the Molnar-Petroff series to which these correspond.

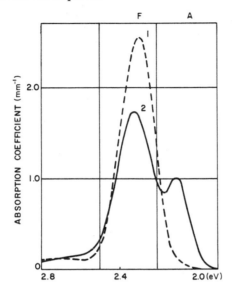

FIG. 14.3. Development of the A-band from additively colored KCl by irradiation of the F-band at 240°K. Measured at 93°K, $N_0 = 6.8 \times 10^{16}$ cm^{-3}. The F'-band which is formed has been bleached. Curve 1 before, and curve 2 after bleaching (after Lüty, 1961S).

Since all bands appear in additively colored crystals, we may assume that they are either due to the trapping of an electron at some lattice imperfection or the formation of small colloids. The absorption band associated with a colloid should be temperature independent (see Section 2). Further, the peaks of the bands associated with a colloidal center vary in a continuous manner and do not have discrete values (see Fig. 2.3). The new series of bands narrow and shift to the violet as θ decreases. These facts indicate that these bands are due to the trapping of electrons. Since

* The notation B seems somewhat appropriate in view of Petroff's nationality (Bulgarian). The B-, N-, and O-bands are not single structures and their shapes vary on bleaching.

the work of Petroff, various growth rate studies have been made of the bands and various models have been suggested. Further detailed studies of the properties of the Molnar-Petroff bands, however, are required for all of them to be established; the few that have been established are complex and will not be discussed.

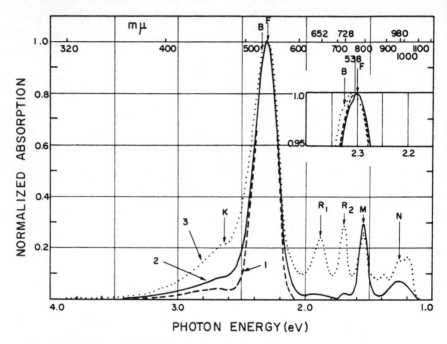

FIG. 14.4. Effect of bleaching at room temperature on the *F*-band (absorption measurements at NT); curve 1, unbleached; curve 2, 5-min bleaching; curve 3, 1 hr bleaching (after Konitzer and Markham, S).

Our point of interest here is in the destruction of the *F*-band. At low temperature, only one band (the *F'*-band) forms, and at high temperature, the Molnar-Petroff series appears.* The exact transition temperature is unknown. Molnar has bleached K–KCl at −80° C, 0° C, 22° C,

---

* The Molnar-Petroff series does not always appear. At times, seven or eight bands appear to the red of the *F* which do not resemble those of Table 14.3. This phenomenon was first found by Uchida and Yagi (see Yagi, S). Konitzer has also observed this complex structure. What causes the presence of the Uchida-Yagi system in place of the Molnar-Petroff system is unknown at present, but it does not seem to be simply due to better absorption measurements or purer host crystals.

$57°$ C, and $100°$ C. At $-80°$ C, the F' forms without a trace of the Molnar-Petroff type structure. At all higher temperatures, the complex structure appeared without the F'-band. On x-irradiating NaCl at RT, the M-bands appear with the F'-band, whereas the complete Molnar-Petroff series forms only after the bleaching of the F-center. The F'-center is probably always formed but is unstable at higher temperatures. When it is unstable, the Molnar-Petroff bands form. An exception is the M-band, which can be formed by x-irradiation; perhaps the x-rays bleach the crystal. Some of these bands can also be formed when the crystal is poorly quenched. Actually, only a few of the bands are stable at a given temperature; hence, the bands formed after a process depend on how rapidly one takes the absorption data after the treatment of the crystal. An extremely complex process seems to occur after bleachings or irradiations which can only be studied by very rapid methods of measuring the absorption. In LiF, R- and M-centers form after an exposure to electron bombardments.

We may relate the bleaching phenomenon to the photoconductivity measurement previously discussed. This is related to the bleaching since in both cases electrons are released to the conduction band. At low temperatures, few electrons are released to the conduction band. At higher temperatures, most of the electrons are released from the excited state of the F-center to form the F'-center. When $n_- \ll n_F$, $P(F')$ is unity and the range of the electron is inversely proportional to the macroscopic cross section $n_F \sigma_F$; this means that T is proportional to n_F^{-1} for a fixed value of θ. This agrees with the observation of Glaser for $\theta < 190°$ K (see Section 7).

At temperatures where the F'-center is unstable, the released electrons do not end up at a second F-center. Its mean free path is determined by the density of imperfections which are involved in the Molnar-Petroff bands. At present, information regarding these bands is too meagre to explain the $n_F^{-0.5}$ dependence of $\eta_c \mu T$ in this range of θ. As our models develop, however, the explanation for this dependence must be found.

For temperatures below the knee of the curve in Fig. 7.8, one would also expect a departure from the n_F^{-1} relation when n_F is small, because ion vacancies trap electrons in place of F-centers. We see from Eq. (9.6) that this occurs when the relation $\sigma_- n_- \ll \sigma_F n_F$ does not apply. Since n_- is produced by the absorbed photons, the relation will tend to break down as n_F decreases. Inchauspé (S) has found a deviation from the n_F^{-1} relation at $80°$ K in KBr in the expected direction. Unfortunately, the data are extremely limited and no reliable conclusion can be drawn from them.

c. The V-Bands

When an electron is excited into the conduction band, a hole remains in the valence band. The word "band" here refers to the energy levels of the electron in the solid, not to an absorption structure. The concept of a conduction and a valence band is more complex in an alkali halide, with its strong polar forces, than in a simple metal or semiconductor; yet such bands exist and holes must be created during an irradiation of a crystal. The hole cannot wander through the crystal since it would eventually meet a trapped electron and destroy the coloration. The color does fade in the dark but not at a rate which could possibly be due to free holes. Seitz (1946), therefore, suggested that optical absorption bands which form to the violet of the F-band during irradiation are due to trapped holes (hole center). Since then, the bands associated with these imperfections have been known generally as V-bands. They seem to form primarily to the violet of the F-band, but the author knows of no good reason for this. Actually, as we shall see, some of the absorption bands due to these imperfections are to the red of the F-band in the Molnar-Petroff region of the spectrum.

Several years ago, models of the V-bands were suggested from our ideas regarding the imperfections which trap electrons. Unfortunately, this approach is questionable. First, we had no reliable knowledge of the imperfections which are responsible for the Molnar-Petroff series. Second, holes do not behave as positive electrons in an alkali halide. The hole is related to the complex chemistry of the halogen molecules and ideas from chemistry are extremely helpful. We must regard the imperfections which have trapped holes as chemical species in the lattice, and we must know why and how the molecule is stabilized. This requires a detailed knowledge of the interaction of the molecule with the host lattice. At present, one cannot answer these complex questions, even in a preliminary manner, and no attempts will be made here to enter into these problems in detail. Three problems have been selected out of the maze of V-band experiments. They are: (1) the V-bands formed by irradiation (x-rays) at NT—the first detailed study of the V-band problem; (2) the V-bands formed by irradiation (x-rays) at HT—the author's introduction to the experimental aspect of the color center field; and (3) the V_k-band—the best-understood imperfection of this kind. We shall only be interested in the optical phases of the phenomena, completely omitting electron spin resonance methods of detection. (This phase would require a lengthy extension of the arguments in the chapters on spin resonance.)

The V-Bands Formed at NT

Between 1946, when Seitz predicted the existence of *V*-bands, and about 1952, a series of papers appeared reporting new bands and describing their properties. Some of these studies are papers by Alexander and Schneider (S); Casler, Pringsheim, and Yuster (S); Dorendorf and Pick (S); Dorendorf (S); and Duerig and Markham (S).

An exposure of KCl to moderately soft x-rays at NT produces the absorption spectra shown in Fig. 14.5. On the right is the *F*-band;

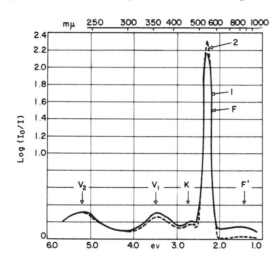

Fig. 14.5. Effect of x-raying KCl at 78° K, and bleaching with *F'*-light at 78° K. Curve 1, after x-raying; curve 2, after bleaching with *F'*-light (after Duerig, S).

proceeding to the left, we notice the *K*-band and two new bands, known as the V_1- and V_2-bands. To the red of the *F*-band is a broad band which is believed to be the *F'*-band. Whereas the data were taken from Duerig's paper, Casler, Pringsheim, and Yuster were the first to make detailed studies on these bands. Warming the crystal to dry ice temperature (about 195° K) decreases the *F*- and *K*-bands; the V_1-band disappears, and the structure in the V_2 region changes. It has been established by Casler *et al.* that two bands exist in the region between 200 mμ and 300 mμ. These bands are known as the V_2, which forms at NT, and the V_3, which forms primarily at RT. By bleaching and by thermal treatment, one may eliminate the V_2 and produce the V_3. The phenomenon of having

V-bands form at one temperature on irradiation and then disappear (or be transformed) by warming to a higher temperature is typical of most V-bands. During this process, the F-band usually decreases.

In 1937, Mollwo (S) additively colored KBr with Br_2 and KI with I_2. He obtained three bands in KBr and two bands in KI. In KBr, a pair is located between 200 and 300 mμ; they resemble the room temperature

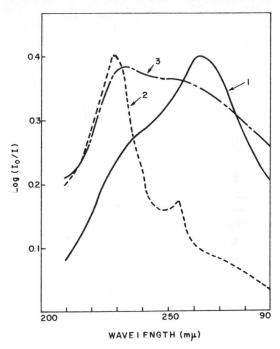

FIG. 14.6. Superposition of V_2- and V_3-bands in KBr obtained by various authors: curve 1, Mollwo; curve 2, Alexander and Schneider; curve 3, Casler, Pringsheim, and Yuster (after Casler *et al.*, S).

bands obtained by the Argonne group and the bands reported by Alexander and Schneider. Since the bands cannot be completely resolved, one cannot measure their ϵ_m and H accurately; hence, a one-to-one correspondence has not been completely established. Several workers have tried to reproduce Mollwo's work in KI with less success. As in the formation of pure F-centers (see Section 6), the quenching of the crystal seems to play an important role. A comparison of the measurements of Mollwo (S), of Alexander and Schneider (S), and the workers at Argonne (see Casler *et al.*, S) is shown in Fig. 14.6. It indicates that the relative sizes of the two bands depend on the way they are produced. Mollwo produced a band at 2.9 ev in KBr which agrees approximately with the band formed in KBr at 3.0 ev by x-irradiation at NT.

Hersh (1957S) has noted an interesting correspondence between these bands and some absorption bands obtained by dissolving Br_2 and I_2 in two types of solutions, one polar, such as water, and the other nonpolar, such as an organic liquid. Part of his data are shown in Table 14.4. The molecule Br_2 seems to be responsible for the V_1-band, while Br_3^- is responsible for the V_2- and V_3-bands.

TABLE 14.4. SOME BANDS OF KBr[a]

Band:	V_1	Br_2[b]	V_2	V_3	$Br_2 + Br^-$[c]
Peak (ev):	3.02	3.10	4.66	5.34	4.60 and 5.40

[a] After Hersh (1957S).

[b] A spectrum of Br_2 dissolved in an inert solvent.

[c] When one dissolves Br_2 in water, the Br_3^- ion seems to form. Some question regarding this reaction exists in the chemical literature.

The correspondence indicated in Table 14.4 is striking. Actually, as we shall see, three bands form in KBr at about 3 ev and they do not have the same properties as is indicated from paramagnetic resonance studies. They must be associated with different imperfections. Hersh's correlation strongly suggests that the imperfection associated with the *V*-centers is a chemical species—not the usual imperfection with which the physicist has been familiar. The correlation is less striking, however, when one includes all the alkali halides. The chemist's understanding of the above types of solutions seems to be in a state of flux; hence, footnote *b* in Table 14.4. Actually, the correlation shown in Table 14.4 is questionable, but Hersh's suggestion that *V*-centers are "molecules" is correct and of major importance.

Dorendorf (S) in a detailed study irradiated both KBr and KCl at several temperatures above NT and obtained bumps on the absorption curve with which he could associate seven *V*-bands. Some of these bands could be due to impurities in the crystal.

The V-Bands Formed at HT

The importance of some of the *V*-bands is that we know both the optical absorption and the electron spin resonance signal associated with the imperfection. This fact has given us a reliable model of the center responsible for some V-bands.

Dutton, Heller, and Maurer (S) were the first to report that the F-center forms on irradiation at HT, whereas Duerig and the author (S) made a more detailed study of the properties of the bands which are produced by irradiation at that temperature. The optical spectra of KCl, KBr, and KI are known and are similar. The work on "pure" KI was

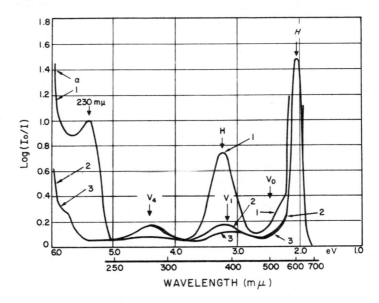

FIG. 14.7. Effects of x-irradiation of KBr at 5° K. The H-band is really the H_1-band. A very small band which forms at about 4.5 is the H_2. Curve 1: after x-irradiation at HT; curve 2: immediately after raising to NT; curve 3: 20 min later (after Duerig and Markham, S).

done by Hersh (1959S), but has not been published in full detail. NaCl does not behave similarly to the above-listed alkali halides for reasons which are not presently understood.

A typical spectrum is shown in Fig. 14.7. We note that two bands form to the violet of the F—a large band at 3.26 ev and a small one at 4.35 ev. They are known as the H_1- and the H_2-bands. The F'-band may or may not form, depending on the origin of the crystal. The band at 230 mµ does not appear in all types of KBr and is believed to be due to an impurity. The position of the H-bands is given in Table 14.5. The H_1-band has been studied in much greater detail and the subscript 1 is usually omitted; we shall do so here.

TABLE 14.5. VALUES FOR THE ϵ_m OF THE H-BANDS[a]

Alkali halide	H_1	H_2
KCl	3.59	4.86
KBr	3.26	4.35
KI	2.3	2.8

[a] The nomenclature can lead to some confusion. In the original paper of Duerig and Markham, the bands were not referred to by name. Duerig in his doctor's thesis refers to the bands as H_1 and H_2 (H for helium or Johns Hopkins University). Subsequently, Seitz (1952) retained the letter H for the H_1-band, and the smaller band at 4.35 ev in KBr was forgotten. Hersh's data established that two bands form at 5° K in KI and that the original analysis of Duerig and co-worker is correct. Data for KI from Hersh (1959S); for KCl and KBr from Duerig and Markham (S).

Warming the crystal to NT causes a disappearance of the H-bands and the reappearance of the bands which are formed by X-raying a sample at NT—that is, the V_1- and V_2-bands in KCl and the V_1- and V_4-bands in KBr. It is occasionally possible to see the transformation from H_1 to V_1. Actual transformation in KBr has been reported by Duerig and co-worker (S) (see Fig. 14.8). These workers employed a heavy metal cell which was quite satisfactory since the crystal was in good thermal contact with the sample. The sample reaches 5° K. The rate of thermal response of the cell was not known, and the temperature at which these data were taken is unknown.

Several interesting properties of the H-band have been established.* One may make H-bands from V_1-bands by first forming V_1-bands (by x-irradiation at NT) and then irradiating the crystal with light in the V_1-band after the crystal has been cooled to 20° K. The bleaching properties of a sample x-rayed at HT are rather complex. It is known that

* We assume that the H-bands are related. This has not been established. Most of the work on the H-bands has been done in KCl and KBr on the H_1-band.

some *H*-centers are destroyed by exposing the sample to light in the *F*-band spectra regions.

By bleaching a band with polarized light, one can occasionally determine the orientation of the dipole moment associated with the optical transition, that is, $\langle \psi_2 | \mathbf{r} | \psi_1 \rangle$ of Eq. (4.3a) depends on the orientation of the vector $\mathbf{r}$ relative to the crystal axes. The moment can depend on ψ_1

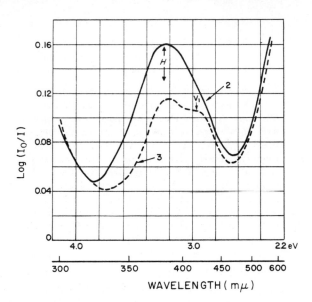

FIG. 14.8. Transformation of the *H*-band to the V_1-band in KBr on warming from 5° K to NT. The actual temperature of the crystal is unknown. Curve 2 was right after putting liquid nitrogen into the cell; curve 3 was taken 20 min later (after Duerig and Markham, S).

and ψ_2. One such fortunate case is the *H*-band, and the work of Compton and Klick (S) indicates that the dipole moment is oriented along the [110] direction.*

In 1959, Kanzig and Woodruff (S) reported an electron spin resonance absorption signal from an imperfection which forms on irradiation at HT. We shall discuss the EPR technique later in this book. The difficulty is to know whether or not this is related to the optical absorption bands which are formed by a similar process, since establishing a one-to-one corre-

* The [110] is the direction between next-nearest neighbors. Actually, this crystallographic notation may be incorrect since it ignores the fact that there are two unlike ions in the unit cell of the NaCl structure; it is, however, generally used.

spondence is always a major problem. From a careful study of the optical and the EPR signal, they were able to establish this relation for the H-band (perhaps we should say the H_1) and their imperfections. At times, one may easily and uniquely build a model of the imperfection from an EPR signal. This is the case for the imperfection studied by Kanzig and Woodruff. We thus have an exact model of the center responsible for the H absorption band.

The model proposed and essentially established is given in Fig. 14.9. It is composed in part of a Cl_2^- ion aligned along the [110] direction. A

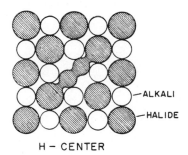

—ALKALI

—HALIDE

H – CENTER

Fig. 14.9. Schematic model for the H-center. The ratio of the ionic radii in the figure corresponds to KCl (after Kanzig and Woodruff, S).

molecule composed of two Cl^- ions should be diamagnetic since it is made of ions with closed shells. If we subtract an electron, we effectively add a hole and make the paramagnetic ion Cl_2^-. The H-center is the Cl_2^- ion with two additional ions on either side. Actually, this means that an additional ion has been added to the lattice. It is most strange that such a complex hole center is formed at these low temperatures. Why the imperfections are of such a complex form is still a complete mystery. Why a simple imperfection such as a hole attached to a positive-ion vacancy has not yet been found is also a mystery. We note that in KBr at NT:

$$\epsilon_m \, (V_1\text{-band}) \qquad 3.02 \text{ ev}$$

$$\epsilon_m \, (H\text{-band}) \qquad 3.26 \text{ ev}$$

$$\epsilon_m \, (Br_2 \text{ molecule}) \qquad 3.10 \text{ ev}$$

The Kanzig-Woodruff model does not resemble the Br_2 molecule in any way since its building block is the Br_2^- molecular ion.

The V_k-Bands

The H-band was discovered optically before the EPR signal was observed. This is also true for the F-center. The reverse occurred in the case of a V-band first discovered by Castner and Kanzig (S). We shall adopt the name V_k-center, although this does not do justice to the workers on this band at the Argonne Laboratory (Delbecq, Smaller, and Yuster, S; Delbecq, Hayes, and Yuster, S) or to the work done at Zenith by Hersh (1957S).

In the next part, we shall briefly present the model of the V_k-center obtained from a very careful study of EPR spectra. These spectra are

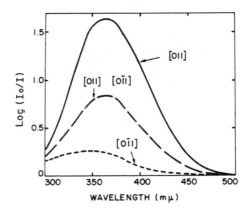

FIG. 14.10. Absorption spectra of KCl-Pb after 10 min x-ray irradiation at liquid nitrogen temperature as measured with either [011] or [0$\bar{1}$1] polarized light; and then after bleaching with [0$\bar{1}$1] polarized light (426 mμ) as measured with [011] polarized light and [0$\bar{1}$1] polarized light (after Delbecq, Smaller, and Yuster, S).

relatively simple when the major magnetic field is along the [100] direction and the alkali halide is KCl. The conclusion of Castner and Kanzig is that a molecular-ion molecule is formed within the crystal in the [110] direction. Two ions trap a hole to form the Cl_2^- ion. No real imperfection is formed (that is, no ion is actually displaced from its position), but two ions move closer to form a molecule due to the chemical bond between them. The interactions of this "molecule" with the other ions are much weaker.

Castner and Kanzig formed this imperfection by exposing their crystals to x-rays at NT. In some respects, it behaved like the V_1-center, and at first the suggestion was made that this imperfection was related to the V_1-band. The study of Delbecq, Smaller, and Yuster (S) indicates, however, that this is not the case, and they found the actual absorption due to the Cl_2^- ion. These workers proved that the V_1 absorption was not related to the Cl_2^- ion by pulse annealing (that is, raising the crystal from NT to a given temperature and rapidly recooling it to this temperature). The V_1-band completely disappeared by the time the crystal was raised to $120°$ K, while the Cl_2^- ion remained at a temperature of $135°$ K. The V_k-center may be produced in pure KCl, but it is formed much more rapidly in KCl to which some impurities have been added. For example, one may add Pb, Tl, or Ag, in which case only the F-band and the new V_k-band form.

Figure 14.10 shows the new optical absorption band which forms in the ultraviolet when one irradiates doped KCl at NT. This band is very sensitive to bleaching with polarized light. If the light falls on the (100) face of the crystal and is polarized along the $[0\bar{1}1]$ direction, then the absorption by light polarized along the $[0\bar{1}1]$ is greatly decreased while the absorption with light polarized along the $[011]$ direction is increased, as if the ions were rotated so their dipoles changed from the $[0\bar{1}1]$ direction to the $[011]$. Similar differences between the EPR signals for molecules oriented along the $[0\bar{1}1]$ and the $[011]$ have been observed. This established the correspondence between the optical and the magnetic resonance absorption. The Cl_2^- ion actually has two absorption bands, one to the violet of the F-band and the other to the red.

We conclude this chapter by listing a few of the properties of the F_2^-, Cl_2^-, Br_2^-, and the I_2^- ions in various alkali halides.

TABLE 14.6. TEMPERATURE OF BLEACHING OF
Cl_2^- ION IN VARIOUS TYPES OF KCl[a]

Pure KCl	$130°$ K
KCl:Tl	$210°$ K
KCl:Ag	$210°$ K
KCl:Pb	$220°$ K

[a] Data from Delbecq, Smaller, and Yuster (S).

(1) The *thermal stability* of the ion depends on a process (or processes) that destroys the ion rather than on the properties of the ion itself (see Table 14.6).

(2) Data on the V_k-band in other alkali halides are summarized in Table 14.7. (A detailed discussion of the EPR properties of the V_k-center has been given by Slichter).

TABLE 14.7. SUMMARY OF DATA ON THE V_k-CENTER[a]

Ion	Matrix	Disorientation temp. (°K)[b]	Band peak (ev)	Half width (ev)	Area under the band
F_2^-	LiF	110	3.65	1.20	200
			1.65		1
Cl_2^-	KCl	170	3.40	0.81	100
			1.65	0.37	1
Br_2^-	KBr	140	3.22	0.73	445
			1.65	0.26	10
			1.38		1
I_2^-	KI	90	3.10	0.55	340
			2.12	0.36	
			1.55	0.22	36
			1.08	0.19	1

[a] From Delbecq, Hayes, and Yuster (S).
[b] The disorientation temperature is that above which one cannot orient the molecule with polarized light.

REFERENCES

J. Alexander and E. E. Schneider, *Nature* **164**, 653 (1949).
E. Burstein and J. J. Oberly, *Phys. Rev.* **76**, 1254 (1949).
R. Casler, P. Pringsheim, and P. Yuster, *J. Chem. Phys.* **18**, 1564 (1950).
T. G. Castner and W. Kanzig, *Phys. Chem. Solids* **3**, 178 (1957).
W. D. Compton and C. C. Klick, *Phys. Rev.* **110**, 349 (1958).
C. J. Delbecq, W. Hayes, and P. Yuster, *Phys. Rev.* **121**, 1043 (1961).
C. J. Delbecq, B. Smaller, and P. Yuster, *Phys. Rev.* **111**, 1235 (1958).
H. Dorendorf, *Z. Physik* **129**, 317 (1951).
H. Dorendorf and H. Pick, *Z. Physik* **128**, 166 (1950).
W. H. Duerig, *Phys. Rev.* **94**, 65 (1954).
W. H. Duerig and J. J. Markham, *Phys. Rev.* **88**, 1043 (1952).
D. Dutton, W. Heller, and R. Maurer, *Phys. Rev.* **84**, 363 (1951).
H. N. Hersh, *J. Chem. Phys.* **31**, 909 (1959).
H. N. Hersh, *Phys. Rev.* **105**, 1410 (1957).
H. N. Hersh (unpublished, a).
N. Inchauspé, *Phys. Rev.* **106**, 898 (1957).
W. Kanzig and T. O. Woodruff, *Phys. Chem. Solids* **9**, 70 (1959).

F. G. Kleinschrod, *Ann. Physik* 27, 97 (1936).

J. D. Konitzer and J. J. Markham, *Phys. Rev.* **107**, 685 (1957).

F. Lüty, *Z. Physik* **160**, 1 (1960).

F. Lüty, *Z. Physik* **165**, 17 (1961).

J. P. Molnar, Thesis, M. I. T. (1940).

E. Mollwo, *Ann. Physik* **29**, 394 (1937).

F. Okamoto, *Phys. Rev.* **124**, 1090 (1961).

A. Okuda, *J. Phys. Soc. Japan* **16**, 1746 (1961).

R. Ottmer, *Z. Physik* **46**, 798 (1928).

R. A. Penneman, AECD 1859 (Argonne National Laboratories).

S. Petroff, *Z. Physik* **127**, 443 (1950).

R. T. Platt and J. J. Markham, *Phys. Rev.* **92**, 40 (1953).

A. B. Scott and L. P. Bupp, *Phys. Rev.* **79**, 341 (1950).

G. E. Stungis, J. J. Markham, and G. A. Noble, *J. Chem. Phys.* **40**, 3634 (1964).

R. L. Wild and F. C. Brown, *Phys. Rev.* **121**, 1296 (1961).

H. Yagi, *J. Phys. Soc. Japan* **11**, 430 (1956).

VI. Electron Paramagnetic Resonance in a Medium without Nuclear Spins

15. INTRODUCTION

In the preceding five chapters, we have studied the various transitions between electronic states associated with the electron trapped at the imperfection which produces the F-center and the F-band. We may study the ground state alone, without considering effects of the excited states, by means of electron paramagnetic resonance (EPR) (for details see Sections 17 and 18). Several very important factors can be obtained from such a study. The detailed structure of the ground-state wave function can be obtained from electron nuclear double resonance (ENDOR) measurements (see Section 22) and by changes in the g-factor (see Section 16). The means by which the energy is transferred between the spin system and the lattice can be studied from the saturation properties of the EPR signal (see Sections 16, 17, and 20). The ability of various imperfections to communicate with each other can be studied by measuring the transverse relaxation times (see Section 17).

Unfortunately, the number of variables in this problem is very large and the experiments themselves are complex, so that one cannot obtain even an elementary feeling regarding these problems without considering the various magnetic quantities associated with imperfections in solids. Although the quantities are usually defined in the more elementary treatments of the problem, the interactions of these quantities are discussed in full detail only in the most advanced texts. We require the most advanced treatment to deal with the experimental data on the F-center. This is unfortunate, but there is no other way to understand the magnetic properties of this center. The interaction of greatest interest is that between the spin of the electron and the spin of the nuclei. Even in a standard treatment, such as Condon and Shortley, this phase of atomic spectra is dealt with only in the last chapter; similar situations exist in other texts.

A systematic development of the required terms is given by Bethe and Salpeter in their detailed treatment of the quantum mechanics of one-

and two-electron atoms. Although it is not practicable to reproduce their beautiful treatment here, we shall review the equations of importance so that they will be in a handy form. The reader who wants the full details will have to study the book by Bethe and Salpeter. Other useful treatments have recently appeared by Abragam, by Slichter, and by Griffith.

Actually, the treatment of Bethe and Salpeter is adopted for a single-center system, whereas we are concerned with a many-center system; hence, even their equations have to be modified.

Most presentations of Pauli's equations are gauge varient. This creates no problem as long as we have only a *single* strong center (a strong center is where the potential field goes as $1/r$ for $r \to 0$). A strong potential occurs at the center of each ion which is overlapped by the wave function associated with the trapped electron. Many such strong centers exist in our imperfection, and the usual treatment (Bethe and Salpeter; Condon and Shortley; Griffith) has to be modified. These modifications have been studied by Griffith and by Slichter. In the appendix at the end of this chapter we consider the mathematical problem associated with these modifications.

Chapter VI summarizes the equations and develops the theory of EPR experiments in its simplest form where the interactions between the electron and the surrounding nuclei are neglected. The theory of nuclear resonance seems to be better developed, and several very useful treatments of this field have appeared. In many respects, the theories are similar, and we shall occasionally refer to books wherein the theory of nuclear magnetism is developed. Chapter VII includes the effects of the surrounding nuclei which have spins and associated magnetic dipole moments, and Chapter VIII summarizes the magnetic properties of the F-center as far as they are known at present.

Although it is not certain, there are many reasons to believe that the resonance associated with the F-center is one of the simplest possible. Indeed, it is so simple that Professor Pryce recently stated it was un-interesting. This is true in the sense that one will not learn much new regarding the model of the center from the electron paramagnetic resonance; it is not true, however, if we employ the F-center as an im-perfection to study the various magnetic forces within solids. The simplicity of the center and its high degree of symmetry make it most attractive for such studies. Further, the fact that it is a many-center imperfection requires that one develop the usual spin equations with greater care; hence it gives a theoretical insight which is unique and of major importance.

16. SUMMARY OF QUANTUM MECHANICAL EFFECTS

a. Basic Properties of the Angular Momentum

In view of the elementary consideration put forward by Ampère, we are concerned with the angular rotation of the species that make up the solid —that is, the electrons and nuclei. Each has six degrees of freedom, three external and three internal. The electron's internal degrees of freedom arise in a straightforward manner if we use Dirac's relativistic equation; hence, the word "internal" is perhaps misleading. For this discussion we do not require explicit forms of the external motion of the nuclei; hence, they will not be stated. The effect of the external motion of the nuclei is discussed in Sections 30–33. The external motion of the electron (which in all cases of interest is trapped at imperfections) is given in terms of an angular momentum vector, $\mathbf{L} = \mathbf{r} \times \mathbf{p}$.* The internal degrees of freedom of the electron and the nucleus are given by the angular momentum vectors $\mathbf{S}$ and $\mathbf{I}$. Here we assume that we are dealing with a single-electron problem and that S always equals $\frac{1}{2}\hbar$. This does not apply to the Molnar-Petroff bands (see Section 14b).

It is impossible to develop a truly satisfactory notation. A complete uniformity with the literature is impossible, since several notations have been used in the past. We shall denote the angular momentum by $\mathbf{L}$, $\mathbf{S}$, and $\mathbf{I}$; $\mathbf{l}$, $\mathbf{s}$, and $\mathbf{i}$ will be employed for $\hbar^{-1}\mathbf{L}$, $\hbar^{-1}\mathbf{S}$, and $\hbar^{-1}\mathbf{I}$; l, s, and i are the magnitude of $\mathbf{l}$, $\mathbf{s}$, and $\mathbf{i}$ (actually the z component); hence, they are integers or half-integers. Our equations agree with Condon and Shortley, who employ $\mathbf{L}$, $\mathbf{S}$, and $\mathbf{I}$, and with Bethe and Salpeter, who use $\mathbf{s}$ and $\mathbf{i}$. Bethe and Salpeter's $\mathbf{k}$ equals our l, although their $\mathbf{l}$ equals ours. In numerous references, our $\mathbf{i}$ and $\mathbf{s}$ will equal their $\mathbf{S}$ and $\mathbf{I}$. We shall employ β for the electron magneton:

$$\beta = e\hbar/2m_e c = 0.927 \times 10^{-20} \quad \text{ergs/gauss;} \qquad (16.1a)$$

and β_I for the nuclear magneton

$$\beta_I = e\hbar/2Mc = 5.05 \times 10^{-24} \quad \text{ergs/gauss} \qquad (16.1b)$$

where m_e is the electron mass; M† is the unit of nuclear mass; c is the

---

* Where $\mathbf{r}$ is a radius vector and $\mathbf{p}$ is the linear momentum.

† m and M are used for the masses and the magnetic quantum number. In general, M is a nuclear mass; m may be an orbital quantum number or an electronic mass. Initially, a subscript e is appended to the electronic mass. In the appendix to this chapter and in the later chapters, the e is omitted when it is evident what meaning it has. In Chapter IX m stands for the true electronic mass and m with a subscript stands for the "effective" mass. In Chapter X m is the mass of a particle in a linear chain.

velocity of light in the vacuum, e is the absolute value of the charge on the electron, and $\hbar$ is Planck's constant divided by 2π.

One should distinguish between vectors, operators, expectation value, and eigenvalue. The eigenfunction in its simplest form is a product of a nuclear wave function and an electron wave function. In turn, the nuclear wave function is made of two parts, one associated with its translational, motion the other associated with the nuclear spin. As stated, we shall ignore the part due to the translational motion here. The electron wave function is also a product of two functions, one associated with its position and the other associated with the electron spin. The total eigenfunction thus has the approximate form:

$$\phi_n(r)\,\eta_s\,\eta_I. \tag{16.1c}$$

The exact eigenfunction is a sum of such functions. No distinction will be made in the notation used for vector, operator, or vector operator, on the commonly made assumption that no confusion will arise. We hope this is actually the case. The eigenvalue will be denoted by its numerical value or a letter, while the expectation value of an operator will be denoted by:

$$\langle\phi_n\eta_I\eta_s|\mathbf{O}|\phi_n\eta_I\eta_s\rangle = \langle|\mathbf{O}|\rangle. \tag{16.1d}$$

Some of the properties of angular momentum operators we require are listed in Table 16.1. $\mathbf{T}$ is any angular momentum operator.

We are interested in the interaction between the $\mathbf{L}$, $\mathbf{S}$, and $\mathbf{I}$. These terms are given in Table 16.3. Before proceeding, some comments may be helpful.

The z-axis is selected completely arbitrarily. Equation (16.2) states that, in general, a wave function cannot be an eigenstate of L_x, L_y, and L_z. We can select only one. Using (16.2), it is possible to show that L_z, $L^2 = L_x{}^2 + L_y{}^2 + L_z{}^2$, and $\mathscr{H} = T + V$ commute. Here, T is the kinetic energy operator, and is not to be confused with the vector operator $\mathbf{T}$, while V is the potential energy, which is assumed here to have spherical symmetry. In a more general case L^2 and $\mathscr{H}$ do not have to commute. Hence, one may obtain eigenstates of the set of operators, $\mathscr{H}$, L^2, S^2, I^2, L_z, S_z, and I_z. The $\mathbf{S}$ and $\mathbf{I}$ refer to different coordinate systems and they commute with any operator associated with the x-, y-, and z-axes of the electron position, as well as with each other. Often, one quantizes the system—that is, selects the coordinates in such a manner that L_z, S_z, and I_z are parallel to each other and to the applied magnetic field. This is done only for the convenience of working a particular problem and, in

TABLE 16.1. GENERAL PROPERTIES OF ANGULAR MOMENTUM[a]

(a) The commutational properties of the components of **T** are

$$[T_x, T_y] = T_x T_y - T_y T_x = i\hbar T_z, \text{ etc.} \tag{16.2}$$

(b) The eigenvalue associated with the square of the angular momentum is given by

$$T^2 = \mathbf{T} \cdot \mathbf{T} \rightarrow \hbar^2 t(t+1) \quad \text{(the eigenvalue),} \tag{16.3}$$

where

$$
\begin{aligned}
t &= l, \quad \text{a positive integer, for} \quad \mathbf{T} = \mathbf{L} \\
t &= s = \tfrac{1}{2} \quad \text{for} \quad\quad\quad\quad\quad\; \mathbf{T} = \mathbf{S} \\
t &= i \quad \text{(see Table 16.2) for} \quad\; \mathbf{T} = \mathbf{I}
\end{aligned}
$$

(c) The eigenvalue of the z component of **T** is $\hbar m_z$ $\qquad\qquad\qquad\qquad$ (16.4)

where

$$
\begin{aligned}
m_z &= m \quad \text{which ranges from } +l \text{ to } -l \text{ for} \quad \mathbf{T} = \mathbf{L} \\
m_z &= m_s \quad \text{which has the value } \pm\tfrac{1}{2} \text{ for} \quad\quad \mathbf{T} = \mathbf{S} \\
m_z &= m_I \quad \text{which ranges from } +i \text{ to } -i \text{ for} \quad \mathbf{T} = \mathbf{I}
\end{aligned}
$$

(d) Associated with **T** is a magnetic moment given by:

$$\mathbf{M}_0 = -\frac{e}{2m_e c}\mathbf{L} = -\gamma_0 \mathbf{L} = -\beta\mathbf{l} \tag{16.5a}$$

-- for $\mathbf{T} = \mathbf{L}$

$$M_{z0} \rightarrow -\beta m$$

$$\mathbf{M}_s = -\frac{g_e\, e}{2m_e c}\mathbf{S} = -\gamma\mathbf{S} = -g_e\beta\mathbf{s} \tag{16.5b}$$

-- for $\mathbf{T} = \mathbf{S}$

$$M_{zs} \rightarrow -g_e\beta m_s$$

$$\mathbf{M}_I = +\frac{e}{2Mc}g_I\mathbf{I} = \gamma_I\mathbf{I} = g_I\beta_I\mathbf{i} \tag{16.5c}$$

-- for $\mathbf{T} = \mathbf{I}$

$$M_{zI} \rightarrow \gamma_I\hbar m_I = g_I\beta_I m_I$$

---

[a] The γ's defined here are the absolute values of the gyromagnetic ratio, except for **T**=**I**. This convention is not commonly employed; it eliminates the necessity of using $|\gamma|$ in the problems of interest.

TABLE 16.1.—*cont.*

$g_e = 2.0023$; g_I is the nuclear g-factor; $\gamma_I = \beta_I g_I / \hbar$ is the nuclear gyromagnetic ratio (see Table 16.2).

(e) The matrix elements of T_x and T_y are:

$$\langle \alpha, t, m_z \pm 1 | T_x | \alpha, t, m_z \rangle = \tfrac{1}{2} \hbar \{ (t \mp m_z)(t \pm m_z + 1) \}^{1/2} \tag{16.6a}$$

$$\langle \alpha, t, m_z \pm 1 | T_y | \alpha, t, m_z \rangle = \mp \tfrac{1}{2} i \hbar \{ (t \mp m_z)(t \pm m_z + 1) \}^{1/2} \tag{16.6b}$$

α stands for the eigenvalue in addition to t and m.

(f) It is useful to define the generation and annihilation operators:

$$T_+ = T_x + i T_y \quad \text{and} \quad T_- = T_x - i T_y \tag{16.7}$$

Their matrix elements have the value:

$$\langle \alpha, T, m_z + 1 | T_+ | \alpha, T, m_z \rangle = \hbar [(t - m_z)(t + m_z + 1)]^{1/2} \tag{16.8a}$$

$$\langle \alpha, T, m_z - 1 | T_- | \alpha, T, m_z \rangle = \hbar [(t + m_z)(t - m_z + 1)]^{1/2} \tag{16.8b}$$

The reader will note that T_+ and T_- do not lead to Hermitian matrices. They do not correspond to physical operators, but are extremely useful tools in the development of concepts associated with angular momentum.

(g) If f is a function which can be expanded in a Taylor series, then:

$$f(t_z) t_+ = t_+ f(t_z + 1) \tag{16.9a}$$

and

$$f(t_z) t_- = t_- f(t_z - 1) \tag{16.9b}$$

(h)

$$\sum_{-l}^{l} m^2 = \tfrac{1}{3}(2l + 1) l(l + 1) \tag{16.10}$$

which can be proved by induction.

(i) The operator, $\mathbf{T} = \mathbf{S}$, for a single electron can be represented by the matrix:

$$s_x = \frac{1}{2} \begin{pmatrix} 0 & 1 \\ 1 & 0 \end{pmatrix} = \tfrac{1}{2} \sigma_x \tag{16.11a}$$

$$s_y = \frac{1}{2} \begin{pmatrix} 0 & -i \\ i & 0 \end{pmatrix} = \tfrac{1}{2} \sigma_y \tag{16.11b}$$

$$s_z = \frac{1}{2} \begin{pmatrix} 1 & 0 \\ 0 & -1 \end{pmatrix} = \tfrac{1}{2} \sigma_z \tag{16.11c}$$

Further, in this case, $s_i s_j - s_j s_i = 0$ when j and i are two *different* electrons.

(j) Field at 10^{-8} cm along the z-axis.
From a stationary s-state electron: $\pm 18{,}600$ gauss.
From nucleus: ~ 10 gauss for $g_I m_I = 1$.

TABLE 16.2. NUCLEAR MOMENT DATA ON THE STABLE ALKALI AND HALIDE NUCLEI[a]

Element	Atomic mass	Natural abundance per cent	i	g_I
Li	6	7.4	1	0.822
	7	92.6	3/2	2.171
Na	22		3	0.582
	23	100	3/2	1.478
K	39	93.1	3/2	0.261
	40	0.012	4	−0.323
	41	6.9	3/2	0.143
Rb	85	72.1	5/2	0.541
	87	27.9	3/2	1.833
Cs	133	100	7/2	0.736
F	19	100	1/2	5.258
Cl	35	75.4	3/2	0.548
	37	24.6	3/2	0.456
Br	79	50.6	3/2	1.404
	81	49.4	3/2	1.513
I	127	100	5/2	1.124

[a] Taken in part from Ramsey (S). The magnetic dipole moment is usually given. We have divided this quantity by the spin. Actually, the total dipole moment should be $g_I \beta_I [i(i+1)]^{1/2}$ but the effective value is $g_I \beta_I \mathbf{I}$ since one can only quantize $\mathbf{I}$ in one direction.

TABLE 16.3. HIGHER ORDER INTERACTIONS BETWEEN AN ELECTRON
AND AN ELECTROMAGNETIC FIELD

	Terms in Pauli's equation
Moving charge:	
(I) Electric	$-(i\beta/2m_e c)\mathbf{E}\cdot\mathbf{p}$
(II) "Magnetic"	$(2\beta/\hbar)\mathbf{A}\cdot\mathbf{p}$
Static dipole	
Electric	None
(III) Magnetic	$(e/2m_e c)g_e\mathbf{S}\cdot\mathbf{H}$
Moving dipole:	
(IV) Electric	$(e/2m_e c^2)\mathbf{S}\cdot(\mathbf{E}\times\mathbf{p})$
Magnetic	None

general, they need not be parallel. The completeness theorem of quantum mechanics assures one that the solution of any real problem does not depend on this selection.

Item (j) indicates that the magnetic field associated with an electron angular momentum is very large. It is of the order of the applied external magnetic field, and in many situations is the largest field acting on a nucleus. This suggests that for some problems one should not quantize $\mathbf{I}$ along the axis of the external field. The nuclear field is small and, as we shall see, of the order of a magnetic line width. This fact makes us handle $\mathbf{I}$ differently from $\mathbf{L}$ and $\mathbf{S}$ (for details, see Abragam). In Table 16.2, we list $\mathbf{i}$ and g_I for the nuclei associated with the alkali and halide atoms. The actual value of the nuclear moment is $g_I\beta_I[i(i+1)]^{1/2}$.

b. *Higher Order Terms in the Hamiltonian as Applied to Atoms*

Numerous interactions exist involving $\mathbf{L}$, $\mathbf{S}$, and $\mathbf{I}$. To summarize these terms, we consider an electron with charge and spin moving in an electromagnetic field, which is characterized by $\mathbf{E}$ and $\mathbf{H}$, or the potentials $\mathbf{A}$ and ϕ.* The major potential energy term is simply the static interaction between the charge and ϕ. Six other types of interaction suggest themselves; they are listed in Table 16.3. (We have omitted the diamagnetic

* $\mathbf{H}=\nabla\times\mathbf{A}$ and $\mathbf{E}=-\nabla\phi-(1/c)\dot{\mathbf{A}}$. A third equation exists relating the divergence of $\mathbf{A}$ to ϕ. Its nature depends on the gauge employed (see Heitler, p. 2). The dot over the $\mathbf{A}$ means the partial differentiation with respect to time.

term, which is proportional to A^2.) Table 16.3 comes from Bethe and Salpeter (p. 56), and is derived from the relativistic theory of the electron due to Dirac. Actually the forms given in Table 16.3 are not completely satisfactory since they are not gauge invariant. One should replace the linear momentum with the kinematic momentum. A rigorous method of doing this has been given by Foldy and Wouthuysen (S). We have derived the gauge-invariant Pauli equation by a simpler and less rigorous method in Appendix a of this chapter; the difference between it and the one given by Bethe and Salpeter is also discussed there. Any complete theoretical treatment must start with a gauge-invariant equation. Term (I) accounts for the "spin-orbit" interaction when $l=0$ (for details see Condon and Shortley, p. 130); it is of no interest to us since it does not involve the spin. Term (II) is not strictly a magnetic one since **A** is not exclusively a magnetic potential. One should note that term (II) in the Schrödinger approximation has the form (see Van Vleck, p. 20)

$$\frac{\beta}{\hbar}(\mathbf{A}\cdot\mathbf{p}+\mathbf{p}\cdot\mathbf{A}),$$

which is not necessarily the same as (II) since **p** is an operator and **A** can be a function of $x, y,$ and z.* The order of **p** and **A** is of no importance when the Coulomb gauge is employed, as will be done here.

Terms (II), (III), and (IV) make the phenomena of paramagnetic resonance possible. These terms, with various expressions of the field, give rise to the following small terms to be added to the Schrödinger equation.

If **E** is the static field term due to a scalar potential ϕ, (IV) gives the spin-orbit interaction. In a central field, $\mathbf{E}=(-1/r)(\partial\phi/\partial r)\mathbf{r}$ and

$$spin\text{-}obit = \frac{-e}{2m_e^2 c^2}\left(\frac{1}{r}\frac{\partial\phi}{\partial r}\right)\mathbf{S}\cdot\mathbf{L}, \qquad (16.12)$$

since
$$\mathbf{L} = \mathbf{r}\times\mathbf{p}. \qquad (16.12a)$$

r is measured from the center of the field. In atomic problems, the origin is the nuclei. In solid state problems, the origin is the atom or ion of interest and, in general, it is not the center of the imperfection. We return to this problem in Section 16c and the appendices. An alternate form of this term is:

$$spin\text{-}orbit = \mathscr{H}(so) = 2\beta^2\langle|1/r^3|\rangle Z_{\text{eff}}\mathbf{s}\cdot\mathbf{l} = \xi\mathbf{s}\cdot\mathbf{l}. \qquad (16.13)$$

* Heitler reverses the order of **p** and **A**. This does not affect the answer in any case of interest to us. $\nabla\cdot\mathbf{A}+(1/c)\dot{\phi}=0$ in the Lorentz gauge, and ϕ is time independent, or $\nabla\cdot\mathbf{A}=0$ in the Coulomb gauge.

In (16.13), we have taken the expectation value of $1/r^3$ over $\phi_n(r)$. For a hole, filled shell with one electron missing, the effective charge is positive and ξ is negative. For a bare nucleus, Z equals the nuclear charge; however, for an ion or atom, Z has to be replaced by an effective charge. Barnes and Smith (S) have given Z_{eff} for some of the orbits of the electron on an alkali atom. These values are given in Table 16.4. The reader will note that the Z_{eff}'s were calculated for an electron that has considerably more energy than one in the ground state of that atom, and hence it is farther away from the nucleus. The use of (16.13) and Table 16.4 in a calculation regarding a point imperfection, such as an F-center, requires an element of caution, and we shall return to this point in Section 16c.

TABLE 16.4. Z_{eff} FOR THE ALKALI METALS[a]

Metal ion	Electronic state	Z	Z_{eff}
Li	$2p$	3	0.94
Na	$6p$	11	7.62
K	$7p$	19	15.1
Rb	$7p$	37	31.3
Cs	$7p$	55	49.3

[a] After Barnes and Smith (S).

The Zeeman and Paschen-Back effects appear because of terms (II) and (III). In a uniform field a form of $\mathbf{A}$ is $\frac{1}{2}(\mathbf{H} \times \mathbf{r})$; hence, with the use of Eq. (16.12a):

Zeeman term due to orbital motion $\mathscr{H}(Zl) = (e/2m_ec)\mathbf{L} \cdot \mathbf{H} = \beta \mathbf{l} \cdot \mathbf{H}$.

$$(16.14)$$

The interaction between $\mathbf{S}$ and the uniform magnetic field is obtained directly from (III), which we rewrite for convenience:

Zeeman term due to spin $\mathscr{H}(Zs) = (e/2m_ec)g_e\mathbf{S} \cdot \mathbf{H} = \beta g_e \mathbf{s} \cdot \mathbf{H}$.   (16.15)

In atomic spectroscopy, where one starts by neglecting $\mathbf{A}$ and the terms from Table 16.3, one may quantize a one-electron atom in terms of:

$$L^2, \quad S^2, \quad L_z, \quad \text{and} \quad S_z \qquad (16.16)$$

or $\qquad L^2, \quad S^2, \quad (\mathbf{L}+\mathbf{S})^2 = J^2, \quad \text{and} \quad J_z.$ (16.17)

When one includes terms of Table 16.3, these quantizations are not equivalent, since L_z and S_z do not commute with J^2. Quantization (16.17) gives only diagonal matrix elements when perturbation (16.13) is employed, since:

$$\mathbf{L} \cdot \mathbf{S} = \tfrac{1}{2}(J^2 - L^2 - S^2). \tag{16.18}$$

The introduction of J is appropriate when there are no external magnetic fields and the spin-orbit interaction is taken into account.

System (16.17), however, does not commute with L_z and S_z of (16.14) and (16.15); hence, if the magnetic interaction is strong (Paschen-Back effect), it is not a good choice. System (16.16) does commute and it is the proper selection since, in this case, (16.13) is a smaller perturbation. For very weak fields (16.14) and (16.15) usually have smaller effects than (16.13) and one may still use (16.17). For intermediate fields, neither quantization is satisfactory, and the problem becomes complex. In these cases, one must use a perturbation theory appropriate for a degenerate system. We shall start our study of the F-center by assuming the simplest quantizations possible, either (16.16) or (16.17), since $l = 0$. We shall then find that more complex treatments are needed.* This is similar to the case of intermediate magnetic fields.

We now assume that $\mathbf{I} \neq 0$ and obtain the interactions between $\mathbf{S}$, $\mathbf{L}$, and $\mathbf{I}$; the hyperfine interactions. These terms arise from (II) and (III) when $\mathbf{H}$ is produced by a magnetic nucleus. In this case:

$$\mathbf{A} = (1/r^3)\boldsymbol{\mu} \times \mathbf{r} = \nabla_f \times (1/r)\boldsymbol{\mu}, \tag{16.19}$$

$\mathbf{r}$ is measured from the nucleus (see, for example, Abraham and Becker, p. 125), and $\boldsymbol{\mu}$ is the nuclear magnetic moment. The subscript f refers to the differentiation with respect to the field point. The origin is assumed to be at the nucleus. The terms to be added to the Hamiltonian have the form

$$\mathscr{H}(hf) = 2(e/2m_ec)(1/r^3)\boldsymbol{\mu} \times \mathbf{r} \cdot \mathbf{p} + 2(e/2m_ec)\mathbf{S} \cdot \nabla_f \times [\nabla_f \times (1/r)\boldsymbol{\mu}] \tag{16.19a}$$

where we have set $g_e = 2$.† Equation (16.19a) can be transformed by the use of vector identities to give the relation:

$$\begin{aligned} \mathscr{H}(hf) = {} & 2\beta[(\mathbf{s} \cdot \nabla_f)(\boldsymbol{\mu} \cdot \nabla_f) - \tfrac{1}{3}(\mathbf{s} \cdot \boldsymbol{\mu})\nabla_f^2](1/r) \\ & + (2\beta/r^3)\boldsymbol{\mu} \cdot \mathbf{1} - (4\beta/3)(\mathbf{s} \cdot \boldsymbol{\mu})\nabla_f^2(1/r) \end{aligned} \tag{16.20}$$

---

* The initial assumption is made that V has spherical symmetry, which is only approximately true.

† The letters hf stand for the word "hyperfine," since in atomic spectra the nuclear interaction is very small.

This is a strange way of writing the equation since ∇_f^2 appears in two separate places. One may show, however, by expansion that the first term on the right equals

$$\mathbf{s} \cdot [\nabla_f (\nabla_f \cdot \boldsymbol{\mu}(1/r))].$$

The term $\mathscr{H}(hf)$ diverges as $1/r^3$ at the origin, and in evaluating the expectation value one must take this carefully into account. To see how this comes about one may expand the first term on the right and three terms of interest appear, namely,

$$s_x \mu_x \frac{\partial^2}{\partial x^2}, \qquad s_y \mu_y \frac{\partial^2}{\partial y^2}, \qquad \text{and} \qquad s_z \mu_z \frac{\partial^2}{\partial z^2}.$$

Since $1/r$ is spherically symmetric

$$\frac{\partial}{\partial x^2} = \frac{1}{3} \nabla^2 \qquad (16.21)$$

and hence the Laplacian operator does not appear in the square brackets as desired. The Laplacian is equivalent to the operator:

$$\nabla^2 \left(\frac{1}{r} \right) = -4\pi \, \delta(0), \qquad (16.21a)$$

where δ is the Dirac delta function (see Panofsky and Phillips, S). Performing the operations indicated in (16.20) gives:

$$\mathscr{H}(hf) = 2\beta\boldsymbol{\mu} \cdot \left[\frac{1}{r^3} \mathbf{1} + \frac{3}{r^5} \mathbf{r}(\mathbf{s} \cdot \mathbf{r}) - \frac{1}{r^3} \mathbf{s} + \frac{8}{3}\pi \mathbf{s}\, \delta(r) \right]. \qquad (16.22)$$

The evaluation of (16.22) requires another consideration. The strong magnetic field at the nucleus is along the $\mathbf{J}$ vector [the quantization (16.17) is being used]. We desire the mean value of the magnetization due to the spin and due to the orbital motion of the electron. This results in

$$\mathscr{H}(hf) = 2\beta \beta_I g_I \langle |1/r^3| \rangle \frac{l(l+1)}{j(j+1)} \mathbf{j} \cdot \mathbf{i} \quad \text{for} \quad l \neq 0 \qquad (16.23)$$

$$= (16\pi/3)\beta \beta_I g_I |\phi_n(0)|^2 \mathbf{s} \cdot \mathbf{i} \quad \text{for} \quad l = 0 \qquad (16.24)$$

(see Bethe and Salpeter, p. 107, or Abragam, p. 170).

An alternate form of Eq. (16.20) has been given by Zevin (S) and is used by the Russian school. The expectation value obtained by both approaches is the same. One can transform the expectation value or matrix element obtained from Eq. (16.20) into Zevin's form by the use of vector identities. Zevin's form may be useful for some applications; it is to be stressed that all its terms are included in our equations. Caution must be employed around the origin because of the divergence.

For an atom, forms (16.23) and (16.24) are satisfactory, but at a point imperfection in a solid additional problems arise. One may show that the expectation value of $\mathbf{l}$ for some ground states of imperfections is zero although $l(l+1) \neq 0$ (see Section 16c). In this situation one omits the first term of (16.22) and considers the expectation values of the terms which involve $\mathbf{s}$. The last term is considered differently. The expectation value obtained from Eq. (16.20) without the last two terms can be written as a traceless three-by-three matrix times a vector $\mathbf{s}$. The matrix also has an inversion symmetry. These properties allow one to write an operator which couples the spins of the electron and the nucleus in the form

$$\mathbf{s} \cdot \mathcal{J} \cdot \mathbf{i} \tag{16.25}$$

where $\mathcal{J}$ is a traceless matrix (see Abragam, p. 191). The form (16.25) is very useful in describing experimental data. The fact that the matrix is traceless and has inversion symmetry can be used in group theoretical arguments.

It should be stressed that (16.24) does not represent a mysterious interaction that comes from some quantum mechanical potential related to relativity. It arises in a straightforward manner from term (III) when an appropriate form of $\mathbf{H}$ is employed. In Fermi's original derivation, it arose from an integration of the type:

$$\int_0^\infty \frac{1}{r^2} \psi \frac{d\psi}{dr} r^2 \, dr \; = \; -\psi^2(0), \tag{16.26}$$

where ψ is an hydrogenic wave function. Equation (16.26) does not suggest a short-range interaction, although it is equivalent to the delta-function of (16.22). In arriving at (16.24), Fermi (S) used the Dirac theory of the electron. This does not introduce a new type of "relativistic" force as the treatment in Bethe and Salpeter indicates.

c. Higher Order Terms in the Hamiltonian as Applied to Imperfections in Solids

The development in Section 16b applies to atoms or ions in free space. To apply it to imperfections in solids, some modifications are required. We may insert an ion in a solid and then explore the quantum numbers and the expressions for the $\mathcal{H}$'s. This procedure is not strictly related to the F-center for, as we shall see, an F-center is due to a missing ion and the geometry of the problem is altered. Some knowledge of the situation that exists when we place an ion in a solid is essential, however. To develop these ideas, consider what happens to the hole associated with the Cu^{2+} ion when it is placed in a crystal. (For a development that applies to *F*-centers see the appendix at the end of this chapter.) That problem is so complex that one requires a simple orientation, which is attempted here. Consider in detail the case of $Cu^{2+}6H_2O$, where the undistorted lattice belongs to the O_h point group. This example has been worked out by Pryce (S). $\xi < 0$ but $\mathscr{H}(Zl)$ is not altered.

TABLE 16.5. ORDER OF MAGNITUDE OF TERMS IN $Cu^{2+}6H_2O$

Term	Value (ev)
Ionic field: V_1	10
Crystal field: V_2	1
Spin orbit: $\mathscr{H}(so)$	0.01
Zeeman terms:	
$\quad\mathscr{H}(Zl)$ and $\mathscr{H}(Zs)$	0.0001
Hyperfine term: $\mathscr{H}(hf)$	0.000001

We start by dividing the potential V (which is referred to before Table 16.1) into two parts: V_1, due to the ion, and V_2, due to the surrounding lattice. Table 16.5 gives a rough estimate of the order of the terms which are involved. In the *F*-center, the term V_1 is missing. In the case of Cu^{2+}, the ground-state term is ^2D (that is, $s = 1/2$ and $l = 2$), and all the m values have to be considered. If we neglect V_2 and the higher order term we may start with the quantum number listed in (16.16). However, since V_2 is larger than $\mathscr{H}(so)$, it is appropriate to start the calculation with another set of eigenfunctions, which we list in Table 16.6.

The angular part of the five degenerate ground-state wave functions associated with a ^2D level are shown in Table 16.6; L_z is not an eigen operator of these functions. This splits the five levels into a set of triply degenerate levels and a set of doubly degenerate levels. For the group theoretical arguments, see Tinkham (S, p. 69) or Hammermesh (S, Chapter IX). Further lattice distortion splits the triply degenerate levels into one single level and one doubly degenerate set. This is illustrated in Fig. 16.1. $\mathscr{H}(so)$ removes the degeneracy of the highest level as shown. Actually, every level is degenerate because of the spin parts of the wave function.

TABLE 16.6. ANGULAR PART OF A ^2D FUNCTION IN $Cu^{2+}6H_2O$

$l = 2$. Nonradial part

$m = 0$

E_1	$\dfrac{\sqrt{5}}{4\sqrt{\pi}}(3\cos^2\theta-1)$	$\dfrac{\sqrt{5}}{4\sqrt{\pi}}\dfrac{1}{r^2}(2z^2-x^2-y^2)$	$\dfrac{1}{r^2}\mathscr{Y}_2^{\,0}$

$m = \pm 1$

E_4	$\dfrac{\sqrt{15}}{2\sqrt{\pi}}\sin\theta\cos\theta\sin\phi$	$\dfrac{\sqrt{15}}{2\sqrt{\pi}}\dfrac{xz}{r^2}$	$\dfrac{1}{\sqrt{2}}\dfrac{1}{r^2}(\mathscr{Y}_2^{\,-1}-\mathscr{Y}_2^{\,1})$
E_3	$\dfrac{\sqrt{15}}{2\sqrt{\pi}}\sin\theta\cos\theta\cos\phi$	$\dfrac{\sqrt{15}}{2\sqrt{\pi}}\dfrac{yz}{r^2}$	$\dfrac{i}{\sqrt{2}}\dfrac{1}{r^2}(\mathscr{Y}_2^{\,1}+\mathscr{Y}_2^{\,-1})$

$m = \pm 2$

E_0	$\dfrac{\sqrt{15}}{4\sqrt{\pi}}\sin^2\theta\cos 2\phi$	$\dfrac{\sqrt{15}}{4\sqrt{\pi}}\dfrac{1}{r^2}(x^2-y^2)$	$\dfrac{1}{\sqrt{2}}\dfrac{1}{r^2}(\mathscr{Y}_2^{\,2}+\mathscr{Y}_2^{\,-2})$
E_2	$\dfrac{\sqrt{15}}{4\sqrt{\pi}}\sin^2\theta\sin 2\phi$	$\dfrac{\sqrt{15}}{2\sqrt{\pi}}\dfrac{1}{r^2}xy$	$\dfrac{i}{\sqrt{2}}\dfrac{1}{r^2}(\mathscr{Y}_2^{\,-2}-\mathscr{Y}_2^{\,-2})$

The last column expresses the eigenfunction in terms of the solid harmonics, which use quantization (16.16) and to which Eq. (16.6) applies. The solid harmonics have the form

$$\mathscr{Y}_2^{\,0} = \frac{1}{4}\left(\frac{5}{\pi}\right)^{1/2}(3z^2-r^2) \tag{16.26a}$$

$$\mathscr{Y}_2^{\,\pm 1} = \mp\frac{1}{2}\left(\frac{15}{2\pi}\right)^{1/2}z(x\pm iy) \tag{16.26b}$$

$$\mathscr{Y}_2^{\,\pm 2} = \frac{1}{4}\left(\frac{15}{2\pi}\right)^{1/2}(x\pm iy)^2. \tag{16.26c}$$

These functions are normalized over an integration with respect to the solid angle. The E's are the energies $Cu^{2+}6H_2O$; $E_0 < E_1 < E_2 < E_3 = E_4$.

We are concerned with the ground state and the effects of a magnetic field on this state, since its behavior will be compared to the ground state of the F-center. The exact position and character of the excited state are of no interest.

While the ground state is not degenerate with respect to the orbital part, $\phi_0(r)$, it has two η_s's, which we shall denote by η_- and η_+. We ignore η_I. The spin-orbit interaction does not modify the energy of the ground state to first order, although it modifies the wave functions $\phi_0\eta_-$ or $\phi_0\eta_+$. These wave functions will be denoted by $|0, -1/2\rangle$ and $|0, 1/2\rangle$.

If the first-order perturbation theory is used with $\mathcal{H}(so)$, one must evaluate expressions such as

$$\langle \mp 1/2|S_z| \mp 1/2\rangle \langle \phi_0|L_z| \phi_0\rangle. \qquad (16.27)$$

The first quantity is real [see Eq. (16.6)], ϕ_0 is real,* $L_z[-i\hbar(\partial/\partial\phi)]$ is imaginary (see Condon and Shortley, p. 50); hence, the expression (16.27)

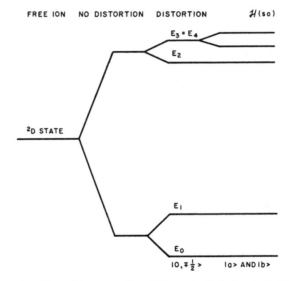

FREE ION   NO DISTORTION   DISTORTION $\mathcal{H}(so)$

FIG. 16.1. Effect of the crystalline field on the Cu^{2+} ion in Cu^{2+} $6H_2O$.

is imaginary. This is impossible unless it is zero, since $\mathcal{H}(so)$ is a real observable.

When we include $\mathcal{H}(so)$ we may obtain imaginary wave functions by using first-order perturbation theory and mixing in the excited states. The ground states have the forms:

$$|a\rangle = |0, -1/2\rangle - \xi \sum_n{}' \frac{|n\rangle}{E_n - E_0} \langle n|\mathbf{s}\cdot\mathbf{l}| 0, -1/2\rangle \qquad (16.28a)$$

and

$$|b\rangle = |0, 1/2\rangle - \xi \sum_n{}' \frac{|n\rangle}{E_n - E_0} \langle n|\mathbf{s}\cdot\mathbf{l}| 0, 1/2\rangle, \qquad (16.28b)$$

* The radial part of ϕ_n is real since the Schrödinger equation with V_1 is real and nondegenerate.

where n stands for any excited state with spin up or down. The terms of $|0, 1/2\rangle$ and $|0, -1/2\rangle$ cannot appear in the sum because of the properties of l (just discussed).

If an external magnetic field is applied to the sample, we must consider the effects of $\mathscr{H}(Zl)$ and $\mathscr{H}(Zs)$, namely:

$$\beta \mathbf{H} \cdot (1 + 2\mathbf{s}), \tag{16.29}$$

where g_e has been set equal to 2. Consider the z component, which gives:

$$\beta H_z \langle a | l_z + 2s_z | a \rangle = \beta H_z \{ \langle a | l_z | a \rangle + 2 \langle a | s_z | a \rangle \}. \tag{16.30}$$

The first term can be written in a more explicit fashion:

$$\beta H_z \left[\langle 0, -1/2 | l_z | 0, -1/2 \rangle \right.$$
$$\left. - \xi \sum_n{}' \left\{ \frac{\langle 0, -1/2 | l_z | n \rangle}{E_n - E_0} \langle n | \mathbf{1} \cdot \mathbf{s} | 0, -1/2 \rangle + \text{comp. conj.} \right\} \right]. \tag{16.30a}$$

The only term which will appear in the sum is that where $l_z s_z | 0, -1/2 \rangle$ gives an eigenfunction with spin $-1/2$. This is due to the first bracket after the sum which has no spin operator. All the other terms will be zero, either because of the first or second square bracket in the sum. From Figure 16.1 and Table 16.6, we note that:

$$l_z | 0, -1/2 \rangle = 2i | 2, -1/2 \rangle, \tag{16.30b}$$

and
$$\langle 2, -1/2 | l_z | 0, -1/2 \rangle = 2i. \tag{16.30c}$$

The expression due to the sum in (16.30a) reduces to:

$$4\xi \beta H_z \frac{1}{E_2 - E_0}, \tag{16.31a}$$

since l_x and l_y do not connect states of equal m, see Eq. (16.6) and $s_z | \tfrac{1}{2} \rangle = \tfrac{1}{2} | \tfrac{1}{2} \rangle$. Likewise, for the $|b\rangle$ state, one obtains the correction:

$$- 4\xi \beta H_z \frac{1}{E_2 - E_0}. \tag{16.31b}$$

The correct eigenvalues of the states are obtained by combining Eq. (16.31) with (16.30), thus

$$- \beta H_z \left(1 - \frac{4\xi}{E_2 - E_0} \right) \tag{16.32a}$$

and
$$\beta H_z \left(1 - \frac{4\xi}{E_2 - E_0} \right). \tag{16.32b}$$

A slightly more careful analysis of the Hamiltonian would indicate that the term "1" does not appear in (16.32), but $\frac{1}{2}g_e$. If we neglect ξ, the energies would be given by the Hamiltonian $2\beta s_z H_z$; if ξ is included, however, the form is:

$$\beta g_z H_z s_z' \tag{16.33}$$

where

$$g_z = 2\left(1 - \xi \frac{4}{E_2 - E_0}\right). \tag{16.33a}$$

Here s_z' operates on a fictitious eigenfunction $\eta_{\mp}'$.

To explore this problem further, consider the term where H_x or H_y does not equal zero. We have to evaluate a few more matrix elements. Let us next apply H along the x-axis. The operators whose matrix elements we are to calculate have the form:

$$\beta H_x(l_x + 2s_x). \tag{16.34}$$

By using the right-hand side of Table 16.6, we may show that:

$$l_x|0, -1/2\rangle = -i|3, -1/2\rangle. \tag{16.35}$$

The only nonvanishing term in (16.30) (with the subscript z replaced by x) comes from the sum of (16.30a) and couples the spin states. The off-diagonal elements arising from l_x have the form:

$$-\xi \frac{1}{E_3 - E_0}\langle 0, 1/2|l_x| 3, 1/2\rangle \langle 3, 1/2|l_x s_x| 0, -1/2\rangle = -\frac{1}{2}\xi \frac{1}{E_3 - E_0} \tag{16.36}$$

since

$$\langle 0, 1/2|s_x| 0, -1/2\rangle = 1/2 \tag{16.36a}$$

by (16.6a). Equation (16.36) can also be established with the use of (16.6). We may return to Eq. (16.11a) and write an operator which will give us the matrix elements of (16.34) correctly, namely:

$$\beta g_x H_x s_x', \tag{16.37}$$

where

$$g_x = 2\left(1 - \xi \frac{1}{E_3 - E_0}\right) \tag{16.37a}$$

using the eigenfunctions $\eta_{\mp}'$ in place of $|a\rangle$ and $|b\rangle$. This simplifies the calculations a great deal since one may employ (16.6). Of course, in reality one cannot substitute η' for the real eigenfunction. The eigenvalues associated with (16.36) are:

$$\pm \beta H_x\left(1 - \xi \frac{1}{E_3 - E_0}\right). \tag{16.38}$$

By the same argument, one may show that when the magnetic field is in the y-direction, the "corrected" operator has the form

$$\beta g_y H_y s_y',$$
(16.39)

where
$$g_y = 2\left(1 - \xi \frac{1}{E_4 - E_0}\right).$$
(16.39a)

$g_x = g_y$ since $E_3 = E_4$. The general Hamiltonian can be written in the form

$$\mathscr{H}(Z) = \beta\{g_z H_z s_z' + g_x H_x s_x' + g_y H_y s_y'\} = \beta \mathbf{H} \cdot \mathbf{g} \cdot \mathbf{s}'$$
(16.40)

where $\mathbf{s}'$ is similar to $\mathbf{s}$ except that it is combined with a fictitious $\mathbf{g}$-factor which is a diad; hence, $\mathbf{s}'$ represents some effects of the orbital motion due to Eq. (16.28) and operates on fictitious spin eigenfunctions. We define $\mathbf{g}$ as due to the interactions of $\mathbf{L}$ and $\mathbf{S}$ with $\mathbf{H}$, but do not include the effects of the hyperfine interactions. This may seem logical and simple, but in the case of actual measurements it can lead to some complex problems which we shall discuss in Section 19. In the case considered, $\mathbf{g}$ happened to be a diagonal matrix and $g_x = g_y$ since $E_3 = E_4$.* This will not be true in general, however. $\mathscr{H}(Z)$ is the spin Hamiltonian for an electron in an s orbital state. Actually, the unity in the definitions of g should be replaced by $g_e/2$ as can be seen from $\mathscr{H}(Zs)$, that is, Eq. (16.15). From it, we may calculate the energy and the magnetic moment associated with the electron. We may not, however, calculate the angular momentum since its operator is $\mathbf{L} + \mathbf{S}$ and has no relation to Eq. (16.30) or (16.39). When $s \neq 1/2$, the spin Hamiltonian (16.40) becomes considerably more complex (see Pryce, S).

The angular momentum must be handled carefully in solid state traps. Since the mean position of the electron is fixed, the average linear momentum is zero; hence, the angular momentum is independent of the selected origin, that is,

$$\langle |\mathbf{r} \times \mathbf{p}| \rangle = \langle |\mathbf{r} \times \mathbf{p}| \rangle + \langle |\mathbf{r}_0 \times \mathbf{p}| \rangle$$
(16.41)

because $\mathbf{r}_0$ is a constant. 1 in Eq. (16.22), however, applies to the instantaneous angular momentum, which depends on the origin of the vector, namely $\mathbf{r}_n$. Let $\mathbf{r}$ be a vector defined by the lattice distortion. For example, if we have an electron trapped at a negative-ion vacancy, the origin of $\mathbf{r}$ could be the position of the missing nucleus. We may approximate the actual state by eigenfunctions of $\mathbf{L} = \mathbf{r} \times \mathbf{p}$; namely, $\phi(\mathbf{r})$. This assumes that the scalar potential is approximately spherical and that to a first approximation, one may smooth out details of the potential around the nuclei of the surrounding ions. Using this simplification, we may

* We neglect the small spin-orbit corrections which apply to states 3 and 4.

assume that L^2, L_z, and $\mathscr{H}$ commute, and that we may use (16.16) or (16.17). When one considers hyperfine interaction, the first term in (16.22) has to be handled with care, for $\mathbf{L} = \mathbf{r}_n \times \mathbf{p}$, since $\mathbf{r}_n$ must be measured from the position of nucleus n. If a wave function is an s function relative to the center of a missing ion, it is not such a function relative to the nuclei of the nearest and next-nearest neighbors. The most careful procedure is to expand $\phi(\mathbf{r})$ in terms of Wannier functions (see Section 27) and then explore the effect of $\mathscr{H}(hf)$ on these functions. In reality, one uses atomic orbitals associated with the neighboring ions to which Eq. (16.22) applies.

The reader should note that in arriving at Eq. (16.40) we have made a very basic assumption—namely, that Eqs. (16.13), (16.14), and (16.15) apply to our problem. Equation (16.14) involves the magnetic field and the vector potential. This assumes that a point of origin exists. Equation (16.13) is derived from term (IV) of Table 16.3 and use was made of the relation $\mathbf{L} = \mathbf{r} \times \mathbf{p}$ where for atoms $\mathbf{r}$ is measured from the nuclei. In general, at point imperfections and even when we substitute foreign atoms the above definition is not meaningful unless one can establish certain properties for the problem. Since $\mathbf{A}$ and ϕ enter into the Schrödinger equation, the gauge-invariant properties of perturbation theory must be established. Further, one needs a systematic method of arriving at a spin Hamiltonian from the true one. These problems are quite involved; further terms, which are obtained from Dirac's relativistic wave equation, must be added to Table 16.3. These problems have been solved in principle and some of the details are in the appendix to this chapter.

Since we are dealing with a crystal, we cannot isolate the centers, and their mutual interaction must be considered. Two effects are the dipole-dipole and spin exchange terms. The *dipole-dipole* term is:

$$\mathscr{H}(di) = \sum_{i>j} \beta^2 g_i g_j \left\{ \frac{1}{r_{ij}^3}(\mathbf{s}_i \cdot \mathbf{s}_j) - \frac{3}{r_{ij}^5}(\mathbf{s}_i \cdot \mathbf{r}_{ij})(\mathbf{s}_j \cdot \mathbf{r}_{ij}) \right\}, \qquad (16.42)$$

where i and j refer to traps which are separated by the distance $\mathbf{r}_{ij}$. Equation (16.42) uses the assumption just made that the net magnetic moment is $(\beta/\hbar)g_i\mathbf{S}_i$. It assumes that the bound electrons do not contribute to $\mathbf{H}$ at the imperfection.

The *exchange* term has the form

$$\mathscr{H}(ex) = \sum_{i>j} a_{ij}\mathbf{s}_i \cdot \mathbf{s}_j. \qquad (16.43)$$

a_{ij} is a constant. It arises because one-electron wave functions have been used (see Van Vleck, p. 316).

d. Paramagnetic Resonance and Relaxation

At the end of this section, two types of experiments are discussed— paramagnetic *relaxation* and paramagnetic *resonance*. For simplicity, assume that $l=0$ and that only one electron, $s = \pm 1/2$ has to be considered. Term (II) will average to zero and we are only concerned with (III) (Table 16.3). Let the magnetic field be of the type $\mathbf{k}H_0 + \mathbf{H}_1 \cos \omega t$ where $H_1 \ll H_0$ and t is the time, ω is the angular frequency and $\mathbf{k}$ is the unit vector along the z-axis. H_0 splits the degenerate level into two with eigenvalues $\pm \beta H_0$. The population of these levels will be governed by Boltzmann's statistics.

Since the word *relaxation* is frequently used, one must be very precise about what it means in any given case. Here it refers to a type of experiment that has similarities to what occurs when sound is absorbed in a medium. (Later, in Section 17, the word *relaxation* will be generalized.) Paramagnetic *relaxation* occurs when $\mathbf{H}_1 = 2h_1 \mathbf{k}$. The time-varying field makes the eigenvalues of the states change with time. Because of (16.4), there are no directly induced transitions between the levels. If the two levels are completely isolated from the rest of the crystal, the field will not affect the population of the levels. In quantum mechanical language, we are dealing with an adiabatic process. (The quantum mechanical and the thermodynamical uses of the word *adiabatic* are not identical—see Abragam, p. 135.) This ideal situation does not actually occur, however. Before one applies the field, the levels are in thermal equilibrium with the lattice. $\mathbf{H}_1$ causes an imbalance and, if the processes which tend to keep a canonical distribution are sufficiently rapid, they will induce transitions between the levels because the actual magnetic field is $\mathbf{k}(H_0 + 2h_1)$. Thus, the magnetic moment per unit volume, $\mathbf{M}$, will vary with time.

At low frequency, the population level will be determined by $\mp (H_0 + 2h_1 \cos \omega t)$ and $\mathbf{M}$ will be in phase with the total field. At very high-frequency fields, $\mathbf{M}$ will not be effected by $2h_1 \cos \omega t$ and will be independent of time. At an appropriate frequency, the magnetic moment and the field will be out of phase. This leads to absorption and dispersion. This process has been treated quantitatively by Casimir and du Pré (S) and is the kind of process studied extensively by Gorter and his co-workers.

Paramagnetic *resonance* occurs when $\mathbf{H}_1 = 2h_1\mathbf{i}$ or $2h_1\mathbf{j}$ where $\mathbf{i}$ and $\mathbf{j}$ are unit vectors along the x- and y-axes. Equation (16.6) and (III) indicate that direct transitions between the levels $\pm\beta H_0$ can occur. To first order, the eigenvalues are not affected; hence, the field induces direct transitions in the crystal, which accounts for the absorption. The first process is similar to the absorption of acoustic waves in fluids, whereas the second resembles the processes which occur when we pass light through matter.

In an actual case where g is not a scalar the distinction cannot be made simply by the geometry of H_0 and H_1. The relaxation and resonance phenomena occur, however, at quite different frequencies (about 10^6 and 10^{10} cps). The relaxation process has not been used so far on color centers. It is used in other material, however, and the reader should bear the distinction in mind.

The basic theory of paramagnetic resonance follows the lines of nuclear resonance, and no separate development is required. In the next section this theory is outlined using primarily classical arguments. A great deal of useful information can be obtained from quantum mechanical considerations. Yet, this approach is not sufficiently well developed to handle all the problems. The assumption that H_1 causes only a very small change in the population is not generally true, and the first-order time-dependent perturbation theory should not be used without modification.

REFERENCES

R. G. Barnes and W. V. Smith, *Phys. Rev.* **93**, 95 (1954).

H. B. G. Casimir and F. K. du Pré, *Physica* **5**, 507 (1938).

E. Feenberg and G. E. Pake, "Notes on the Quantum Theory of Angular Momentum." Addison-Wesley, 1953.

E. Fermi, *Z. Physik* **60**, 320 (1930).

L. L. Foldy and S. A. Wouthuysen, *Phys. Rev.* **78**, 29 (1950).

M. Hammermesh, "Group Theory," Addison-Wesley, 1962.

W. K. H. Panofsky and M. Phillips, "Classical Electricity and Magnetism," p. 1. Addison-Wesley, 1955.

M. H. L. Pryce, *Nuovo Cimento* 6 *Suppl.* 3, 817 (1957).

M. Tinkham, "Group Theory and Quantum Mechanics." McGraw-Hill, New York, 1964.

N. F. Ramsey, "Nuclear Moments." Wiley, New York, 1953.

B. R. Zevin, *Optika i Spektroskopiia* **3**, 660 (1957).

17. Solution of Dynamic Equations for an Isolated System

a. General Phenomenological Equations

Consider n_0 electrons (per unit volume) trapped at imperfections. Associated with every trap is a total angular momentum. We assume that $l=0$, hence it is given by $\mathbf{S}$. Any required correction to the spin will be reflected in g [see Eq. (16.40)]. We neglect the difference between the angular momentum operator and the magnetic moment associated with the electron spin and orbital motion. Thus, to every imperfection, the magnetic moment is given by $\mathbf{M} = -\beta g\mathbf{s}$, and the total magnetic moment per unit volume is obtained from Brillouin's equation:

$$\mathbf{M} = \left[\frac{1}{2}n_0\beta g\tanh\frac{\beta gH_0}{2k\theta}\right]\mathbf{k} = M_0\mathbf{k} \qquad (17.1)$$

(see Fowler-Guggenheim, p. 629).

$\mathbf{H}$ is assumed to have the form $H_0\mathbf{k}$; θ is the absolute temperature, and k is Boltzmann's constant. At "high" temperatures (a few degrees absolute), if $H \sim 3000$ gauss, this gives the Curie law, namely:

$$\mathbf{M} = \frac{1}{4}n_0\frac{\beta^2 g^2}{k}\frac{1}{\theta}H_0\mathbf{k} = \chi_0 H_0\mathbf{k}. \qquad (17.1a)$$

We define the static susceptibility as M/H_0. It is given by

$$\chi_0 = \tfrac{1}{2}(g^2\beta^2/\hbar\omega_0)n_\theta = \tfrac{1}{2}(\gamma^2\hbar/\omega_0)n_\theta \qquad (17.1b)$$

where

$$\omega_0 = (g\beta/\hbar)H_0 - \gamma H_0, \qquad (17.1c)$$

and

$$n_\theta = n_0\tanh(\beta gH_0/2k\theta) \approx \tfrac{1}{2}(g\beta H_0/k\theta)n_0. \qquad (17.1d)$$

n_θ is the difference in the populations between the spins pointing against the magnetic field and those pointing along the field, since the gyromagnetic ratio for the electronic spin is negative.

To develop the theory, consider first a single spin which does not interact with the lattice; later we shall return to Eq. (17.1). From Eqs. (16.5b) and (16.40), with $g_x=g_y=g_z=g_e=g$, a relation between the magnetic moment and the angular momentum is obtained, namely,

$$\mathbf{M} = -(g\beta/\hbar)\mathbf{S} = -\gamma\mathbf{S}. \qquad (17.2)$$

As pointed out in the last section, s' of Eq. (16.40) is a fictitious spin function and, in this case, one may not relate the total angular momentum, $(\mathbf{L}+\mathbf{S})$, in a simple manner to the total magnetic moment, $(\beta/\hbar)(\mathbf{L}+g\mathbf{S})$.

In (17.2), we ignore the effects of $\mathbf{L}$. This complication does not arise in nuclear spin problems since an $\mathbf{L}$ does not exist.

Let us apply a field oscillating along the x-direction

$$H_x = 2h_1 \cos \omega t = H_1 \cos \omega t. \tag{17.3}$$

H_x can be resolved into two fields as follows:

clockwise　　　　　$\mathbf{h} = \mathbf{i}h_1 \cos \omega t - \mathbf{j}h_1 \sin \omega t, \quad \boldsymbol{\omega} = -\omega\mathbf{k}$　(17.4a)

counterclockwise　$\mathbf{h} = \mathbf{i}h_1 \cos \omega t + \mathbf{j}h_1 \sin \omega t, \quad \boldsymbol{\omega} = \omega\mathbf{k}.$　(17.4b)

The sum gives (17.3). Equation (17.4a) is a clockwise rotating field, (ω along $-\mathbf{k}$), whereas (17.4b) rotates counterclockwise. Since H_x is at right angles to H_0, it does not to first order affect the thermal distribution. However, it exerts a torque on $\mathbf{S}$. By Newton's second law:

$$(d/dt)\,\mathbf{S} = \mathbf{M}\times\mathbf{H} = -\gamma\mathbf{S}\times\mathbf{H} \tag{17.5}$$

here $\mathbf{H}$ is $H_0\mathbf{k}$ plus Eq. (17.4b), that is, a rotation given by the vector $\omega\mathbf{k}$.* We shall later consider the effects of (17.4a). The z component of (17.5) has the form

$$(d/dt)\,S_z = -\gamma[H_y\,S_x - H_x S_y]. \tag{17.5a}$$

We would now like to show that one can derive (17.5a) from Schrödinger's equation where $\mathbf{S}$ is the expectation value. In general, for any time-independent operator, $\mathbf{O}$:

$$\frac{d}{dt}\langle|\mathbf{O}|\rangle = \int\left(\frac{\partial}{\partial t}\psi^*\right)\int \mathbf{O}\psi\,dt + \int \psi^*\mathbf{O}\left(\frac{\partial}{\partial t}\psi\right)dt = \frac{1}{i\hbar}\langle|\mathbf{O}\mathcal{H} - \mathcal{H}\mathbf{O}|\rangle \tag{17.6}$$

where use has been made of Schrödinger's time-dependent equation and the fact that the real operators are Hermitian. $\mathcal{H}$ is the Schrödinger form of the Hamiltonian. If $\mathbf{O} = S_z$, the only part of $\mathcal{H}$ which does not commute with S_z is $\mathbf{S}$, hence:

$$\frac{d}{dt}\langle|S_z|\rangle = -\frac{1}{i\hbar}\left\langle\left|\frac{\beta g}{\hbar}[(\mathbf{S}\cdot\mathbf{H})\,S_z - S_z(\mathbf{S}\cdot\mathbf{H})]\right|\right\rangle. \tag{17.7}$$

---

* d/dt is the derivative with respect to time in the laboratory frame of reference. One might use partial derivatives since we are going to employ Schrödinger's equation. The partial derivative with respect to time will, however, be used later when a rotating frame is introduced. The rotating field employed depends on the sign of the gyromagnetic ratio. For electrons and the stable nuclei which make up the alkali halide, as defined in Table 16.2, γ is always positive. Note, however, the *signs* in Eqs. (16.5a), (16.5b), and (16.5c). The positive and negative values of the gyromagnetic ratio require some care in the solutions of the equations [that is Eqs. (17.12a), (17.12b), and (17.14)]. Bloch considers this problem in some detail.

This reduces to (17.5a) with the use of Eq. (16.2). The reader will note that (17.6) is similar, but not identical, to Heisenberg's equation of motion. We may thus assume that Eq. (17.5) is a classical equation or an equation which relates expectation values.

If we consider an actual crystal, one never deals with a single spin and M is given by Eq. (17.1). Therefore, it has a temperature dependence. Associated with this M is an angular momentum, $-(1/\gamma)M$. For the remainder of this section or where the problem is treated classically we shall use $S = -(1/\gamma)M$.

It is convenient to introduce a coordinate system that rotates with (17.4b). Its k-axis is the same as the laboratory system. One may show (see Joos, p. 232) that in this case, the time derivative with respect to the rotating coordinates, $\partial/\partial t$, corresponds to the operator

$$\frac{\partial}{\partial t} = \frac{d}{dt} - \omega k \times, \tag{17.8}$$

where $\times$ indicates the cross product, d/dt is the time derivative with respect to the laboratory system, and ω is the angular velocity of the rotating coordinate system. Combining (17.5) and (17.8) and writing $H = H_0 k + h_1 i'$, where i' is a unit vector in the rotating system, we obtain:

$$-\frac{1}{\gamma}\frac{\partial}{\partial t}S = S \times k\left[H_0 - \frac{\omega}{\gamma}\right] + h_1 S \times i' \tag{17.9}$$

$$= S \times H_e \tag{17.9a}$$

where

$$H_e = (H_0 - H^*)k + h_1 i' \tag{17.9b}$$

and

$$H^* = \omega/\gamma. \tag{17.9c}$$

The sign of ω must be selected in such a manner that $\omega/\gamma > 0$. This can always be done by either selecting (17.4a) or (17.4b). In an experiment, one usually varies H_0. As one passes through the value where $H_0 = H^*$, the effective field is reduced to almost zero. The desired solutions are those where the absolute magnitude of M does not change. One thus passes through a series of stationary states. Such a solution is referred to as adiabatic, that is, the population in the quantized states does not change relative to H_e. Let α be the angle of H_e relative to the z-axis (see Bloch, S, and Rabi, Ramsey, and Schwinger, S), then

$$\cos\alpha = \frac{\delta}{(1+\delta^2)^{1/2}}, \tag{17.10}$$

where

$$\delta = (1/h_1)(H_0 - H^*).$$ (17.11a)

Further, in the rotating coordinate system:

$$M_{x'}(\text{rot}) = M \frac{1}{(1+\delta^2)^{1/2}}$$ (17.11b)

and

$$M_z(\text{rot}) = M \frac{\delta}{(1+\delta^2)^{1/2}}.$$ (17.11c)

In an experiment we start with a large value of δ and the spins align themselves along $H_0\mathbf{k}$. Now, H_0 is varied slowly, without changing h_1, in such a manner that δ goes through zero and finally has a large negative value. Equation (17.11c) indicates that the final $\mathbf{M}$ is the negative of the original $[M_z(\text{final}) = -M_z(\text{initial})$, and $M_x(\text{final}) = 0]$; that is, the spins have been flipped. In the laboratory system:

$$M_x(\text{lab}) = M \frac{1}{(1+\delta^2)^{1/2}} \cos \omega t$$ (17.12a)

and

$$M_y(\text{lab}) = M \frac{1}{(1+\delta^2)^{1/2}} \sin \omega t$$ (17.12b)

One should note that our gyromagnetic ratio is really $-\gamma$ for the electron; hence, our equation for M_y is slightly different from Bloch's original expressions for nuclei. In an experiment, one may measure M_x or M_y, detect when $\delta = 0$, and hence may evaluate γ and g. We note that M is in phase with the counterclockwise field and that no energy is transferred from the h_1 microwave field to the system, provided H_0 is not varied. The energy stored in the system comes from the time variation of H_0, which has not been included in our solutions.

The geometry of our solution is as follows: Before passing through resonance, $\mathbf{H}$ is up (along the z-axis), $\mathbf{M}$ is up, but $\mathbf{S}$ is down because the gyromagnetic ratio is negative. Effectively, our spins are rotating counterclockwise. It is for this reason that we use (17.4b).

If the system passes through resonance for this field, it will not pass through resonance for (17.4a). Since resonance occurs in the region $H_0 - H_e \approx h_1$, we may ignore (17.4a) when the system goes through the resonance of (17.4b). Field (17.4a) produces a time-varying torque on $\mathbf{S}$ which averages to zero (see Abragam, p. 21). For a general reference to these problems see Bloch (S).

b. Bloch's Equations and the Solution for Slow Passage

Unfortunately, Eq. (17.5) ignores the spin-spin interactions, terms (16.42) and (16.43). Further, it does not include terms such as (III), from Table 16.3, where $\mathbf{A}$ is due to the lattice vibrations. These terms are responsible for the spin-lattice interactions. Equation (17.5) also excludes the effects of the nuclear magnetism. One way to include these is by using Bloch's phenomenological equations, which is now derived.

Consider first a system where the spins cannot interact with the lattice and where $H_0 \neq 0$.* Assume further that at $t = 0$, H_1 is turned off, but at that moment $M_x \neq 0$. As time goes on, M_x will tend to die out since its expectation value is zero. An elementary way to describe this is to assume that M_x is governed by the equation

$$(d/dt) M_x = -(1/T_2) M_x. \qquad (17.13a)$$

T_2 has the dimension of time and is called the *transverse relaxation time*. If $M_x \neq 0$ there is a phase relation between the spins in the lattice. To deal with this problem rigorously involves the use of density matrices (see Slichter, Chapter V).

A change in the z component (direction of H_0) of M requires the transfer of energy from the spin system to the lattice vibrations, since $\mathscr{H}(Zs)$ changes. Further, M_z wants to return to its stationary value given by (17.1); hence, in place of (17.13a), we write:

$$(d/dt) M_z = -(1/T_1)(M_z - M_0). \qquad (17.13b)$$

T_1 is the *spin-lattice relaxation time*. One would not expect that $T_1 > T_2$ since the time it takes to restore the system to an equilibrium value, T_1 (which requires energy) cannot be longer than the time it takes for changes in the x and y directions to occur (T_2) where no energy transfer is involved.

Combining Eqs. (17.5), (17.13a), and (17.13b) results in Bloch's equation:

$$\frac{d}{dt}\mathbf{M} = -\gamma(\mathbf{M}\times\mathbf{H}) - \frac{1}{T_2}(M_x\mathbf{i} + M_y\mathbf{j}) - \frac{1}{T_1}(M_z - M_0)\mathbf{k}. \qquad (17.14)$$

$\mathbf{H}$ is the total field, H_0 plus (17.4a) or (17.4b).

Many solutions for this equation exist. Only the steady-state solution in the presence of H_0 and the rotating field will be considered. In the first case, adiabatic rapid passage, no energy was transferred to the lattice. This is a limiting case. Here there is always a transfer of energy, first to

* Actually, the lattice interacts with the spins.

the spin system and then to the lattice. We consider the equilibrium case, where the field transfers energy to the spin system. The energy transferred to the spin system, because of the interaction given by Eq. (17.5), equals the energy transferred to the lattice. In this case again, **M** is time independent on the rotating coordinate system introduced previously. In this case, however, **M** will not be aligned with the rotating field. This situation is known as *slow passage*. Under these conditions we have the solution

$$M_x = \frac{1}{2}\chi_0\,\omega_0\,T_2\left[\frac{(\omega_0-\omega)\,T_2(2h_1\cos\omega t)+2h_1\cos(\omega t-\pi/2)}{1+(\omega_0-\omega)^2\,T_2{}^2+\gamma^2\,h_1{}^2\,T_1\,T_2}\right] \quad (17.15)$$

where

$$\omega_0 = \gamma H_0 \quad (17.15a)$$

and

$$\chi_0 = M_0/H_0, \quad \text{the static susceptibility, see Eq. (17.1b).}$$

Equation (17.15) is derived many places (see Andrews, p. 221, for a positive gyromagnetic ratio). Expressions for M_y and M_z are known but are not required here. Using the total H_1, i.e., (17.3), we define a frequency-dependent susceptibility:

$$M_x = 2h_1\,re\{\chi\,e^{i\omega t}\}, \qquad \chi = \chi'-i\chi'' \quad (17.16)$$

where

$$\chi' = \frac{1}{2}\chi_0\,\omega_0\,T_2\left[\frac{(\omega_0-\omega)\,T_2}{1+(\omega_0-\omega)^2\,T_2{}^2+\gamma^2\,h_1{}^2\,T_1\,T_2}\right] \quad (17.17a)$$

and

$$\chi'' = \frac{1}{2}\chi_0\,\omega_0\,T_2\left[\frac{1}{1+(\omega_0-\omega)^2\,T_2{}^2+\gamma^2\,h_1{}^2\,T_1\,T_2}\right]. \quad (17.17b)$$

If h_1 is small, we may neglect the last term in the denominator and write

$$\chi' = \frac{1}{2}\chi_0\,\omega_0\left[\frac{(\omega_0-\omega)\,T_2{}^2}{1+(\omega_0-\omega)^2\,T_2{}^2}\right] \quad (17.18a)$$

$$\chi'' = \frac{1}{2}\chi_0\,\omega_0\left[\frac{T_2}{1+(\omega_0-\omega)^2\,T_2{}^2}\right]. \quad (17.18b)$$

χ' and χ'' are the susceptibilities for the total field, Eq. (17.3). One may differentiate between the χ's defined here and the χ's for which both (17.4a) and (17.4b) are used (in Abragam, p. 40). We shall not do so however. Our χ's are related as follows:

$$\chi'(\omega_0+\omega) = \frac{1}{\pi}\mathscr{P}\int_{-\infty}^{\infty}\frac{\chi''(\omega_0+\omega')\,d\omega'}{\omega'-\omega} \quad (17.19a)$$

and

$$\chi''(\omega_0+\omega) = -\frac{1}{\pi}\mathscr{P}\int_{-\infty}^{\infty}\frac{\chi'(\omega_0+\omega')}{\omega'-\omega}\,d\omega' \qquad (17.19b)$$

where

$$\mathscr{P}\int_{\infty}^{\infty}\frac{g(\omega')\,d\omega'}{\omega'-\omega} = \lim_{\epsilon\to 0}\left[\int_{\infty}^{-\omega\epsilon} + \int_{\omega+\epsilon}^{\infty}\right]. \qquad (17.19c)$$

Near resonance one measures χ_R even with the field described by (17.3) since the contribution of the off-resonance term is very small compared to the on-resonance one; hence, χ_R and Eq. (17.19) can be used even with a linear field. These are known as the *Kramers-Krönig relations*. The Kramers-Krönig relations apply to *linear* systems, that is, only in the case of χ' and χ'' as given by Eqs. (17.17a) and (17.17b), where $\gamma^2 h_1{}^2 T_1 T_2 \ll 1$.

One would like to establish similar relations when the above restrictions do not apply. This can be done by a method, due to Abragam (p. 44), which (as we shall see) is of major importance in understanding the *F*-center. For this purpose, the Lorentz function is introduced

$$f_T(\omega) = \frac{T}{\pi}\frac{1}{1+(\omega-\omega_0)^2 T^2}, \qquad (17.20)$$

which is normalized with respect to an integration over ω from $-\infty$ to $+\infty$. The points at half height are:

$$\omega-\omega_0 = \pm 1/T. \qquad (17.20a)$$

Using this definition, Eqs. (17.18) can be written in the form:

$$\chi' = (\pi/2)\chi_0\,\omega_0(\omega_0-\omega)\,T_2 f_{T_2}(\omega) \qquad (17.21a)$$

$$\chi'' = (\pi/2)\chi_0\,\omega_0 f_{T_2}(\omega), \qquad (17.21b)$$

while, in the case of saturation, one obtains almost the same equation if one introduces a fictitious T_2, namely,

$$\chi' = (\pi/2)\chi_0\,\omega_0\,T_2'(\omega_0-\omega)f_{T_2'}(\omega) \qquad (17.22a)$$

$$\chi'' = (\pi/2)\chi_0\,\omega_0\frac{1}{[1+\gamma^2 h_1{}^2 T_1 T_2]^{1/2}}f_{T_2'}(\omega) \qquad (17.22b)$$

$$(1/T_2') = (1/T_2)(1+\gamma^2 h_1{}^2 T_1 T_2)^{1/2}. \qquad (17.22c)$$

Since Eqs. (17.21) and (17.22) are similar, one may use the Kramers-Krönig relation even when there is saturation. The actual relation for χ' (due to the absorption characterized by χ'') is

$$\chi'(\omega_0+\omega) = [1+\gamma^2 h_1{}^2 T_1 T_2]^{1/2}\frac{1}{\pi}\mathscr{P}\int\limits_{-\infty}^{\infty}\frac{\chi''(\omega_0+\omega')}{\omega'-\omega}\,d\omega'. \quad (17.22d)$$

This is a very important result, as we shall see later (Section 20).

Let us briefly consider what use we may make of χ' and χ'' in the laboratory. We are interested in frequencies where $\omega = \omega_0$. For $H_0 = 5000$ gauss, this corresponds to a frequency of the order of 10^{10} cps, which is in the microwave range. To obtain a high value of h_1, the sample must be in a resonance cavity. It is the effect of χ on the resonance cavity which one can measure.

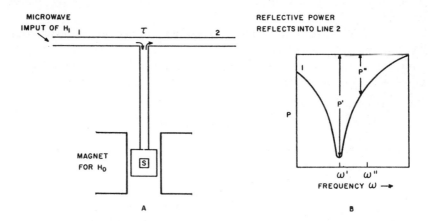

FIG. 17.1. Principle of measuring χ' and χ''; τ is a magnetic microwave tee.

One possible arrangement of the equipment is shown in Fig. 17.1. We transmit an electromagnetic wave down a wave guide (arm 1); it gets reflected at the tee (τ) and power is transmitted to the sample S. The field H_0 is applied by means of an external magnet. When $H_0 = 0$, the reflected power in arm 2 is given in Fig. 17.1B. For an appropriate iris size, energy will be stored in the cavity. For a perfect system $\rho \to 0$ and the resistances associated with the cavity disappear. This accounts for the sharp drop in power at ω'. ρ is a measure of the energy absorbed in the cavity. For much higher and lower frequencies, little power will enter the cavity and its resistive properties play only a minor role. The actual shape of the dip in the figure depends on the iris size and its coupling to the cavity. The resonance frequency occurs when the inductive and capacitive terms associated with the iris and cavity are equal.

Consider now what happens when we turn on H_0. We will have in the cavity a complex magnetic element giving a total magnetization of the form

$$M = M' + iM'', \tag{17.23}$$

where M' and M'' equal χ' and χ'' times an effective volume and H_x. M' contributes to the reactive component of a cavity and affects the resonance frequency. M'' contributes to the resistive properties of the cavity and affects the absorption.

If we tune to ω' when H_0 is applied, the amount of reflected power will change because the resistive component of the cavity has been altered. (The very small change of the resonance frequency will have a minor effect at ω'.) The power dissipated in the sample may be calculated as follows: M_z is time independent and does not contribute to the dissipation; the energy absorbed, therefore, is

$$-\frac{\omega}{2\pi} \int_0^{2\pi/\omega} M_x \frac{d}{dt} H_x \, dt = 2\omega h_1^2 \chi'' V_c \tag{17.24}$$

where (17.3) and (17.15) have been used. V_c is the effective volume of the crystal. This means that changes in resistance of the cavity ρ will be proportional to χ''.

If we are tuned to ω'', χ' can be measured. H_0 will again cause changes in the energy absorbed and in the frequency. Because of the extreme steepness of the curve at ω'', the major effect of the variation of the impedance is a shift of the resonance. Since these changes are very small, the variation of the impedance is proportional to χ'. Thus, what we measure, χ' or χ'', depends on where the system is on the resonance curve.

c. Comparison of the Two Solutions

We have obtained two solutions for **M**, namely (17.12) and (17.17). For the following arguments we shall assume that h_1 is very small and that one may ignore the last term in the denominator of Eq. (17.17). Equation (17.12) applies to this case if $T_1 = T_2 = \infty$. The experiment must proceed rapidly compared to T_1 and T_2 for solution (17.12) to apply. It is for this reason that this solution is referred to as *adiabatic rapid passage*. Shortly the limitations on the field will be considered. Using (17.12), we obtain the following expression for the susceptibilities:

$$\chi' = \frac{M}{2h_1}\frac{1}{(1+\delta^2)^{1/2}} = \frac{M}{2}\frac{1}{[h_1{}^2+(H_0-H)^2]^{1/2}} \qquad (17.25a)$$

$$\chi'' = 0. \qquad (17.25b)$$

Equation (17.25b) states that no energy is being put into the system as can be seen from Eq. (17.24). In Fig. (17.2) we have plotted χ' and χ'' as functions of H for adiabatic rapid passage, that is, Eq. (17.25), as well as those values for slow passage [Eqs. (17.18) $(\gamma^2 h_1{}^2 T_1 T_2 \ll 1)$].

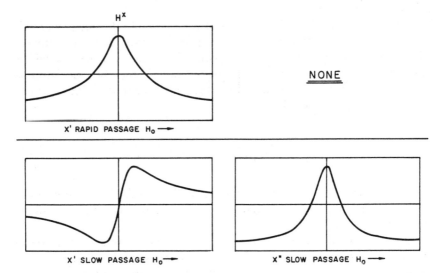

FIG. 17.2. Comparison of two possible solutions of Bloch's equations.

Actually, H_0 varies with time. Magnetic energy is stored in the system when the spins are flipped after an adiabatic passage. Equations (17.3), (17.12a), and (17.24) indicate that no energy is transferred to the system. Actually, since H_0 is a function of time, the solution (17.12a) does not apply exactly and there must be an imaginary part of the susceptibility.

These are not the only solutions of the equations and a general one has been given by Bloch. We shall not consider other solutions, but shall discuss briefly the conditions in which Eq. (17.12) applies. We follow an argument of Abragam (pp. 34; 65).

Consider what happens to **M** when field (17.4b) is applied and H_0 is made time dependent. We first apply the transformation (17.8) to eliminate the time dependence of the microwave field [that is, Eq. 17.4b)]; the gyromagnetic ratio for the electron is $-\gamma$ (it is negative). Thus, the field employed in (17.9a),

$$\mathbf{H}_{\mathrm{eff}} = \mathbf{H}_e = [H_0 - (\omega/\gamma)] \mathbf{k} + h_1 \mathbf{i}' \qquad (17.26)$$

is used. A change in a vector, that is, $\mathbf{H}_e$, can be represented by two terms in the following manner:

$$\frac{\partial}{\partial t} \mathbf{H}_e = \mathbf{\Omega} \times \mathbf{H}_e + \Omega_1 \mathbf{H}_e \qquad (17.27)$$

where $\mathbf{\Omega}$ is a vector and Ω_1 is a scalar. The Ω's have the dimension of $(\text{time})^{-1}$ and $\mathbf{\Omega}$ is the instantaneous rotation $\mathbf{H}_e$. At any instant there is a pure rotation, which causes a change in the direction of $\mathbf{H}_e$, that is given by the first term of (17.27). This quantity will shortly be determined. The second term is responsible for a change in the magnitude of $\mathbf{H}_e$. We now employ a second rotating frame, about $\mathbf{\Omega}$, the double prime system. Differentiation in this frame is denoted by the symbol D. Then it follows from (17.5) and (17.8) that:

$$(D/Dt)\mathbf{M} = -\gamma \mathbf{M} \times [\mathbf{H}_e - (1/\gamma)\mathbf{\Omega}]. \qquad (17.28)$$

The z''-axis is taken along $\mathbf{H}_e$; hence, in the double prime system, the x and y components of $\mathbf{H}_e$ are zero. The z component of $\mathbf{M}$ has the form:

$$(D/Dt) M_z = M_x \Omega_y - M_y \Omega_x \qquad (17.29)$$

or

$$\Delta M_z = M_z(t) - M_z(0) = \int_0^t [M_x(t')\Omega_y(t') - M_y(t')\Omega_x(t')]\, dt'. \qquad (17.29a)$$

If in the first rotating frame, $\Delta M_z \to 0$ for the period of one revolution, γH_e, the following condition is obtained:

$$\Delta M_z \sim \left| \frac{M\Omega}{\gamma H_e} \right| \ll M \qquad (17.30)$$

where M_x or M_y is replaced by the absolute value of $\mathbf{M}$ and the magnitude of Ω is employed. M can be much larger than M_x and M_y.

To evaluate Ω, let $\mathbf{H}_e$ be time dependent due to changes in H_0; then in the first rotating frame we have

$$\frac{\partial}{\partial t} \mathbf{H}_e = \cos \alpha \frac{\dot{H}_0}{H_e} \mathbf{H}_e + \sin \alpha \frac{\dot{H}_0}{H_e} (\mathbf{n} \times \mathbf{H}_e) \qquad (17.31)$$

where $\mathbf{n}$ is a unit vector at right angles to H_e and h_1.* The dot is employed for differentiation with respect to time in the laboratory frame of reference; α is the angle between H_e and the z-axis in that reference frame. Comparing (17.27) and (17.31) the following relation is established:

$$|\Omega| = \frac{\sin \alpha}{H_e} H_0 = \frac{h_1}{H_e^2} H_0 \tag{17.32}$$

substituting in (17.30) finally results in

$$\frac{h_1}{\gamma H_e^3} H_0 \ll 1 \tag{17.33}$$

or the slightly stronger condition,

$$\dot{H}_0 \ll \gamma h_1^2. \tag{17.34}$$

which is the criterion first given by Bloch for adiabatic passage.

In the preceding equation nothing has been said regarding the relaxation times introduced when we obtained Bloch's equation. If the passage through resonance is slow, energy will be transferred to the lattice and the spins will be out of phase with $\mathbf{H}_e$.

The width of the resonance is h_1 and the time to pass through it is $h_1/\dot{H}_0$. This quantity must be small compared to T_1 or T_2. Since $T_2 \leqslant T_1$ we have the additional condition for adiabatic rapid passage:

$$(1/h_1)\dot{H}_0 \gg (1/T_2). \tag{17.35}$$

REFERENCES

F. Bloch, *Phys. Rev.* **70**, 460 (1946).
I. I. Rabi, N. F. Ramsey, and J. Schwinger, *Rev. Mod. Phys.* **26**, 167 (1954).

18. GENERAL THEORY OF PARAMAGNETIC RESONANCE (QUANTUM CONCEPTS)

Although the treatment in Section 17 is of great value, it is not sufficient. Observed shapes of χ' and χ'' during slow passage are not always given by (17.17a) and (17.17b). One reason for this is that many solutions of (17.14) exist, and one should solve this equation using correct expressions for $\mathbf{H}_0$ and $\mathbf{H}_1$, that is, solutions that include the switching on and off

* $\mathbf{n}$'s positive direction is chosen properly so that Eq. (17.31) applies.

of the fields. Another reason is that Eqs. (17.13a) and (17.13b) are only first-order approximations. For some calculations it is most desirable to have a microscopic picture of the phenomenon; thus, we develop the quantum treatment using perturbation theory and using in part the development of Bloembergen, Purcell, and Pound (S).

a. Introduction to the Quantum Mechanical Approach

As in the previous sections, we consider n_0 (per unit volume) magnetic dipoles ($\mathbf{M} = -\beta g\mathbf{s}$) in a field $\mathbf{H}_0$. The magnets are assumed to have two orientations and their magnetic energies are $\mp \frac{1}{2}g\beta H_0$. This causes a difference in the population of the levels when in contact with a heat bath. The fraction in the lower state is $e^{\alpha}(e^{\alpha}+e^{-\alpha})^{-1}$ where $\alpha = \frac{1}{2}\beta g H_0/k\theta$. Likewise, the fraction in the upper state is given by $e^{-\alpha}(e^{\alpha}+e^{-\alpha})^{-1}$. When we apply a field H_1 along the x-axis it causes upward and downward transitions. The probability of these transitions is equal.* An absorption of energy occurs because of the difference in the population of the levels. Thus, if P is the transition probability, the energy absorbed will be:

$$A = P\hbar\omega n_0 \tanh\{\beta g H_0/2k\theta\} \qquad (18.1)$$

To calculate P we use first-order theory. The perturbation Hamiltonian has the form [see Eq. (17.3)]:

$$\gamma S_x h_1(e^{i\omega t} + e^{-i\omega t}); \qquad (18.2)$$

and the number of transitions per unit time is†

$$P = (1/\hbar^2)\gamma^2 h_1^2 |\langle \pm 1/2|S_x| \mp 1/2\rangle|^2 = \tfrac{1}{4}\gamma^2 h_1^2, \qquad (18.3)$$

provided that the energy is conserved, that is,

$$\omega_0 = \gamma H_0. \qquad (18.4)$$

In the last step of (18.3) we have used (16.6a). In the derivation of (18.3) we have resorted to a Dirac delta-function and assumed that condition (18.4) applied rigorously. We have not considered all the perturbations on the system. Equation (18.3) envisages a solid made of nuclei without

---

* This is true in the semiclassical treatment, but not when one quantizes the electromagnetic field.

† For the steps between (18.2) and (18.3) the reader is referred to Seitz (1940, p. 215). Our Eq. (18.2) is equivalent to his Eq. (1), and his Eq. (20) equals our (18.3) provided his ρ_ν is set equal to $h_1^2/2\pi$, which is the density of the electromagnetic field if the dielectric constant is set equal to unity. This procedure is proper even if $\kappa \neq 1$, since one must actually replace Seitz's $E^2/2\pi$ by our $h_1^2/2\pi$.

spins, that is, $\mathbf{I} = 0$. This means that there is no hyperfine interaction [Eqs. (16.23) and (16.24)]. The interactions with the lattice have also been ignored. Further, the trapped electrons can interact with each other because of dipole-dipole effects and exchange terms in the Hamiltonian. When these interactions are included, the two discrete levels assumed in deriving (18.3) are replaced by two bands and one must introduce a shape function, as was done in Section 4. Now the transition probability has the form

$$P = \tfrac{1}{4}\gamma^2 h_1^{\,2} g_s(\nu) \qquad (18.5)$$

where Eq. (4.8) applies. Using (17.24) we may obtain the following expression for the imaginary part of the susceptibility:

$$\chi'' = \tfrac{1}{8}\gamma^2 \hbar g_s(\nu)\, n_0 \tanh\{\tfrac{1}{2}(\beta g H_0/k\theta)\} = \tfrac{1}{4}\omega_0 \chi_0 g_s(\nu). \qquad (18.6)$$

ω_0 is defined by Eq. (18.4). If $\theta > 5°$ K and $H_0 < 3000$ gauss, the hyperbolic tangent can be approximated by $\tfrac{1}{2}(\beta g H_0/k\theta)$. The use of (18.3) assumes that h_1 only perturbs the energy levels a very small amount. If the spin-lattice interaction is strong, one should expect that the thermal vibrations of the lattice will keep the spin population in equilibrium with the lattice temperatures. As P increases, however, the level distribution will not be able to maintain itself and the population will become equalized. We may define a spin temperature by the relation:

$$1/\theta_s = (k/\beta g H_0)\ln(n_1/n_2). \qquad (18.7)$$

n_1 is the population of the ground state while n_2 is the population of the upper state. This equation applies rigorously and does not require any special equilibrium condition between n_1 and n_2. When more than two spin states exist, the introduction of θ_s requires more detailed considerations (see Abragam, Chapter V).

If θ_s is appreciably higher than the lattice (crystal temperature), first-order perturbation theory does not apply and (18.6) requires modification. We shall discuss these problems in Section 21. $g_s(\nu)$ does not have to equal the expression in the square brackets of Eq. (17.17b); that is, the Bloch equations do not necessarily hold (see Section 18c for details). By comparing Eq. (18.6) with the results for χ'' obtained from Bloch's equation for small h_1, we find that $g_s(\nu)$ equals the expression in the square brackets of (17.18b). In this case, $g_{max} = 2T_2$ since g_s is normalized over the frequency. The advantage of (18.6) over (17.18b) is that in principle $g_s(\nu)$ can be obtained from theory (see Slichter, as well as Abragam). The development here, on the other hand, does not include saturation or higher order perturbation theory. This can be included (see Section 21).

Two quantum mechanical calculations of g_s are of interest. We will discuss the one using the dipole-dipole interaction term first, then the one that employs $\mathscr{H}(hf)$, Eq. (16.24).

b. Spin-Spin Interaction

In this section, the dipole-dipole term, Eq. (16.42), is included in the Hamiltonian. Our interest in (18.3) is limited to transitions where only one of the spins flip over, say the ith jumps from its ground to its excited state. Since $\beta H_0/k\theta$ is very small, a random distribution of all the states is assumed. The interactions between individual spins is neglected (except those at the same spin level).

The introduction of g_s in (18.5) can be due to a spin-spin interaction, as was explained in Section 4. The magnetic Hamiltonian used so far is of the form

$$g\beta H_0 \sum_i s_z{}^i = g\beta H_0 s_z{}^T. \tag{18.8}$$

Its eigenvalues are determined by the sums of the z-components of the spins of the whole crystal, m_T. The associated eigenfunctions are products of individual ones and, in general, highly degenerate. The perturbation operator, Eq. (18.2), only induces transitions where the z-component of s^T changes by unity, as long as (18.8) is employed.

When $\mathscr{H}(di)$ is added to (18.8) this condition still applies, but the degeneracy is at least in part removed, and bands of levels (see Fig. 4.1) replace the discrete levels that are obtained without Eq. (16.42). One would like to calculate the band shape (that is, its width on an energy scale and the distribution of states within the allowed band), but this cannot actually be done. What one may do is to calculate the moments of the absorption band. g_s is no longer a delta-function. In this calculation one must limit oneself to transitions where the z-component of s^T changes only by unity. This limitation is imposed for *experimental*, not theoretical, reasons. Weak transitions, where the z-component changes by 2 or more, are possible, theoretically, when $\mathscr{H}(di)$ is added to (18.8). Being very weak, they can never be measured (resolved from the background). Since their position in an energy scale is appreciably different from condition (18.4), they would have a *major* effect on the moments and a comparison between the theoretical and experimental values would be impossible. This is why one considers only broadening that does not modify the selection rule obtained without the dipole interaction.

Let the frequency of the absorbed photon during the transition from state n to state n' be $\nu_{nn'}$. Then, the mean-square absorption frequency is given by:

$$\langle \nu^2 \rangle = \int_0^\infty \nu^2 g_s(\nu)\, d\nu = \frac{\sum_{nn'} \nu_{nn'}^2 |(s_x^T)_{nn'}|^2}{\sum_{nn'} |(s_x^T)_{nn'}|^2} \qquad (18.9)$$

where the quantity is summed over all possible orientations of the spins; $s_x^T = \sum_i s_x^i$ is the total spin operator for the solid and $(s_x^T)_{nn'}$ is the matrix element of s_x^T which connects state n to state n'. When $\mathscr{H}(di)$ is neglected, the spin wave function of the solid is a product of individual spin functions, so that s_x^T flips only those spins whose external field is given by $h\nu_{nn'}/g\beta$, that is, Eq. (18.4). A representation exists in which s_x^T is diagonal and $\sum_{nn'} |(s_x^T)_{nn'}|^2$ equals $\mathrm{Tr}(s_x^T)^2$; Tr is the trace or the diagonal sum. The trace is invariant to the representation, hence, one may evaluate $\mathrm{Tr}(s_x^T)^2$ without finding the representation. Likewise, we may evaluate the numerator. Because of the time dependence of $|(s_x^T)_{nn'}|^2$, that is, $\exp(2\pi i \nu_{nn'} t)$, $\sum \nu_{nn'}^2 |(s_x^T)_{nn'}|^2$ can be replaced by (Slichter, p. 50)

$$\sum_{nn'} \nu_{nn'}^2 |(s_x^T)_{nn'}|^2 = -\mathrm{Tr}[(1/h^2)(\mathscr{H} s_x^T - s_x^T \mathscr{H})^2] \qquad (18.10)$$

where the relation between expectation values derived in Section 17 has been employed, Eq. (17.6). One may also obtain (18.10) directly, since one is dealing with Hermitian operators. The only part of $\mathscr{H}(di)$ of interest is that which does not commute with s_x. In our case, it is Eqs. (18.8), (16.42), and (16.43). One cannot include all the terms in $\mathscr{H}(di)$, but only those that do not commute with s_x. Further, "satellite" terms are omitted (see Section 18c). The actual Hamiltonian is:

$$\begin{aligned}
\mathscr{H} = {}& \beta g H_0 s_z^T + \sum_{i>j} a_{ij} \mathbf{s}_i \cdot \mathbf{s}_j \\
&+ \sum_{i>j} \frac{g^2 \beta^2}{r_{ij}^3} (1 - 3\cos^2 \theta_{ij})(\tfrac{3}{2} s_{iz} s_{jz} - \tfrac{1}{2}\mathbf{s}_i \cdot \mathbf{s}_j)
\end{aligned} \qquad (18.11)$$

where θ_{ij} is the angle between the z-axis (axis of H_0) and $\mathbf{r}_{ij}$. The exchange term, (16.43), does not affect the second moment.

Using Eqs. (18.9), (18.10), (18.11) Van Vleck (S) has shown that

$$\langle (\nu - g\beta H/h)^2 \rangle_{\mathrm{Av}} = \langle \Delta \nu^2 \rangle_{\mathrm{Av}} = \frac{1}{4n_0 h^2} \sum_{ji}{}' B_{ji}^2 \qquad (18.12)$$

for $s = \tfrac{1}{2}$ where

$$B_{jk} = -\frac{3g^2 \beta^2}{r_{jk}^3}\left[\frac{3}{2}\cos^2\theta_{jk} - \frac{1}{2}\right]. \qquad (18.12a)$$

$\sum_m'$ is a sum over all magnetic species (n_0), the term $i = j$ being omitted. A sum over all the lattice points will be denoted by $\sum$. If f is the probability that a lattice site is occupied, then

$$\sum_m \sum_k' B_{jk}^2 = \sum_m \sum_k' f B_{jk}^2 = \sum_m f \sum_k' B_{jk}^2 = n_0 f \sum_k' B_{jk}^2 \quad (18.13)$$

since $\sum_k' B_{jk}^2$ is independent of j and there are n_0 magnetic species. Returning to (18.12) we obtain

$$\langle \Delta \nu^2 \rangle = \frac{1}{4h^2} f \sum_k B_{jk}^2. \quad (18.14)$$

Van Vlcck has evaluated the sum in (18.14) for a simple cubic lattice. He obtains

$$\langle \Delta \nu^2 \rangle = 9.2 \frac{g^4 \beta^4}{h^2} \frac{f}{d^6} [(\lambda_1^4 + \lambda_2^4 + \lambda_3^4) - 0.187] \quad (18.15)$$

where d is the distance between the nearest neighbors and λ_1, λ_2, and λ_3 are the direction cosines of H_0 relative to the principle cubic lattice. If $\mathbf{H}_0$ is along one axis, then

$$\langle \Delta \nu^2 \rangle = 7.48 f A^2 \quad (18.16)$$

where

$$A = g^2 \beta^2 / h d^3. \quad (18.17)$$

In a similar manner one may show that

$$\langle \Delta \nu^4 \rangle = 11.7 f A^4. \quad (18.18)$$

provided $f \ll 1$ and one omits a_{ij} of (18.11).

$\langle \Delta \nu^2 \rangle$ and $\langle \Delta \nu^4 \rangle$ have to be related to the width of the absorption line. Following Kittel and Abrahams (S), whose analysis is being combined with Van Vleck's, we assume that the line shape is Lorentzian, Eq. (17.20), with its tails cut off so that the second and fourth moments will exist.

$$g_s = \frac{\Delta}{\pi} \frac{1}{(\nu_0 - \nu)^2 + \Delta^2} \quad \text{for} \quad |\nu_0 - \nu| < \eta \quad (18.19)$$

$$= 0 \quad \text{for} \quad |\nu_0 - \nu| > \eta$$

η is large compared to Δ. Then

$$\langle \Delta \nu^2 \rangle = 2\eta \Delta / \pi, \quad (18.20a)$$

and

$$\langle \Delta \nu^4 \rangle = (2/3\pi) \eta^3 \Delta. \quad (18.20b)$$

Comparing Eqs. (18.16), (18.18), and (18.20), one finds:

$$\Delta = 5.3fA \qquad (18.21)$$

or $$\Delta(\text{gauss}) = (h/g\beta)\Delta = 10^{-19}n_0. \qquad (18.21a)$$

We have assumed a simple cubic structure; n_0 is the number of imperfections per unit volume. For concentrations of 10^{17} or 10^{18} the width of the resonance is of the order of 10^{-2} gauss. This value is many orders of magnitude too small. As we shall see, the measured widths of the F-band range from 35 to 250 gauss. The width of the V-center EPR lines is much smaller (Section 14c). Some measured values range from 1 to 15 gauss. That this figure is still several orders of magnitude larger than the value given by the theory developed here is a very essential point, and should be kept in mind.*

The just-mentioned theory assumes that the local fields of all the spins are identical. If the local field is a result of a combination of the external field and the field due to the arrangement of the magnetic species around the F-center, then the problem becomes more complex. In an experiment, the external field is of the order of 3000 gauss, whereas the field due to the nuclei is of the order of 20 gauss. This means that the local field may vary, from one center to another, by an order of 20 gauss, depending on the orientation of the surrounding nuclei. In some traps the electronic distribution may be such that the effective local field may vary by as much as 2000 gauss. To understand the width under this situation, we need to develop the theory of hyperfine interactions due to Kip, Kittel, Levy, and Portis (S). The word hyperfine has a historic significance and a meaning in atomic spectra. For the problems we are considering, it is not a small effect and the term hyperfine may be misleading.

c. Physical Ideas in Van Vleck and Bloch Broadening

Before proceeding with our analysis, we would like to present the physical concepts behind the Van Vleck, Kittel, and Abrahams theory which perhaps are not always apparent from the involved mathematical deductions. In particular, we would like to relate this theory with the one obtained previously in Section 17. At this point it is useful to write the interaction between the two dipoles [Eq. (16.42)] in the form

$$\mathscr{H}(di) = \sum_{q=-2}^{q=2} F^{(q)} A^{(q)} \qquad (18.22)$$

---

* The fact that the NaCl lattice is body centered will only change the coefficient of Eq. (18.21) by a small amount.

where

$$F^{(1)} = \frac{\sin\theta\cos\theta\,e^{-i\phi}}{r^3}, \tag{18.22a}$$

$$F^{(2)} = \frac{\sin^2\theta\,e^{-2i\phi}}{r^3}, \tag{18.22b}$$

$$F^{(0)} = \frac{1 - 3\cos^2\theta}{r^3}, \tag{18.22c}$$

$$F^{(-q)} = F^{(q)*}, \tag{18.22d}$$

$$A^{(2)} = \tfrac{1}{2}\alpha s_+{}^i s_+{}^j, \qquad A^{(-2)} = \tfrac{1}{2}\alpha s_-{}^i s_-, \tag{18.22e}$$

$$A^{(1)} = \alpha(s_z{}^i s_+{}^j + s_+{}^i s_z{}^j), \tag{18.22f}$$

$$A^{(-1)} = \alpha(s_z{}^i s_-{}^j + s_-{}^i s_z{}^j), \tag{18.22g}$$

$$A^{(0)} = \alpha\{-\tfrac{2}{3}s_z{}^i s_z{}^j + \tfrac{1}{6}(s_{\upharpoonright}{}^i s_-{}^j + s_-{}^i s_+{}^j)\}, \tag{18.22h}$$

and

$$\alpha = (-3/2)g^2\beta^2. \tag{18.22i}$$

This complex form is the one employed by Abragam (pp. 103 and 289), and has some advantages for the discussion to follow: The F's have to do with the space involving the lattice, while the A's are spin operators. The F's have two parts: (1) the mean value $\bar{F}$, and (2) a fluctuating, time-dependent part.

If we ignore the time variations of the F's, we obtain Van Vleck's theory. Van Vleck starts with the unperturbed Hamiltonian of the form

$$\mathcal{H}_0 = \sum_i g\beta s_z{}^i H_0. \tag{18.23}$$

Assume that the imperfections in the solid have a spin of $1/2$, and that there are only ten imperfections, then (18.23) will give 11 levels, with $\sum_i m_s{}^i$ ranging from 5 to -5 (see Fig. 18.1). If $\bar{F}^{(0)}A^{(0)}$, the "truncated" part (also known as *secular* or *adiabatic*) of the static Hamiltonian is applied, the degeneracy of the levels is at least in part removed. One may show that $\bar{F}^{(0)}A^{(0)}$ connects only those levels where $\sum_i m_s{}^i$ does not change. Hence, the levels have some breadth, as in Fig. 18.1. The microwave signal introduces a time-dependent perturbation whose spin operator is $s_x{}^T = \sum_i s_x{}^i$; this connects only adjacent levels in Fig. 18.1. The spacing of the level within a band on the right of Fig. 18.1 is not uniform, and it is this nonuniformity that produces the shape whose moment Van Vleck calculates. Since $\bar{F}^{(0)}$ is time independent, this calculation does not involve the lattice in any way. $\bar{F}^{(0)}$ simply describes the orientation and distribution of the spin systems.

If we now permit the F's to fluctuate, they will induce transitions between the levels. For these calculations we may ignore the Van Vleck broadening and use the energy scheme to the left in Fig. 18.1. Further, we employ the total Hamiltonian $\mathscr{H}(di)$ of Eq. (18.22). The calculation

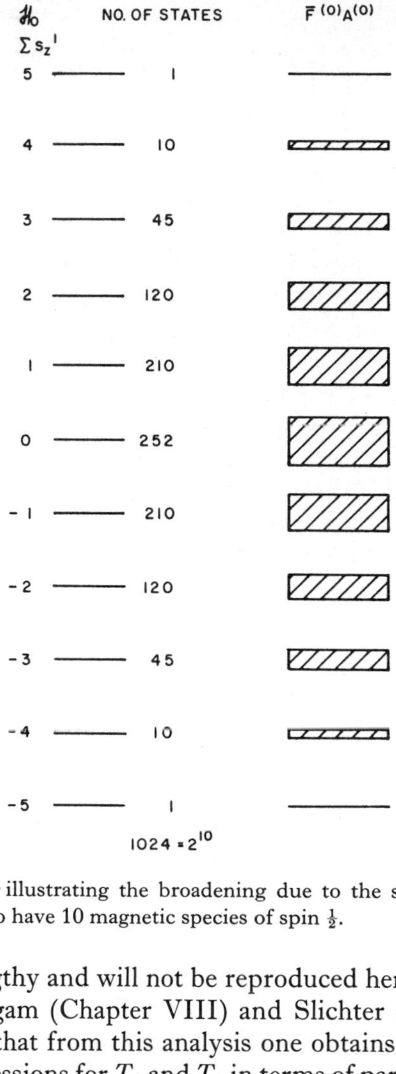

FIG. 18.1. Diagram illustrating the broadening due to the spin-spin interactions. The solid is assumed to have 10 magnetic species of spin $\frac{1}{2}$.

of this effect is lengthy and will not be reproduced here. The problem is discussed in Abragam (Chapter VIII) and Slichter (Chapter V). It is important to note that from this analysis one obtains Eqs. (17.13a) and (17.13b) with expressions for T_1 and T_2 in terms of parameters associated with the lattice. Under *some* conditions, one may show that $T_1 = T_2$. In reality we have two distinct types of broadening, one due to Bloch, the other to Van Vleck. The Bloch type of broadening arises not only from (16.42) but may include the other perturbations mentioned in Section 16.

In an alkali halide one knows that the vibration and polarization of the ions will set up a time-dependent electromagnetic field at the F-center which will most probably lead to a Bloch type of relaxation. In addition, the vibrating nuclei will have a similar effect due to $\mathscr{H}(hf)$. The author believes that these two effects are the most important and that one may not calculate the width by the theory of Van Vleck, Kittel, and Abrahams. This above assumption does not necessarily mean that $T_1 = T_2$, as has often been assumed. These relaxation processes become very complex and one cannot even be sure if Eq. (17.13) applies to the F-center.

There may always be some questions regarding the use of perturbation theory (18.3) when h_1 is not too small. Rabi has given an exact solution of the time-dependent equation. For small signals, his exact results agree with the ones given here but deviate from them when h_1 is large and one does not consider the interaction of the spin with the lattice. If one considers the realistic case when there is a coupling between the spin system and the lattice, the difference between the two approaches disappears and the Rabi equation gives the same results as those presented here, provided $g_s(\nu)$ has a Lorentzian form. This most probably is not a real limitation since different spin-lattice couplings than those considered are possible. A complete discussion of this problem is given again by Abragam (Chapter II). Several years ago Hyde (S) suggested that the Rabi approach does not give a result identical with that obtained from perturbation theory or the Bloch equations. The more careful treatment seems to indicate that it does, however.

REFERENCES

N. Bloembergen, E. M. Purcell, and R. V. Pound, *Phys. Rev.* **73**, 679 (1948).
J. S. Hyde, *Phys. Rev.* **119**, 1492 (1960).
A. F. Kip, C. Kittel, R. A. Levy, and A. M. Portis, *Phys. Rev.* **91**, 1066 (1953).
C. Kittel and E. Abrahams, *Phys. Rev.* **90**, 238 (1953).
J. H. Van Vleck, *Phys. Rev.* **74**, 1168 (1948).

19. THEORY OF THE g-FACTOR AS APPLIED TO THE F-CENTER

In Section 16c we discussed the g-factor and the spin Hamiltonian for $Cu^{2+}6H_2O$. Herein the general ideas developed there will be applied to the F-center.

The g-factor could be defined as follows: If a resonance of frequency ν occurs in an external field H_0, then

$$h\nu = E_u - E_g = g\beta H_0. \tag{19.1}$$

When $g_s(\nu)$ of Eq. (18.5) is not a δ-function, then there is no single value of $E_u - E_g$ and no definite value of ν. Hence, Eq. (19.1) does not define g. One might associate g for the frequency where $g_s(\nu)$ is a maximum. This is a proper procedure if there are no nuclear dipoles surrounding the imperfection. Δg, $(g - g_e)$, is then due only to the interaction of $\phi(r)$ and η_s of (16.1c), where the effects of η_I are completely neglected. Another way of saying this is that it includes the effects of $\mathscr{H}(so)$ [Eq. (16.13)], but not the effects of $\mathscr{H}(hf)$. This is the traditional approach used in atomic spectroscopy where $\mathscr{H}(hf)$ is very small. Actually, the maximum of g_s can be influenced by η_I as we shall see in Section 20.

The above definition has the *theoretical advantage* of associating Δg with interactions between the ϕ and η_s. It has an *experimental disadvantage* since, in general, g cannot be measured directly. As we shall see, for the F-center in LiF $\Delta g = g - g_e$ uncorrected was believed to be positive; when corrected for the nuclear interactions, however, it is negative, as in the case of the other alkali halides (Section 24). We shall see that it should be negative as defined earlier. (For more details, see Section 20.) $g = g_e$ provided $\phi(F)$ can be expanded only in terms of s-functions. If some p-functions have to be added, the spin-orbit interaction must be considered, Eq. (16.13). This additional term perturbs both spin states, that is, $\eta_s = \eta_-$ or $\eta_s = \eta_+$. This perturbation, however, is not equal. Hence, the resonance frequency is slightly altered and the g no longer equals g_e.

A simple assumption to make in order to show how a change in the g can occur is to combine the following wave function with the η_- and η_+ spin functions:

$$\phi(F) = \frac{1}{\sqrt{6}} \sum_j^6 \phi(j). \tag{19.2}$$

Equation (19.2) assumes that the F-center is a negative-ion vacancy with six nearest neighbors. $\phi(j)$ is on each of these neighbors. If $\phi(j)$ is a pure s-function, then $g = g_e$. Measurements indicate this is not the case. Hence, for ion $a\{1, 0, 0\}$ we take it in the form

$$\phi(j) = \frac{1}{(1+\epsilon^2)^{1/2}} \left[\phi_s + \frac{\epsilon}{\sqrt{2}} (\phi_p^+ - \phi_p^-) \right]. \tag{19.3}$$

ϕ_s is an s-function, ϕ_p^+ is a p-function such that $L_z^j \phi_p^+ = \hbar \phi_p^+$, while for ϕ_p^-, $L_z^j \phi_p^- = -\hbar \phi_p^-$ and ϵ is the fraction of non-s-state in $\phi(j)$. The second term arises from the wave-function distortion due to the vacancy Consider the ion located at $a\{1,0,0\}$. The coordinates in Eq. (19.3) are relative to the nucleus of the ion. Using solid harmonics, it follows that

$$\phi_p^+ - \phi_p^- = (\mathscr{Y}_1{}^1 - \mathscr{Y}_{\bar{1}}{}^{-1})f(r) = -\frac{1}{2}\left(\frac{3}{2\pi}\right)^{1/2}(2x)f(r) \quad (19.3\text{a})$$

hence the correction term adds to the s-function for $x < 0$ and subtracts for $x > 0$. The $\{-1,0,0\}$ correction has the form $-\{\mathscr{Y}_1{}^1 - \mathscr{Y}_{\bar{1}}{}^{-1}\}$ and in the general case, see Table 19.1. We shall assume that the ϕ's are orthogonal

TABLE 19.1. CORRECTIONS TO $\phi_s(j)^a$

Ion	
$a\{1,0,0\}$	$\dfrac{\epsilon}{\sqrt{2}}(\mathscr{Y}_1{}^1 - \mathscr{Y}_{\bar{1}}{}^{-1})$
$a\{-1,0,0\}$	$-\dfrac{\epsilon}{\sqrt{2}}(\mathscr{Y}_1{}^1 - \mathscr{Y}_{\bar{1}}{}^{-1})$
$a\{0,1,0\}$	$-i\dfrac{\epsilon}{\sqrt{2}}(\mathscr{Y}_1{}^1 + \mathscr{Y}_{\bar{1}}{}^{-1})$
$a\{0,-1,0\}$	$i\dfrac{\epsilon}{\sqrt{2}}(\mathscr{Y}_1{}^1 \mathscr{Y}_{\bar{1}}{}^{-1})$
$a\{0,0,1\}$	$-\epsilon\mathscr{Y}_1{}^0$
$a\{0,0,-1\}$	$\epsilon\mathscr{Y}_1{}^0$

^{a} Where $\mathscr{Y}_1{}^0 = \frac{1}{2}(3/\pi)^{1/2}z$ and $\mathscr{Y}_{\bar{1}}^{+1} = \mp\frac{1}{2}(3/2\pi)^{1/2}(x \perp iy)$.

to each other, i.e., no overlap between $\phi(j)$ and $\phi(j')$, for $j \neq j'$ and, of course, ϕ_s is orthogonal to ϕ_p^+ and ϕ_p^-, etc. Hence $\phi(F)$ is normalized. The total zeroth order wave functions are

$$\eta_+\phi(F) \quad \text{and} \quad \eta_-\phi(F). \quad (19.4)$$

η_- is η_s whose eigenvalue of S_z is $-\frac{1}{2}\hbar$, etc.; $\eta_+\phi(F)$ and $\eta_-\phi(F)$ are eigenfunctions of the operator

$$\mathscr{H}_0 + g_e\beta s_z H_0 \quad (19.5)$$

where $\mathscr{H}_0$ is the Hamiltonian for zero magnetic field without the spin-orbit term and the magnetic field is along the z-axis.

l^j is the angular momentum relative to the jth nucleus. The use of l^j in place of the angular momentum centered at the imperfection has to be justified; this is done in the appendix (Sections c and d) to this chapter. It is easy to understand the g-shift using Eq. (19.3); however, it is only an approximate wave function. It has neven been rigorously derived from first principle. (See Section 27.) We now drop the superscript j.

Consider now what happens when the following perturbation is added:

$$\Delta\mathcal{H} = \beta\mathbf{l}\cdot\mathbf{H}_0 + \xi\mathbf{l}\cdot\mathbf{s}. \tag{19.6}$$

The first term comes from (16.14), while the second arises from (16.13). We note that

$$\xi = (e^2/2m_e{}^2c^2)\hbar^2\langle|1/r^3|\rangle Z_{\text{eff}} \tag{19.7}$$

and that $\mathbf{l}$ in the second term is relative to the origin of the nuclei that surround the imperfection. In the first term, however, $\mathbf{l}$ does not depend on a particular origin. This can be seen from the form of $\mathbf{A}$ used to obtain (16.14) from (II) of Table 16.3. We thus may assume that $\mathbf{l}$ and $\mathbf{s}$ are the usual "atomic" operators associated with the ions that surround the point imperfection in the crystal. A real limitation is the overlap integrals which arise in such a calculation. These are ignored. For values of the actual Z to be employed, see Table 16.4.

Consider first a single $\eta\phi(j)$. Since H_0 is along the z-axis, (19.6) takes the form:

$$\Delta\mathcal{H} = \beta l_z H_0 + \xi l_z s_z. \tag{19.8}$$

$\Delta\mathcal{H}$ does not affect the energy when first-order perturbation theory is used, since $\langle|l_z|\rangle = \langle|l|\rangle = 0$, as can be seen from (16.6) and Table 19.1. For this reason, second-order perturbation theory is used and the excited states associated with the ions must be included in the calculation. Now, the additional energy has the form

$$\sum_n{}' \frac{1}{E_0 - E_n} \langle 0|\Delta\mathcal{H}|n\rangle\langle n|\Delta\mathcal{H}|0\rangle \tag{19.9}$$

where n refers to a wave function of an excited state with energy E_n, and E_0 is the energy of the ground state. The main contribution to (19.9) comes from the first excited state; hence, the closure theorem (see Schiff, p. 46) can be invoked and one may obtain approximately

$$\delta E = \frac{1}{E_0 - E_n}\langle 0|\Delta\mathcal{H}^2|0\rangle \tag{19.10}$$

$$= \frac{1}{E_0 - E_n}\langle\phi(j)|\beta^2 l_z{}^2 H_0{}^2 \pm \beta\xi l_z{}^2 H_0 + \tfrac{1}{4}\xi^2 l_z{}^2|\phi(j)\rangle. \tag{19.11}$$

The minus term corresponds to the eigenfunction related to η_- and the plus term is the one related to η_+. The spin-orbit term of (19.8) lowers and raises the energy of the levels. The other terms do not affect the relative energy of the levels. The net energy difference is therefore

$$g\beta H_0 = \beta[g_e + (2/\Delta E)\langle\phi(j)|\xi l_z^2|\phi(j)\rangle]H_0.\qquad(19.12)$$

The first term in (19.12) comes from (19.5). Thus

$$g(j) - g_e = \Delta g(j) = (2/\Delta E)\langle\phi(j)|\xi l_z^2|\phi(j)\rangle\qquad(19.13)$$

$$= \frac{4\beta^2}{\Delta E}\left\langle\phi(j)\left|\frac{Z_{\text{eff}}}{r^3}l_z^2\right|\phi(j)\right\rangle\qquad(19.14)$$

The four ions at $a\{\pm 1,0,0\}$ and $a\{0,\pm 1,0\}$ give

$$\Delta g(j) = \frac{4\beta^2}{\Delta E}Z_{\text{eff}}\frac{\epsilon^2}{1+\epsilon^2}\left\langle\left|\frac{1}{r^3}\right|\right\rangle_{\text{av}}\qquad(19.14a)$$

while the $a\{0,0,\pm 1\}$ make no contribution so that

$$\Delta g = \Delta g(\text{total}) = \frac{16\beta^2}{6\Delta E}Z_{\text{eff}}\frac{\epsilon^2}{1+\epsilon^2}\left\langle\left|\frac{1}{r^3}\right|\right\rangle_{\text{av}}\qquad(19.15a)$$

$$= \frac{4}{3}\frac{1}{\Delta E}\frac{\epsilon^2}{1+\epsilon^2}\xi\qquad(19.15b)$$

which is a negative quantity since $\Delta E < 0$ and ξ is positive. Here $\langle|1/r^3|\rangle_{\text{av}}$ is $1/r^3$ averaged over $\phi_p^{\pm}$ state. One may obtain this number from a Hartree-type calculation using Eq. (19.14). If we assume that Z_{eff} and $\langle|1/r^3|\rangle_{\text{av}}$ are known from the wave functions of the ions (see Table 16.4), one may use the empirical values of Δg to evaluate ϵ. This value can also be obtained from ENDOR experiments.

The reader will note that (19.3) was used in two places, first to prove that second-order perturbation theory is required, and second, to evaluate (19.14).

The derivation here of the g-shift is similar to the derivation of the spin Hamiltonian for $Cu^{2+}6H_2O$ in Section 16c. The reader will note that ΔE at times cannot be simply described by a shift in g but involves other terms, one proportional to H_0^2, and the other independent of H_0. In actual problems it is these terms that can make the spin Hamiltonian a good deal more complex than Eq. (16.40).

REFERENCES

F. J. Adrian, *Phys. Rev.* **107**, 488 (1957).
A. H. Kahn and C. Kittel, *Phys. Rev.* **89**, 315 (1953).

APPENDIX

SOME BASIC THEOREMS RELATED TO ELECTRON PARAMAGNETIC RESONANCE

a. The Pauli Hamiltonian

The problem of angular momentum is so basic in atomic physics that one employs it without question in all problems where there is a single strong center field. In a large class of problems the concept of angular momentum is much less useful. Unless handled with special care it ceases to be a useful concept and many notions used throughout quantum mechanics do not apply. We may recover the usefulness of this concept if we are extremely careful in our development (more careful, that is, than we were earlier, in Section 16). We must first obtain Pauli's equation in a gauge-invariant form. Two additional theorems, one regarding gauge invariance and the other regarding the reduction of matrix equations, are required.

The history of this field, a long one, will not be pursued here. The most fundamental method of arriving at Pauli's equation is that of Foldy and Wouthuysen (S); their approach, however, is beyond the scope of this book. We shall use a method based on some notes of Löwdin (S), combined with an approach due to Griffith. The reader will note that we employ the operator of Löwdin, which is quite rigorous, and then switch to the approach of Griffith and of Condon and Shortley, who basically assume that one is operating only on the eigenstate of the Dirac equation. This assumption is hard to justify. The reason for deriving the equation is that this is a "simple" manner of obtaining a Pauli equation in a gauge-invariant form, the only form that can be employed for an imperfection without a single strong center field. A simple derivation of this equation does not seem to exist.

We start with the general Dirac two-dimensional equation (see Griffith, p. 123), but we recognize that Griffith's f is really an operator. One may break up Dirac's equation into two parts; the one of interest here is

$$\left\{\frac{1}{2m}(\boldsymbol{\sigma}\cdot\boldsymbol{\pi})\,k_{\mathrm{op}}(\boldsymbol{\sigma}\cdot\boldsymbol{\pi})-eA_0-\epsilon_{\mathrm{op}}\right\}\psi = 0 \qquad (A1)$$

where $\boldsymbol{\pi}$ is the kinetic momentum $[\mathbf{p}+(e/c)\mathbf{A}]$, A_0 the scalar potential, $-e$ the charge on the electron, $\mathbf{A}$ the vector potential, k_{op} an operator to be described shortly, m is the *mass* and the Coulomb gauge is used (i.e., $\nabla \cdot \mathbf{A} = 0$). The $\boldsymbol{\sigma}$'s are matrices and ψ is a two-column matrix. Some explicit useful equations are:

$$\epsilon_{op} = -(\hbar/i)(\partial/\partial t) \tag{A2}$$

$$k_{op}^{-1} = 1 + (1/2mc^2)(\epsilon_{op} + eA_0). \tag{A3}$$

Later, when Griffith's form is used, the following relation will apply

$$k_{op}^{-1} \to f^{-1} = 1 + (1/2mc^2)\{E + eA_0\} \tag{A4}$$

where E is the Schrödinger energy (excluding the rest mass). Further, one should note that

$$\partial f/\partial x_i = -(e/2mc^2)(\partial A_0/\partial x_i) \quad \text{(for } x_i = x, y, \text{ or } z\text{).} \tag{A5}$$

Griffith (p. 126), and Condon and Shortley (p. 130 ff.), have shown that (A5) and (A4) do not lead to divergent terms for hydrogenic functions. The $\boldsymbol{\sigma}$ and ψ are matrices. Equations (A1), (A4), (A5) can be found in Griffith. Equation (A1) appears in Condon and Shortley (p. 129) with the kinematic momentum replaced by the linear momentum. Explicit expressions are required for $\boldsymbol{\sigma}$. They are:

$$\sigma_x = \begin{bmatrix} 0 & 1 \\ 1 & 0 \end{bmatrix} \quad \sigma_y = \begin{bmatrix} 0 & -i \\ i & 0 \end{bmatrix} \quad \sigma_z = \begin{bmatrix} 1 & 0 \\ 0 & -1 \end{bmatrix} \tag{A6}$$

$$\mathbf{1} = \begin{bmatrix} 1 & 0 \\ 0 & 1 \end{bmatrix}. \tag{A7}$$

Thus

$$\sigma_x\sigma_y = i\sigma_z; \quad \sigma_y\sigma_z = i\sigma_x; \quad \sigma_z\sigma_x = i\sigma_y; \tag{A8}$$

$$\sigma_x{}^2 = \sigma_y{}^2 = \sigma_z{}^2 = \mathbf{1} \tag{A9}$$

and

$$\sigma_i\sigma_j + \sigma_j\sigma_i = 0 \quad \text{for} \quad i \neq j. \tag{A10}$$

Because of (A8) and (A10), it follows that for any two vectors $\mathbf{B}$ and $\mathbf{C}$,

$$(\boldsymbol{\sigma} \cdot \mathbf{B})(\boldsymbol{\sigma} \cdot \mathbf{C}) = \mathbf{B} \cdot \mathbf{C} + i\boldsymbol{\sigma} \cdot (\mathbf{B} \times \mathbf{C}). \tag{A11}$$

$\mathbf{C} \times \mathbf{C}$ need not be zero because these quantities can be operators.

Using the above definitions and the relation between the vector and scalar potential of a field we may establish the relation

$$\boldsymbol{\pi} \times \boldsymbol{\pi} = -i(e\hbar/c)\mathbf{H}. \tag{A12}$$

Using (A3) it follows that for any function F

$$k_{op}^{-1}F - Fk_{op}^{-1} = (1/2mc^2)[\epsilon_{op} + eA_0, F] \tag{A13}$$

where
$$[A, B] = AB - BA$$

and
$$Fk_{op} - k_{op}F = (1/2mc^2) k_{op}[\epsilon_{op} + eA_0, F]k_{op}. \tag{A14}$$

Since
$$[\epsilon_{op} + eA_0, \pi] = -ie\hbar\mathbf{E}$$

we have
$$\pi k_{op} - k_{op}\pi = (-ie\hbar/2mc^2) k_{op}\mathbf{E}k_{op} = i(\beta/c) k_{op}\mathbf{E}k_{op}. \tag{A15}$$

The final form of interest follows from (A15)

$$\pi \times k_{op}\pi = k_{op}\pi \times \pi - i(\beta/c) k_{op}\mathbf{E} \times k_{op}\pi \tag{A16}$$

$$= -i(e\hbar/c) \{k_{op}\mathbf{H} + (1/2mc) k_{op}\mathbf{E} \times k_{op}\pi\} \tag{A17}$$

where we have used (A12), k_{op} is a scalar operator. Returning to Eq. (A1) we proceed as follows: (1) employ Eqs. (A11) and (A17); (2) replace k_{op} by f and the desired equation is obtained. For terms proportional to σ we use only the first term in the expansion (A4). Thus

$$\{(1/2m) \pi \cdot k_{op}\pi + (1/2m)i\sigma \cdot (\pi \times k_{op}\pi) - eA_0 - \epsilon_{op}\}\psi = 0. \tag{A18}$$

Since

$$(1/2m) \pi \cdot k_{op}\pi = (1/2m)(\pi \cdot f\pi) = (1/2m)\pi^2 f - (1/2m)\pi \cdot [(\hbar/i)\nabla f]$$

$$= \frac{1}{2m}\pi^2 \left\{1 - \frac{E + eA_0}{2mc^2}\right\} + \frac{e}{4m^2c^2}\frac{\hbar}{i}(\nabla A_0) \cdot \pi \tag{A19}$$

and

$$(i/2m)\sigma \cdot (\pi \times k_{op}\pi) = \tfrac{1}{2}(e\hbar/mc)\sigma \cdot \mathbf{H} + (1/4m^2c^2)e\hbar\sigma \cdot (\mathbf{E} \times \pi)$$

$$= \beta\sigma \cdot \mathbf{H} + (1/2mc)\beta\sigma \cdot (\mathbf{E} \times \pi) \tag{A20}$$

we obtain

$$\left\{(1/2m)\pi^2 - (1/2m)\pi^2\left\{\frac{E + eA_0}{2mc^2}\right\} + \frac{e}{4m^2c^2}(\hbar/i)(\nabla A_0) \cdot \pi \right.$$

$$\left. + \beta\sigma \cdot \mathbf{H} + (1/2mc)\beta\sigma \cdot (\mathbf{E} \times \pi) - eA_0 - \epsilon_{op}\right\}\psi = 0. \tag{A21}$$

The first term with the last two is the "standard" Schrödinger equation when there is an external field. The second is a relativistic correction. The third is the spin-orbit term for an s electron in an atomic field in a gauge-invariant form (see Condon and Shortley, p. 130; there is an error in sign in Condon and Shortley). The fourth term is the Zeeman term for the spin, and the last is the spin-orbit term again, in a gauge-invariant form. The above equation indicates that, in terms (I) and (IV), but not in term (II), of Table 16.3, **p** should be replaced by π.

b. The Spin-Hamiltonian Techniques

If the electron that is trapped at an imperfection did not interact with the strong electric fields of the nearby ions, and if the electronic spatial wave function is an s-state, then its magnetic behavior would be described simply by the relation

$$\beta \boldsymbol{\sigma} \cdot \mathbf{H} = g_e \beta \mathbf{s} \cdot \mathbf{H} \tag{B1}$$

since $\boldsymbol{\sigma}$ is equivalent to $g_e \mathbf{s}$ and the problem of paramagnetic resonance would be extremely simple. In the example considered in Section 16c, we saw that the additional interactions given in (A21) could be described by a $\mathbf{g}$ tensor which was composed of (B1) plus additional terms. We encountered exactly the same problem in Section 19. Some careful manipulations were done which require justification.

A systematic way of handling the problem has been given by Löwdin (S) and by Pryce (S) at approximately the same time. We shall present Löwdin's technique, since in this field the approach of Pryce is usually employed. Although the resonance spectrum of the F-center is actually very simple, theoretically it is a much more involved problem than the one considered by Pryce; it requires consideration of the whole problem of gauge invariance in great detail.

The spin-orbit terms have contributions from many of the ions which surround the F-center trap. This problem becomes involved, but can be handled rigorously and the final results give relatively simple equations. Here we must develop a type of perturbation theory appropriate for the problem.

Ordinarily in degenerate perturbation theory one attempts to obtain the proper linear combination of states using a secular equation associated with first-order perturbation theory. If higher terms are required, then ordinary second-order theory is employed. Here we calculate the matrix elements to any degree of accuracy desired and then solve for the energy by using almost exact matrix elements. At this point we shall not specify the perturbation, but shall assume that the exact Hamiltonian has the form $\mathscr{H} = \mathscr{H}_0 + \mathscr{H}_1$. The eigenfunctions associated with $\mathscr{H}_0$ form an orthonormal complete set. Let the ground states of $\mathscr{H}_0$ be degenerate, and let them be denoted by ψ_α, ψ_β, ψ_γ, etc. In the simplest case $\mathscr{H}_0$ may be spin independent and the degeneracy will arise from the spin functions $|\frac{1}{2}\rangle$ and $|-\frac{1}{2}\rangle$ as in the case of $Cu^{2+}6H_2O$. If these functions are combined with (B1) they give two diagonal elements from which the energy can be obtained. We now proceed to calculate the matrix elements, which give the energy, and then to obtain the operators that give these matrix elements when operating on spin functions of the types $|\frac{1}{2}\rangle$ and $|-\frac{1}{2}\rangle$. This spin Hamiltonian replaces (B1). The functions associated with the higher state (spatial time spin) are denoted by ψ_i, ψ_j, ψ_k, etc. The exact ground state will be given by

$$\Psi = \sum_a c_\alpha \psi_\alpha + \sum_i c_i \psi_i. \tag{B2}$$

One might use a double subscript since there are more than one ψ and one set of c's. They are determined by solving a secular equation for the energy. This makes the notation unnecessarily complex, however. To determine the c's we must solve the equation

$$\delta E = \delta \left\{ \frac{1}{\langle \psi | \psi \rangle} \langle \psi | \mathcal{H}_0 + \mathcal{H}_1 | \psi \rangle \right\}$$

$$= (1/B)(\delta A - E \delta B) = 0 \tag{B3}$$

where
$$A = \sum_{a,\beta} H_{\alpha\beta} c_\alpha^* c_\beta + \sum_{ai} H_{\alpha i} c_\alpha^* c_i + \sum_{ai} H_{i\alpha} c_i^* c_\alpha$$
$$+ \sum_{ij} H_{ij} c_i^* c_j, \tag{B3a}$$

$$B = \sum_a c_\alpha^* c_\alpha + \sum_i c_i^* c_i, \tag{B3b}$$

and
$$H_{i\alpha} = \langle \psi_i | \mathcal{H}_0 + \mathcal{H}_1 | \psi_\alpha \rangle, \quad \text{etc.} \tag{B3c}$$

Since the ψ's form a complete set, Eq. (B3) gives the exact solution to the Schrödinger equation and E is independent of the c's. Substituting into (B3) results in the equations

$$(E - H_{\alpha\alpha}) c_\alpha = \sum_\beta' H_{\alpha\beta} c_\beta + \sum_i H_{\alpha i} c_i \tag{B4a}$$

and
$$(E - H_{ii}) c_i = \sum_a H_{i\alpha} c_\alpha + \sum_j' H_{ij} c_j. \tag{B4b}$$

The prime on the sum means that $\alpha \neq \beta$ or $i \neq j$. The equations can be rewritten in the form

$$c_\alpha = \sum_\beta h_{\alpha\beta} c_\beta + \sum_i h_{\alpha i} c_i \tag{B5a}$$

$$c_i = \sum_a h_{i\alpha} c_\alpha + \sum_j h_{ij} c \tag{B5b}$$

where
$$h_{\alpha\beta} = \frac{1}{E - H_{\alpha\alpha}} H_{\alpha\beta}(1 - \delta_{\alpha\beta}), \tag{B6a}$$

$$h_{ij} = \frac{1}{E - II_{ii}} H_{ij}(1 - \delta_{ij}), \tag{B6b}$$

and
$$h_{i\alpha} = \frac{1}{E - H_{ii}} H_{i\alpha}. \tag{B6c}$$

The δ eliminates the necessity of the prime on the sum. Assuming that the second sum in (B5b) is small, we write

$$c_i = \sum_{\alpha} h_{i\alpha} c_{\alpha}$$

and

$$c_{\alpha} = \sum_{\beta} h_{\alpha\beta} c_{\beta} + \sum_{i,\beta} h_{\alpha i} h_{i\beta} c_{\beta}$$

$$= \sum_{\beta} \{h_{\alpha\beta} + \sum_{i} h_{\alpha i} h_{i\beta}\} c_{\beta}. \tag{B7}$$

Further iteration results in

$$c_{\alpha} = \frac{1}{E - H_{\alpha\alpha}} \sum_{\beta} (U_{\alpha\beta} - H_{\alpha\beta} \delta_{\alpha\beta}) c_{\beta} \tag{B8}$$

here

$$U_{\alpha\beta} = H_{\alpha\beta} + \sum_{i} \frac{1}{E - H_{ii}} H_{\alpha i} H_{i\beta} + \sum_{i,j}' \frac{1}{(E - H_{ii})(E - H_{jj})} H_{\alpha i} H_{ij} H_{j\beta},$$
$$\text{etc.} \quad \text{(B8a)}$$

Equation (B8) gives

$$\sum_{\beta} \{U_{\alpha\beta} - E\delta_{\alpha\alpha}\} c_{\beta} = 0 \tag{B8b}$$

from which we obtain a secular equation whose solution gives E and the c's. Löwdin gives an expression for the c_i's and they may be required in some complex relaxation processes. The effects of the higher states are suppressed by the sums of (B8a). These terms are identical to the Brillouin perturbation theory since the matrix elements of $\mathcal{H}_0$ and $\mathcal{H}_1$ appear in the denominator, not the eigenvalues of $\mathcal{H}_0$. The difference in this case is small (note that the denominator terms are $E - H_{ii}$ and $H_{\alpha\alpha}$ does not appear). We replace E by E_0, the eigenvalues of $\mathcal{H}_0$, namely,

$$U_{\alpha\beta} = H_{\alpha\beta} + \sum_{i} \frac{1}{E_0 - E_i} H_{\alpha i} H_{i\beta} + \sum_{i,j} \frac{1}{(E_0 - E_i)(E_0 - E_j)} H_{\alpha i} H_{ij} H_{j\beta}.$$
$$\text{(B8c)}$$

The U's are numbers since to obtain the H's we have integrated over the position of the electron and over its spin values both in the ground and in the excited states. We now define the V where we do not sum over the spin coordinates of the *ground* state. This is possible because each term ends and starts with an $\left|-\frac{1}{2}\right\rangle$ or a $\left|\frac{1}{2}\right\rangle$, thus

$$V = \langle 0|\mathscr{H}|0\rangle + \sum_i \frac{1}{E_0 - E_i}\langle 0|\mathscr{H}|i\rangle \langle i|\mathscr{H}|0\rangle$$

$$+ \sum_{i,j}' \frac{1}{(E_0 - E_i)(E_0 - E_j)}\langle 0|\mathscr{H}|i\rangle \langle i|\mathscr{H}|j\rangle \langle j|\mathscr{H}|0\rangle,$$

$$\text{etc.} \quad \text{(B9)}$$

where $|0\rangle$ is only the *spatial* part of the ground-state wave function. The sum over the spin is included in the $|i\rangle$, $|j\rangle$, etc., however. Equation (B9) is the general form of the spin operator. Its terms resemble those obtained from standard Schrödinger perturbation theory.

c. Gauge Invariance with Spin-Orbit Coupling

The problem of gauge invariance is extremely fundamental in considering the behavior of an electron in a solid in the presence of a magnetic field. It can be dodged in the class of imperfections where one has a single strong central field. This is impossible, however, for the F-center. One may arrive, without difficulties, at a gauge-invariant formulation of the Schrödinger equation provided one does not employ perturbation theory. The problem of gauge invariance and perturbation theory is more involved, however; Griffith (p. 434) has shown that if one neglects the spin-orbit interaction, the first-order and second-order perturbation terms are gauge invariant.

We shall now show that to second order in perturbation theory the contribution to the spin Hamiltonian of the spin-orbit term from every force center [Eq. (16.14) and term (IV) of Table 16.3] is gauge invariant (see Casselman and Markham, S, also Stone, S).

Physically one requires that observable quantities obtained from Schrödinger's equation be gauge invariant. The Hamiltonian $\mathscr{H}$ itself is not gauge invariant; upon changing the gauge, however, compensating terms appear in the phase factor of the wave function ψ such that the observable quantities are independent of the gauge. For example, the energy eigenvalue

$$\langle \psi|\mathscr{H}|\psi\rangle \quad \text{(C1)}$$

is independent of the gauge (see Griffith, p. 41). A problem arises if (C1) cannot be solved *exactly*.

As stated, Griffith has shown that for an electron in an electromagnetic field, the results of perturbation theory are gauge invariant to second order provided the *spin-orbit* effects are neglected. The Hamiltonian used has the form

$$\mathcal{H} = \frac{1}{2m}\left(\mathbf{p}+\frac{e}{c}\mathbf{A}\right)^2 + V \tag{C2}$$

where $\mathbf{A}$ is the vector potential and V contains terms independent of $\mathbf{A}$. This can be obtained from the appendix, Eq. (A21) where the spin-orbit and higher order relativistic terms are neglected. Using Eq. (C2) we define

$$\mathcal{H}_0 = (p^2/2m) + V \tag{C3}$$

$$\mathcal{H}_p = \frac{e}{mc}\mathbf{A}\cdot\mathbf{p} + \frac{e^2}{2m^2c^2}A^2 \tag{C4}$$

where again a Coulomb gauge is employed. Consider the eigenvalue to second order

$$E_i - E_i^{(0)} = \langle i|\mathcal{H}_p|i\rangle + \sum_j{}' \frac{\langle i|\mathcal{H}_p|j\rangle\langle j|\mathcal{H}_p|i\rangle}{E_i^{(0)} - E_j^{(0)}} \tag{C5}*$$

since no spin operators are involved in the $\mathcal{H}$'s, identical terms to these appear in the spin Hamiltonian. This will be indicated shortly.

The proof of the gauge invariance of (C5) depends on a theorem due to Griffith. For any scalar function ξ of r we have:

$$(E_i - E_j)\langle i|\xi|j\rangle = \langle i|(\mathcal{H}_0\xi - \xi\mathcal{H}_0)|j\rangle$$

$$= \left\langle i\left|\frac{1}{2m}(p^2\xi - \xi p^2)\right|j\right\rangle$$

$$= \frac{1}{2m}\langle i|\{p^2\xi\}|j\rangle + \frac{1}{m}\langle i|(\mathbf{p}\xi)\cdot\mathbf{p}|j\rangle. \tag{C6a}$$

The curly brackets define the extent to which p operates. The $|i\rangle$ and the $|j\rangle$ are the bras and the kets associated with $\mathcal{H}_0$. If we assume that ξ is a gauge transformation such that $\nabla^2\xi = 0$ (i.e., the Coulomb gauge is employed) it follows that

$$(E_i - E_j)\langle i|\xi|j\rangle = \frac{1}{m}\langle i|\{\mathbf{p}\xi\}\cdot\mathbf{p}|j\rangle. \tag{C6b}$$

Now the gauge properties of perturbation theory are examined with the spin-orbit term. The Hamiltonian is:

$$\mathcal{H} = \frac{1}{2m}\left(\mathbf{p}+\frac{e}{c}\mathbf{A}\right)^2 + V + \sum_l \mathbf{B}(l)\cdot\left(\mathbf{p}+\frac{e}{c}\mathbf{A}\right) \tag{C7}†$$

---

* State i is assumed to be nondegenerate with regard to the spatial part of the wave function. It is the ground state.

† We have excluded the Zeeman-spin interaction in (C7) as it does not involve $\mathbf{A}$.

where

$$\mathbf{B}(l) = (e\hbar/2m^2 c^2)\mathbf{s} \times \mathbf{E}(l). \qquad (C7a)$$

The reader will note that we have not included all the terms in (A21) and that $\mathbf{s} = \frac{1}{2}\boldsymbol{\sigma}$. The above terms complicate the problem for two reasons: First, they add terms in $\mathbf{A}$, and second, more than one force center is involved and the effect of a gauge change for each center must be included. Consider first

$$E^1(A) = (e/mc)\langle i|\mathbf{A} \cdot \mathbf{p}|i\rangle \qquad (C8)$$

obtained from the first terms of (C4) and (C5). The condition for the gauge invariance of $E^{(1)}$ is

$$\delta E^{(1)} = [E^{(1)}(A - \nabla\chi') - E^{(1)}(A)] \qquad (C9)$$

where χ' is an arbitrary gauge. We let $\mathbf{p} = -i\hbar\nabla$, and $\chi' = i\hbar\chi$; hence,

$$-\nabla\chi' = \mathbf{p}\chi. \qquad (C10)$$

Then

$$\delta E^{(1)} = -\frac{e}{mc}\langle i|\nabla\chi' \cdot \mathbf{p}|i\rangle = \frac{e}{mc}\langle i|\{\mathbf{p}\chi\} \cdot \mathbf{p}|i\rangle = 0, \qquad (C11)$$

where we have used Eq. (C6b). Equation (C8) is gauge invariant, independent of the other terms arising from (C4) and (C5). When spin-orbit coupling is introduced, the perturbation operator has the form

$$\mathscr{H}_p = (e/mc)\mathbf{A} \cdot \mathbf{p} + (e^2/2mc^2)A^2 + \sum_l [\mathbf{B}(l) \cdot \mathbf{p} + (e/c)\mathbf{B}(l) \cdot \mathbf{A}]. \qquad (C12)$$

We denote spin states by α and β, eigenstates of $\mathscr{H}_0$ by i and j, and individual ions by l. For the usual fields encountered, the terms in $(e/c)\mathbf{A}$ will be much smaller than V. In addition, terms containing $\mathbf{B}(l)$ are small compared to this quantity. One may write Eq. (C12) symbolically as follows:

$$\mathscr{H}_p = \mathscr{H}(\mathbf{A}) + \mathscr{H}(A^2) + \mathscr{H}(\mathbf{B}) + \mathscr{H}(BA). \qquad (C13)*$$

We may not solve for the eigenvalue of $\mathscr{H}$ directly. One may employ either first-order degenerate perturbation theory using $\mathscr{H}_p$ (and then correct these values by the use of standard second-order perturbation theory) or the development presented earlier in the appendix to this chapter. Here one calculates matrix elements to a higher order than by the conventional method of solving for the eigenvalues. Our interest here is in the matrix element, not the eigenvalues themselves. We now assume that the α's and β's are due to spin states, Eq. (B8c) gives:

---

* Griffith, p. 434, has shown that $\mathscr{H}(A^2) + \mathscr{H}(\mathbf{A})$ is gauge invariant.

$$U_{\alpha\beta} = \left\{ E_0 + \langle 0|\mathscr{H}(\mathbf{A})|0\rangle + \langle 0|\mathscr{H}(A^2)|0\rangle \right.$$

$$+ {\sum_{j}}' \frac{1}{E_0 - E_j} \langle 0|\mathscr{H}(\mathbf{A})|j\rangle\langle j|\mathscr{H}(\mathbf{A})|0\rangle \Big\} \delta_{\alpha\beta}$$

$$+ \left\{ \langle 0\alpha|\mathscr{H}(\mathbf{B})|0\beta\rangle + {\sum_{j}}' \frac{1}{E_0 - E_j} \langle 0\alpha|\mathscr{H}(\mathbf{B})|j\rangle\langle j|\mathscr{H}(\mathbf{B})|0\beta\rangle \right\}$$

$$+ \left\{ \langle 0\alpha|\mathscr{H}(AB)|0\beta\rangle \right.$$

$$+ {\sum_{j}}' \frac{1}{E_0 - E_j} |\langle 0\alpha|\mathscr{H}(\mathbf{A})|j\rangle\langle j|\mathscr{H}(\mathbf{B})|0\beta\rangle$$

$$\left. + \langle 0\alpha|\mathscr{H}(\mathbf{B})|j\rangle\langle j|\mathscr{H}(\mathbf{A})|0\beta\rangle \right\} = \mathrm{I} + \mathrm{II} + \mathrm{III}. \tag{C14}$$

where I, II, and III are the expressions in the three curly brackets. In obtaining (C14) we have used the fact that $\mathscr{H}(\mathbf{A})$ has no spin operators. The first term, I, are expressions arising from ordinary perturbation theory; Eq. (C4) is used. It is gauge invariant, as indicated earlier; II does not involve the gauge. Finally, if we write III without the integration over the ground spin states, it follows that

$$V(\mathrm{III}) = a\mathbf{s} \cdot \sum_{l} \left\langle 0 \left| \sum_{l} \mathbf{E}(l) \times \mathbf{A} \right| 0 \right\rangle$$

$$+ \frac{a}{m} \mathbf{s} \cdot {\sum_{j}}' \frac{1}{E_0 - E_j} \left[\langle 0|\mathbf{A} \cdot \mathbf{p}|j\rangle\langle j| \sum_{l} \mathbf{E}(l) \times \mathbf{p} |0\rangle \right.$$

$$\left. + \text{comp. conj.} \right]. \tag{C15}$$

Here $a = (e^2\hbar/2m^2c^3)$ and $\mathbf{E}(l)$ is the field due to the lth ion. As $r_l \to 0$ it goes to infinity. For the lth term of (C15) to be gauge invariant we must establish the relation

$$a\mathbf{s} \cdot \left\{ \langle 0|\mathbf{E}(l) \times \{\mathbf{p}\chi\}|0\rangle + \frac{1}{m} \sum_{j} \frac{1}{E_0 - E_j} [\langle 0|\{\mathbf{p}\chi\} \cdot \mathbf{p}|j\rangle\langle j|\mathbf{E}(l) \times \mathbf{p}|0\rangle \right.$$

$$\left. + \langle 0|\mathbf{E}(l) \times \mathbf{p}|j\rangle\langle j|\{\mathbf{p}\chi\} \cdot \mathbf{p}|0\rangle] \right\} \tag{C16}$$

[where we are using the identical arguments which lead up to (C10)].

Employing (C6) once more, the above expression becomes

$$a\mathbf{s}\cdot\left\{\langle 0|\mathbf{E}(l)\times\{\mathbf{p}\chi\}|0\rangle+\frac{1}{m}\sum_{j}'\left[\langle 0|\chi|j\rangle\langle j|\mathbf{E}(l)\times\mathbf{p}|0\rangle\right.\right.$$
$$\left.\left.-\langle 0|\mathbf{E}(l)\times\mathbf{p}|j\rangle\langle j|\chi|0\rangle\right]\right\}. \quad (C17)$$

One may now remove the prime on the sum by adding and subtracting the term $\langle 0|\mathbf{E}(l)\times\mathbf{p}|0\rangle\langle 0|\chi|0\rangle$. The completeness theorem then gives

$$a\mathbf{s}\cdot[\langle 0|\mathbf{E}(l)\times\{\mathbf{p}\chi\}|0\rangle+\langle 0|\chi\mathbf{E}(l)\times\mathbf{p}|0\rangle-\langle 0|\mathbf{E}(l)\times\mathbf{p}\chi|0\rangle]$$
$$= a\mathbf{s}\cdot[\langle 0|\mathbf{E}(l)\times\{\mathbf{p}\chi\}|0\rangle+\langle 0|\chi\mathbf{E}(l)\times\mathbf{p}|0\rangle-\langle 0|\mathbf{E}(l)\times\{\mathbf{p}\chi\}|0\rangle$$
$$-\langle 0|\chi\mathbf{E}(l)\times\mathbf{p}|0\rangle] = 0 \quad\quad (C18)$$

which proves the gauge invariance of the spin-orbit term due to the lth nuclei.

Thus, we have proved:

(1) The terms that are of second order in small quantities are collectively gauge invariant independent of all other terms in the perturbation expansion.

(2) The contribution to the Hamiltonian from the spin-orbit coupling is gauge invariant independent of all other terms in the perturbation expansion.

(3) The spin-orbit term is gauge invariant ion by ion separately.

This is of major importance since it means that a different gauge may be selected for every ion, thus greatly simplifying some calculations involving an imperfection with many strong centers. This problem is discussed in the next section (d) of this appendix.

d. The Spin-Hamiltonian for a Many-Center Imperfection

In this section we combine the results of Sections b and c to obtain the spin-Hamiltonian for a "many-center" imperfection. As stated before, we obtain "exact" matrix elements associated with the ground state by the use of Eq. (B9). The degeneracy arises from the spin, not from the orbital part of the wave function, which is assumed to be nondegenerate. The eigenvalues of the determinant are the eigenvalues of $\mathscr{H}_0+\mathscr{H}_p$. By the use of various gauges it is possible to formally simplify the form of V. Although the form is simplified, when one carries through actual calculations the problem of overlap arises. The latter cannot be solved simply by a judicious choice of gauge, and in many actual problems it leads to involved calculations.

V has the form

$$V = h_0 + g_e\beta\mathbf{H}\cdot\mathbf{s} + \mathbf{s}\cdot\sum_l \langle 0|\mathbf{C}(l)|0\rangle$$

$$+ \mathbf{s}\cdot\sum_l \left[\frac{e}{c}\langle 0|\mathbf{C}(l)\times\mathbf{A}|0\rangle + \frac{e}{mc}\sum_j{}' \frac{1}{E_0 - E_j}\right.$$

$$\left. \times \langle 0|\mathbf{A}\cdot\mathbf{p}|j\rangle\langle j|\mathbf{C}(l)\times\mathbf{p}|0\rangle + \text{comp. conj.}\right] \quad (D1)$$

where

$$h_0 = E_0^{(0)} + E_0^{(1)} + E_0^{(2)}. \quad (D1a)$$

E_0 is the ground-state eigenvalue associated with $\mathcal{H}_0$, that is, Eq. (C3);

$$E_0^{(1)} = \langle 0|\mathcal{H}(\mathbf{A})|0\rangle; \quad (D1b)$$

$$E_{(2)}^0 = \langle 0|\mathcal{H}(A^2)|0\rangle + \sum_j{}' \frac{1}{E_j - E_0}\langle 0|\mathcal{H}(\mathbf{A})|j\rangle\langle j|\mathcal{H}(\mathbf{A})|0\rangle; \quad (D1c)$$

and

$$\mathbf{C}(l) = (e\hbar/2m^2 c^2)\,\mathbf{E}(l). \quad (D1d)$$

We have added the spin-Zeeman term in Eq. (D1). The first term is spin independent and does not actually require a Kronecker delta; h_0, being in every diagonal term, is just added to the eigenvalues obtained by solving the determinant for the energy values. As stressed before, it is most important to establish that h_0 is gauge invariant and will not be affected by changes of gauge in the remaining terms of (D1). The third term of (D1) is the spin-orbit term, also of no interest since (as will be shown shortly) it is zero. The second-order spin-orbit term, which is small, has not been written down in Eq. (D1). Hence, the Hamiltonian—the spin-Hamiltonian—of interest to us has the form

$$\mathcal{H}(\text{spin}) = g_e\beta\mathbf{s}\cdot\mathbf{H}$$

$$\mathbf{s}\cdot\sum_l \left\{\frac{e}{c}\langle 0|\mathbf{C}(l)\times\mathbf{A}|0\rangle + \frac{e}{mc}\sum_j{}' \frac{1}{E_0 - E_j}\right.$$

$$\left. \times [\langle 0|\mathbf{A}\cdot\mathbf{p}|j\rangle\langle j|\mathbf{C}(l)\times\mathbf{p}|0\rangle + \text{comp. conj.}].\right\}. \quad (D2)$$

The orbital-Zeeman term—Eq. (16.14)—does not appear in Eq. (D2) since it does not contribute to V when the ground state is spatially non-degenerate; this will be proven shortly. To establish that the spin-orbit term can be omitted we proceed as follows

$$\mathcal{H}(\mathbf{B}) = \sum_l \mathbf{B}(l)\cdot\mathbf{p} = (e\hbar/2m^2 c^2)\sum_l \mathbf{s}\times\mathbf{E}(l)\cdot\mathbf{p}. \quad (D3)$$

The major contribution to matrix elements involving $\mathscr{H}(\mathbf{B})$ arises from the region near the nucleus where

$$\mathbf{E}(l) \rightarrow (e/r_l{}^3)Z_{\text{eff}}\mathbf{r}_l. \tag{D4}$$

Z_{eff} is the effective nuclear charge, $\mathbf{r}_l$ is the distance from the lth nucleus. Some of the values of Z_{eff} are given in Table 16.4. It depends on the atomic orbital in question. The argument to follow applies even if Z is a function of r_l. Substituting Eq. (D4) into (D3) results in

$$\mathbf{B}(l) \times \mathbf{p} = (e^2 \hbar/2m^2 c^2)(1/r_l{}^3)Z_{\text{eff}}\mathbf{s} \times \mathbf{r}_l \cdot \mathbf{p} = \xi(l)\mathbf{s} \cdot \mathbf{l}(l) \tag{D5}$$

where

$$\xi(l) = (e^2 \hbar^2/2m^2 c^2)(1/r_l{}^3)Z_{\text{eff}} \tag{D5a}$$

$$= 2\beta^2(1/r_l{}^3)Z_{\text{eff}}. \tag{D5b}$$

Further, $\hbar l(l) = |\mathbf{r}_l \times \mathbf{p}|$. This agrees with (16.13) except that Z could be a function of the distance from the lth nucleus; $\mathbf{l}(l)$ is a pure imaginary radial operator (see Condon and Shortley, p. 50). Hence, $\langle 0|\mathscr{H}(\mathbf{B})|0\rangle$ is zero, since $\mathbf{l}$ is Hermitian and the ground state of $\mathscr{H}_0$ is real.* An exception might occur if ξ has an angular dependence, which is not true near the nucleus. It may not apply in the region beyond the Goldschmidt radii, but this contribution to spin-orbit coupling is very small and will be ignored.

Consider next the magnitude of $(e/c)|\langle 0|\mathbf{C}(l) \times \mathbf{A}|0\rangle|$. Let us take a gauge where

$$\mathbf{A} = \tfrac{1}{2}\mathbf{H} \times \mathbf{r}_l. \tag{D6}$$

Hence

$$\frac{e}{c}\langle 0|\mathbf{C}(l) \times \mathbf{A}|0\rangle \approx \frac{Z}{2}(e^2/mc^2)(1/r_l)\beta H \tag{D7}$$

and the change in g due to this term is of the order of 10^{-5} when we take $r_l \approx 10^{-8}$ cm, which is too small to measure. This value is too small even if Z is as large as 100. Hence, the shift in the g-factor arises from the second term of Eq. (D2). We may write (D2) in the form

$$\mathscr{H}(\text{spin}) = g_e\beta\mathbf{s} \cdot \mathbf{H} + \beta\mathbf{s} \cdot \delta\bar{\bar{\mathbf{g}}} \cdot \mathbf{H} \tag{D8}$$

* $\mathbf{l}$ is Hermitian, and so is $f(r_l)\mathbf{l}$. If f depends on the angle, the argument may not apply. The same argument applies to the term $\mathscr{H}(\mathbf{A})$ where now $\mathbf{l}$ is centered at the imperfection. As indicated in Section 16, the orbital Zeeman term arises from the expression $\mathscr{H}(\mathbf{A})$.

where

$$\delta\bar{\bar{\mathbf{g}}} = \sum_{l} \delta\bar{\bar{\mathbf{g}}}(l)$$

$$= \sum_{l} \sum_{j}{}' \frac{1}{E_0 - E_j} [\langle 0|\xi(l)\mathbf{1}(l)|j\rangle\langle j|\mathbf{1}(l)|0\rangle$$

$$+ \langle 0|\mathbf{1}(l)|j\rangle\langle j|\xi(l)\mathbf{1}(l)|0\rangle]. \tag{D8a}$$

To obtain Eq. (D8a) we have used a different gauge for every nucleus—the nuclear gauge—which is permitted because of our proofs in Section c. This treatment agrees with that given in Sections 16c and 19. The treatment given here is more general and the gauge problem was not handled properly in Section 19.

REFERENCES

T. N. Casselman and J. J. Markham, *J. Chem. Phys.* **42**, 4178 (1965).
L. L. Foldy and S. A. Wouthuysen, *Phys. Rev.* **78**, 29 (1950).
P. Löwdin, *J. Chem. Phys.* **19**, 1396 (1951).
P. Löwdin, *Studies Perturbation Theory* **8** (Winter Institute, 1963–1964).
M. H. L. Pryce, *Proc. Phys. Soc.* (*London*) A**63**, 25 (1950).
A. J. Stone, *Proc. Roy. Soc.* (*London*) A**271**, 424 (1963).

VII. Effect of the Nuclear Spins on the Electron Paramagnetic Resonance

In Chapter VI we presented the various magnetic interactions which occur in solids, and developed the theory of electron paramagnetic resonance on the assumption that the nuclear spins surrounding the imperfection are zero (that is, that term (16.22) need not be considered); it has many very important effects on the F-center, and is one of the reasons why this center is so interesting. We shall, therefore, develop here the effects to be expected when $\mathbf{i}$ is not zero.

The idea that the hyperfine interaction can be of major importance comes from a group working in Berkeley. Since then many refinements have been added to the theory and the experimental results, but the basic idea of Kip, Kittel, Levy, and Portis remains. These will be presented first in their simplest form, then in greater detail; all these ideas will be needed in the next chapter when the actual data are given.

20. Hyperfine or Inhomogeneous Broadening

We now consider $\mathscr{H}(hf)$, Eqs. (16.23) and (16.24), and the effect of the nuclei that surround an imperfection. These considerations will lead to concepts of homogeneous and inhomogeneous broadening. They play a very important role in the development of the magnetic concepts associated with the F-center.

Three approaches exist: one due to Kip, Kittel, Levy, and Portis (S); one to Wolga and Strandberg (S); and one to Holton and Blum (S). The paper of Wolga and Strandberg oversimplifies the problem. It gives a beautiful solution for the imperfection it considers and a deep insight into the problem. Holton and Blum use a modified form of their equations, which is of major importance. We first develop the original idea of the Berkeley group and then give the theory of Wolga and Strandberg. The latter will be modified later, and the important equation of Holton and Blum will be presented.

In the interest of clarity, the F-center is assumed to be an electron trapped at a negative-ion vacancy. Consider the case of KCl: the nuclei which surround the vacancy have spins equal to 3/2 (see Table 16.2). Let us introduce the wave function $\phi(F)$ of the electron trapped at the vacancy. Further, the wave functions associated with an extra electron attached to an ion which may surround the vacancies are required. These will be denoted by $\phi(n, l)$ where n states the location of the ions relative to the vacancy (not a quantum number) and l gives the angular momentum of the state. Thus, n can take the values {100}, {110}, {111}, etc., and $l = s, p, d, f$, etc. By means of the completeness theorem we know that

$$\phi(F) = \sum_{n,l} a(n, l) \phi(n, l). \qquad (20.1)^*$$

In this expansion the distortion of the wave functions in the filled shells is ignored. This is an oversimplification. ϕ does not include the spin parts of the eigenfunction. We must multiply it by the usual α or β of the Pauli theory, η_s. The simplest wave function of this form that one might assume is

$$\phi(F) = \frac{1}{\sqrt{6}} \sum_{n}^{6} \phi(n, s) \qquad (20.2)$$

where the sum is over the six nearest neighbors, Fig. 20.1. Equation (20.2) is similar to Eq. (19.2) except the $\phi(j)$'s were not pure s-functions. To explain the observed g-shift one has to have some non-s character. In (20.2) one assumes that $\phi(F)$ can be built up only from s-functions. Further, we assume that $\langle \phi(n,s)|\phi(n',s)\rangle = \delta_{nn'}$ and ignore the overlap problem. A further limitation of (20.2) is that shells beyond the nearest neighbors are not included.

To calculate $\phi(F)$ we require the actual scalar potential, that is, the part due to the nuclei plus the part due to the bound electron. Perhaps one may use the average field of the bound electrons. Detailed calculations using Hartree wave functions indicate that this field bears no relation to the field calculated using the assumptions that the ions are point-positive or -negative charges; indeed, the true potential at a negative ion is positive. The halide ion behaves as a negatively charged particle only at distances beyond the Goldschmidt radii. The actual field near the nucleus is complex and will not be considered here.

Since we are dealing with s-states, the electron-nuclear interaction is given by Eq. (16.24), namely,

$$\Delta \mathcal{H} = (16\pi/18)g_I\beta_I\beta|\phi_s(0)|^2 \mathbf{s} \cdot \sum_{j} \mathbf{i}^j \qquad (20.3)$$

---

* Actually, all the $\phi(n, l)$ should be included in the sum, not just the one associated with an extra electron. Curly brackets denote the position of the ion.

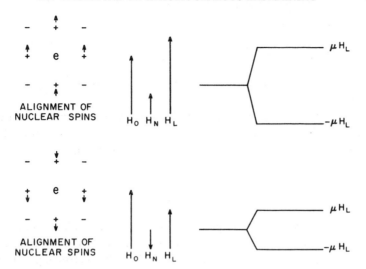

FIG. 20.1. Two-dimensional diagrams of the F-center showing the effects of in-homogeneous broadening. H_0 is the external field. H_N is due to the magnetic moments associated with the "four" nearest neighbors. H_L is the local field seen by the electron.

where $\phi_s(0)$ is $\phi(n,s)$ evaluated at the nucleus. The representation is selected in such a manner that the dot product can be replaced by the product of the z-component of $\mathbf{s}$ and $\sum \mathbf{i}^j$.*

Except for very low temperatures, the nuclear moments are oriented at random along the external field and a statistical average of $\sum_j \mathbf{i}^j$ can be used. Since $i = 3/2$ and s is along the z-axis, $\langle \sum_j i^j \rangle_{\mathrm{av}} = \sum_j m_I^j$. It takes values from $+9$ to -9 in unit steps. There is one combination that gives 9 (or -9); six that give 8 (or -8); $6 + \frac{1}{2}(6)(5) = 21$ that give 7 (or -7), etc. Table 20.1 may be easily obtained.

TABLE 20.1

$\sum_j m_I^j$	9	8	7	6	5	4	3	2	1	0
Number of arrangements:	1	6	21	56	120	216	336	456	546	580

* Actually the dot product in (20.3) includes terms orthogonal to the z-axis. The expectation values of these terms are zero. However, they give off-diagonal terms. The spin wave functions, electronic and nuclear, are nearly $\eta_I \eta_s$. We shall consider these corrections later in this section.

For every value of $\sum m_I$ there is a different effective field on the F-electron. To calculate it, the energy associated with the external field, $g\beta \mathbf{s} \cdot H_0 \mathbf{k}$,* is combined with (20.3). This results in

$$H_{\text{local}} = H_L = H_0 + (8\pi/3)g_I\beta_I[\tfrac{1}{6}|\phi_s(0)|^2] \sum_j^6 m_I{}^j. \qquad (20.4)$$

If we include the next-nearest neighbors, another term must be added to (20.4), and $\tfrac{1}{6}|\phi_s(0)|^2$ must be replaced by $|\phi_F(100)|^2$, the value of the F wave function at the $\{100\}$ nucleus. Thus, in general,

$$H_L = H_0 + \sum_j a_j i_z{}^j \qquad (20.5)$$

where
$$a_j = (8\pi/3)g_I{}^j\beta_I|\phi_F(n_j)|^2. \qquad (20.5a)$$

$\phi_F(n_j)$ is the value of $\phi(F)$ at position n_j and $g_I{}^j$ corresponds to the g value of the jth nucleus. Equation (20.5) neglects part of (16.22) or assumes that only s-functions enter into the expansion of the F-electron eigenfunction, Eq. (20.1). This is an oversimplification.

Equation (20.5) means that χ'' will have a Gaussian shape, since $m_z{}^j$ takes random values. (It is the one-dimensional random walk process.) If the interaction were with only the nearest neighbors, from Eq. (20.3) we would observe only 19 lines, and their distribution in intensity would be Gaussian (see Fig. 20.2). The individual lines would be slightly widened due to T_2 or to the Van Vleck mechanism. When Eq. (20.5) has to be used there would be many more than 19 lines, and we may actually obtain a continuous distribution of individual χ'', giving an over-all distribution of absorption that is Gaussian. The peak is for the case where $\sum_j m^j$ for all the shells is zero and $H_L = H_0$. To calculate the second moment, we proceed as follows:

$$\langle (H_0 - H_L)^2 \rangle_{\text{av}} = \langle \Delta H^2 \rangle_{\text{av}} = \tfrac{1}{3} \sum_j a_j{}^2 i^j(i^j+1) \qquad (20.6)$$

where the fact that

$$\frac{1}{(2i+1)} \sum_i m_i = 0 \qquad (20.6a)$$

and
$$\frac{1}{(2i+1)} \sum_i m_i^2 = \tfrac{1}{3}i(i+1) \qquad (20.6b)$$

has been used [see Eq. (16.10)].

Estimates of a_j indicate that the individual lines would be about 10

---

* g is the g value calculated from the spin Hamiltonian; it is assumed to be isotropic; $g = 2$ in Eq. (20.4).

gauss apart. Hence the Kittel-Abrahams width is much too small to explain the lack of structure of many of the F-center paramagnetic absorptions. We believe that this indicates that the F-center interacts with the nuclei far beyond the inner shell. Further, it is believed that the theory of Kittel and Abrahams does not apply (see Section 18c).

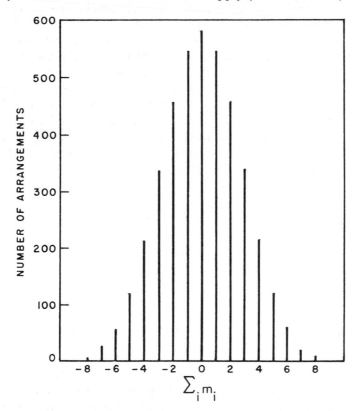

FIG. 20.2. Shape of χ'' obtained from Table 20.1. It is approximately Gaussian.

Equation (20.6) gives the mean square deviation of this field; it includes not only the nearest neighbors, however, but any number of shells. $\langle \Delta H^2 \rangle_{av}$ can be obtained from experimentally measuring the resonance width at half height, or the width between points of maximum slope.* To

---

* For a Gaussian shape $(1a/\sqrt{\pi}) \exp\{-(1/a^2)(H_L - H_0)^2\}$; $\langle \Delta H^2 \rangle = a^2/2 = W^2/5.545$ where W is the width at half height. The experimentalist usually employs a derivative technique, that is, he measures $d\chi''/dH_0$, hence w, the point between maximum slope, is obtained. For a Gaussian it is given by $a^2/2 = \frac{1}{4}w^2$ and $W/w = 1.18$.

use Eq. (20.6) we need to know how many outer shells to include. If the two first shells are used, Eq. (20.6) gives

$$\langle \Delta H^2 \rangle_{av} = 7.5\, a_1^2 + 15\, a_2^2 . \qquad (20.7)$$

Kip et al. (S) employed Eq. (20.7) for natural KCl (see Table 20.2) and a crystal made of enriched K^{41} (99.2%). K^{41} has a smaller nuclear moment than K^{39}. They obtained two values of $\langle \Delta H^2 \rangle_{av}$ (235 and 530 gauss^2). The ratio of a_1(natural) to a_1(enriched) can be calculated from the changes of the K^{41} concentrations and the data in Table 16.2. The shape of $\phi(F)$ does not change, and it is not affected by the nuclear isotopes. Further, a_2 was assumed to be invariant. Using this procedure, one may evaluate $|\phi(F)|^2$ at the various nuclei. The data of Kip et al. are given in Table 20.2. The value of a is usually given in megacycles (mc). The procedure is not completely correct since there is no reason for breaking off (20.6) after the first two terms. The relation between the $\phi(F)$ calculated from the a's and the theory will be discussed more fully later (see also the experimental results—24e).

TABLE 20.2. a_j'S AND ϕ_F'S FOR KCl[a]

	Gauss	$|\phi_F|^2 \times 10^{21}$ cm^{-3}
$a_1\{100\}$ K	7.6	670
$a_2\{110\}$ Cl	2.6	110

[a] From Kip et al. (S).

The foregoing theory and experiments indicate that the width of the F-center is due to the interaction of the electron with the nuclear spin. This is referred to in the literature as *hyperfine interaction* and is a type of inhomogeneous broadening.

The assumption used in arriving at the foregoing equations should not be looked on as mysterious, although some quantum concepts are used. The electron finds itself in a medium having nuclei with magnetic moments and an external field. One assumes that the nuclear magnetic moments are quantized by the external magnetic field H_0.* All possible

* Near the imperfection the major field a nucleus sees is not H_0 but that due to the hyperfine interaction. This is approximately along the z direction, since the electron has been quantized.

alignments are assumed to have equal probability. Now the interaction between the electronic magnetic moment and the external field, as well as the internal field, is calculated assuming that the average position of the electron is given by $|\phi|^2$. All the interactions arise from (III) of Table 16.3, where the Dirac theory of an electron is used, since spin is considered.

The theory of Kip *et al.* (California group) has a limitation. It assumes that the term giving the interaction with the external field is much larger than the terms arising from (16.22). This assumption permits us to neglect s_x and s_y to first order. Actually, terms such as $s_x i_x{}^j$ and $s_y i_y{}^j$ cause a perturbation of the eigenvalues. The largest field at a nucleus may be due to a trapped electron. The wave function can no longer be a single term such as (16.1c), but is a sum of such terms. These sums we can obtain from the matrix elements of $s_x i_x{}^j$ and $s_y i_y{}^j$. A procedure has been employed by Wolga and Strandberg which includes these terms. Actually, it is based on a calculation of Breit and Rabi (S). The spin Hamiltonian has the form

$$\Delta\mathscr{H} = [g\beta s_z - g_I\beta_I \sum_j i_z(j)] H_0 + ag\beta s \cdot \sum_j^6 \mathbf{i}^j \qquad (20.8)$$

where again only the six nearest neighbors are considered and Eq. (20.5a) is used. In Eq. (20.8), a is the a_j appropriate to the nearest neighbors. We must remember that the $\mathbf{i}^j$'s are angular momenta and that they obey the laws of addition for such quantities. We therefore introduce the vector $\mathbf{i}$:

$$\mathbf{i} = \sum_j^6 \mathbf{i}^j \qquad (20.9)$$

The reason for introducing $\mathbf{i}$ may be somewhat mysterious. $\mathbf{i}^j$ does not enter into $\mathscr{H}_0$. It is the spherical symmetry of the problem which suggests the introduction of an $\mathbf{i}$. Further, a coupling occurs because of the isotropic hyperfine interaction in a manner similar to the coupling of the $\mathbf{l}$ and $\mathbf{s}$ vectors to give $\mathbf{j}$ in atomic spectroscopy. The relations between the $\eta_I(j)$ of the individual nuclei and the total η, denoted now by η_I, are complex and given by group theory (or other methods). This procedure greatly simplifies the problem if only the nearest neighbors shell is considered. The procedure of adding $\mathbf{i}$ must follow the law for the addition of such quantities. Consider the case where the spin is 3/2; the i, which is the absolute value of $\mathbf{i}$, ranges from 9 to 0.* There is only one combination which makes $i = 9$. There are more than one which give i less than 9. To obtain this number, we must add two of the spins together, then add a

---

* Actually the absolute value of $\mathbf{i}$ is $[i(i+1)]^{1/2}$.

third, etc. This process is straightforward but laborious, and the details will not be carried through here. The z component of $\mathbf{i}$ will be denoted by m_i:

The wave function to be used with (20.8) is a product of three functions: (1) $\phi(F)$, the spatial part, which we can ignore, except that it gives the a's; (2) the part associated with the electron spin, η_- or η_+; and (3) the part associated with i, which is denoted by $\eta_I(i, m_i)$. $\Delta\mathscr{H}$ can be put in the form

$$\Delta\mathscr{H} = (g\beta s_z - g_I\beta_I i_z)H_0 + ag\beta s_z i_z + \tfrac{1}{2}ag\beta(s_+i_- + s_-i_+). \quad (20.10)$$

When $\Delta\mathscr{H}$ operates on our wave function, the first two terms give only diagonal terms, while the last term gives off-diagonal ones. The latter vanish unless m_i increases by unity when m_s decreases by unity or vice versa [see (16.8a) and (16.8b)]; that is, the sum of $m_s + m_i$ is conserved. One may therefore introduce $m = m_i + m_s$ and reduce the problem to the solution of a quadratic equation. The actual matrix elements have the form

$$\langle i, m_s, m_i | \Delta\mathscr{H} | i', m_s', m_i' \rangle$$
$$= \delta(i, i')[\delta(m_s, m_s')\,\delta(m_i, m_i')(\gamma m_s + \gamma_n m_i)$$
$$+ A\delta(m, m')\{\delta(m_s, m_s')\,m_i m_s + \tfrac{1}{2}\delta(m_s', m_s \pm 1)$$
$$\times (i - m + \tfrac{1}{2})^{1/2}(i + m + \tfrac{1}{2})^{1/2}\}] \quad (20.11)$$

where
$$\gamma = g\beta H_0, \quad (20.11a)$$

$$A = ag\beta, \quad (20.11b)$$

and
$$\gamma_n = -g_I\beta_I H_0. \quad (20.11c)$$

For every value of i and m, there are two values of ϵ: $\epsilon_-(m)$ and $\epsilon_+(m)$. ϵ_+ corresponds to the case where the electron spin is almost anti-paralleled to H_0 while ϵ_- occurs when it is almost parallel. The actual energy expressions are:

$$\epsilon_\pm(m) = \frac{-A}{4} - g_I\beta_I m H_0$$
$$\pm \tfrac{1}{2}[(g\beta + g_I\beta_I)^2 H_0^2 + 4D^2 + A^2 m^2 + 2Am(g\beta + g_I\beta_I)H_0]^{1/2} \quad (20.11d)$$

where
$$D = (A/2)[(i - m + \tfrac{1}{2})(i + m + \tfrac{1}{2})]^{1/2}. \quad (20.11e)$$

Equation (20.11d) is known as the Breit-Rabi formula, given in 1931 in connection with another problem. The equation usually appears in an alternate form [see Kusch and Hughes (S), p. 83]. In the original derivation the second term was omitted. The eigenfunctions are now linear combinations of the product of the three functions discussed earlier. Strong and weak transitions occur. Neglecting the ϕ part, the eigenfunctions have the forms:

$$\chi_+ = T_1\eta_+\eta(i, m-\tfrac{1}{2}) + T_2\eta_-\eta(i; m+\tfrac{1}{2})$$

$$\chi_- = -T_2\eta_+\eta(i, m-\tfrac{1}{2}) + T_1\eta_-\eta(i; m+\tfrac{1}{2}) \qquad (20.12)$$

where

$$T_1 = \left[\frac{Am + (g\beta + g_I\beta_I)H_0 + B}{2B}\right]^{1/2}, \qquad (20.12a)^*$$

$$T_2 = \left[\frac{B - Am - (g\beta + g_I\beta_I)H_0}{2B}\right]^{1/2}, \qquad (20.12b) \quad \text{and}$$

$$B^2 = (g\beta + g_I\beta_I)^2 H_0{}^2 + 4D^2 + A^2 m^2 + 2Am(g\beta + g_I\beta_I)H_0. \qquad (20.12c)$$

We note that $T_1 \to 1$, and $T_2 \to 0$ as $A \to 0$. Strong and weak transitions occur. The transitions of interest are where $\Delta m_I = 0$.

The eigenvalues can be expanded. Thus, we obtain

$$\epsilon_+(m) = \tfrac{1}{2}g\beta H_0 - g_I\beta_I(m-\tfrac{1}{2})H_0 + \frac{A}{2}(m-\tfrac{1}{2})$$

$$+ \frac{A^2}{4(g\beta + g_I\beta_I)H_0}[i(i+1) + \tfrac{1}{4}] - \frac{A^2 m^2}{4(g\beta + g_I\beta_I)H_0} \qquad (20.13a)$$

for a given m. The major spin eigenfunction is η_+. Likewise for $\epsilon_-(m-1)$ whose major spin function is η_-, we have

$$\epsilon_-(m-1) = -\tfrac{1}{2}g\beta H_0 - g_I\beta_I(m-\tfrac{1}{2})H_0 - \frac{A}{2}(m-\tfrac{1}{2})$$

$$- \frac{A^2}{4(g\beta + g_I\beta_I)H_0}[i(i+1) + \tfrac{1}{4}] + \frac{A^2(m-1)^2}{4(g\beta + g_I\beta_I)H_0}. \qquad (20.13b)$$

The hyperfine interaction mixes electronic spin states η_+ and η_- with states where the z component of i changes only by unity and the whole manifold of nuclear states is not involved. In the levels $\epsilon_+(m)$ and $\epsilon_-(m-1)$ the nuclear spins do not change, although the electron spin flips. This gives a strong transition. The energy difference is:

$$\Delta\epsilon = g\beta H_0\left\{1 + \frac{a^2}{2H_0{}^2}[i(i+1) - m_i{}^2]\right\} + g\beta a m_i. \qquad (20.14)$$

---

* T_1 and T_2 are defined by Eqs. (20.12a) and (20.12b) and are in no way related to the relaxation times.

To obtain (20.14) from (20.11) one must expand the second expression and then consider transitions where m_s changes by unity while m_i does not. The term in the square brackets is an interesting correction which one might assume to be measurable if a/H_0 is of the order of 0.01 or larger. The experimentalist measures a frequency ν which equals the expression (20.14) divided by h. It is easily possible to measure the frequency to one or two parts per thousand; hence, if the Wolga-Strandberg correction is of the order of 1 or 0.5%, it is of importance. If a/H_0 equals 0.01, a

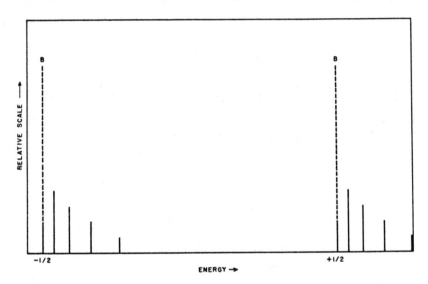

FIG. 20.3. An illustration of the Breit-Rabi effect as calculated by Wolga and Strandberg, for the interaction of an electron with three nuclei of spin 3/2, $m_i = \pm \frac{1}{2}$ lines. The lines marked B are the results of the theory due to Kip *et al.* Note that the average value obtained from the Breit-Rabi equation is not the same as the average position obtained by the Berkeley group. This is the correction of Holton and Blum.

reasonable value for some F-centers, then the Wolga-Strandberg term is 0.0045 if $i = 9$; hence we would expect to observe it.

The simplified theory neglects the second term in the curly brackets and the spread of the lines is due only to $g\beta a m_i$. The Wolga-Strandberg treatment shows that the degeneracy of the levels is partially removed.

To illustrate the problem, let us assume that the electron interacts with only two nuclei, as in the case of a diatomic molecule. If $i^j = 3/2$, i can have the values 3, 2, 1, 0, and each value gives one state when $m_i = 0$. If a/H_0 is not too small, we will have four lines instead of one, spaced as follows:

$a^2/2H_0^2$ (12, 6, 2, 0) relative to the value given by the elementary theory. Since the hyperfine broadening at times can be very large (2000 gauss), the Wolga-Strandberg term is important. If the electron interacts with three nuclei, i can have the values 9/2, 7/2, 5/2, 3/2, and 1/2. There is no $m_i = 0$ line but there are two lines for $m_i = \pm 1/2$. The Wolga-Strandberg theory now gives the pattern shown in Fig. 20.3. The lines marked B result from the theory of Kip et al., (B, Berkeley), while the lines marked W-S result from Eq. (20.14). The method of weighing the lines is shown in Table 20.3.

TABLE 20.3. WEIGHING FACTOR IN THE BREIT-RABI EQUATION[a]

i	Time occurring	Correction $i(i+1) - m^2$
9/2	1	49/2
7/2	2	31/2
5/2	3	17/2
3/2	4	7/2
1/2	2	1/2

[a] Three nuclei with spin 3/2; $m_i = \frac{1}{2}$ line.

Patterns shown in Fig. 20.3 are not generally observed. The Wolga-Strandberg or Breit-Rabi effect is masked by the hyperfine interaction with the nuclei in the shells beyond the nearest neighbors. For states where $l > 0$, we must use (16.23). In this case the symmetry of the wave function enters into the problem.

It is interesting to note that the hyperfine interaction decreases as l increases, since one deals with wave functions that are farther away from the nuclei. This type of calculation has been carried through for a hydrogen atom and the net interaction (16.23) and (16.24) can be calculated. In Table 20.4 are presented some values (Bethe and Salpeter, p. 107).

TABLE 20.4. RELATIVE VALUE OF THE HYPERFINE INTERACTION OF THE HYDROGEN ATOM

State	$1S_{1/2}$	$2S_{1/2}$	$3S_{1/2}$	$2P_{1/2}$	$2P_{3/2}$
Relative value	1	1/8	1/27	1/24	1/60

Kittel (S) has made an estimate of the width of all the alkali halides by using Eq. (20.7) and estimating the new a's from the hyperfine coupling constant of the free ions. The estimates are in fair agreement with the measured value. See Kip *et al.* (S), as well as Kittel in the next chapter.

Holton and Blum (S) handled (16.24) in an alternate manner. They considered the interaction between a single nucleus and an electron. Then Eqs. (20.8) to (20.13) apply with $i = i^j = 3/2$, say for KCl. We may now use fictitious "spin wave functions," namely η_-' and η_+' of (20.12) with a fictitious g value obtained from (20.14) with m_i replaced by the average value and i by i^j. One may now proceed and include a second nucleus, etc. This avoids the use of (20.9) and allows one to include more than the first shell. In this manner we obtain Holton and Blum's equation for the g value:

$$g_n = g\left\{1 + \sum_j \frac{1}{2H_0{}^2} a_j{}^2 i^j(i^j+1) - m_j{}^2\right\}. \qquad (20.15)$$

a_j is the a associated with the jth nucleus. Actually, one may use an effective a to include term (16.23); g is the g due to spin-orbit interactions, while g_n includes both spin-orbit and hyperfine interactions.

Equation (20.15) arises directly from second-order perturbation theory, the last term comes from $ag\beta s_z i_z$ and first-order perturbation theory, while the first term comes from $ag\beta(s_x i_x + s_y i_y)$ with the use of second-order perturbation theory. A factor of $\frac{1}{4}$ of (20.13) does not appear in this treatment; this is of no interest since we are concerned with the difference between two levels. The advantage of the complete development of Wolga and Strandberg is that one obtains a feeling for the eigenfunctions that cannot be obtained immediately from the usual development of perturbation theory. Hence, one can justify the procedure of Holton and Blum directly, although the equations equivalent to (20.12) must be very complex.

In Eq. (20.15), g_n is the total g due to the spin-orbit interaction and the hyperfine interaction. This is a very important point to keep in mind. The results of Holton and Blum indicate that for LiF $g_n = 2.0014$, while the g corrected for the nuclear interaction is 2.0005. Note the Δg changes from -0.0009 to -0.0018.

REFERENCES

G. Breit and I. I. Rabi, *Phys. Rev.* **38**, 2082 (1931).
W. C. Holton and H. Blum, *Phys. Rev.* **125**, 89 (1962).
A. F. Kip, C. Kittel, R. A. Levy, and A. M. Portis, *Phys. Rev.* **91**, 1066 (1953).

C. Kittel, Conference on *Defects in Crystalline Solids* (Physical Society, London, 1955) p. 33.

P. Kusch and V. W. Hughes, *in* "Handbuch der Physik" (S. Flügge, ed.), Vol. 37, Part I, p. 81. Springer, Berlin, 1959.

G. J. Wolga and M. W. P. Strandberg, *Phys. Chem. Solids* **9**, 309 (1959).

21. SATURATION AND HYPERFINE BROADENING

One of the most dramatic properties of F-centers is their saturation. We have just seen that various centers find themselves in different local fields. This fact has to be combined with (17.17a) and (17.17b), if one is to obtain the actual behavior of χ' and χ''. The original expressions were obtained by Portis (S). The saturation behavior of χ' is not the same as that for χ'' when there are various local fields. The experimental data regarding this point is meager, but the theoretical arguments support this conclusion. It is due to Abragam.

We shall now derive Portis's relations for χ''. Returning to (17.17b), we note that:

$$\int \chi'' \, d\omega = \frac{\pi}{2} \chi_0 \, \omega_0 \left\{ \frac{1}{[1 + \frac{1}{4}\gamma^2 H_1^2 T_1 T_2]^{1/2}} \right\} \tag{21.1}$$

and that χ'' peaks at $\omega = \omega_0$. In this section H_1 will be employed in place of h_1—see Eq. (17.3). This is to keep the notation in agreement with the literature. Equation (21.1) states that the absorption "area" decreases as $[1 + \frac{1}{4}\gamma^2 H_1^2 T_1 T_2]^{-1/2}$, while from (17.17b) one notes that the point of maximum absorption decreases as $[1 + \frac{1}{4}\gamma^2 H_1^2 T_1 T_2]^{-1}$. Hence, for large values of H_1, the "area" absorption decreases as H_1^{-1}, although the point of maximum absorption decreases as H_1^{-2}.

Portis's equation, which combines the quantum mechanical approach of Section 18 with the problem of inhomogeneous broadening, leads to a very important equation which goes by his name. We shall now derive it without using the approach of Bloch. Part of the derivation is based on a paper of Bloembergen, Purcell, and Pound (S). Let there be n^+ electrons with spin pointing up in a local field $H_0 + \Delta H$ and n^- electrons whose spins point downward. Using n_0 which now is the total number of spins in the *local field*, $H_0 + \Delta H$ we know that $n_0 = n^+ + n^-$. Further, we define $n = n^- - n^+$. The equation of detailed balance states that

$$\frac{dn}{dt} = \left(\frac{dn}{dt}\right)_{mf} + \left(\frac{dn}{dt}\right)_{lat}. \tag{21.2}$$

The first term on the right is due to transitions induced by the microwave field (*mf*), while the second is due to the lattice.

From Eq. (18.5) we obtain the expression

$$\left(\frac{dn}{dt}\right)_{mf} = -\frac{\pi}{4}\gamma^2 H_1^2 g_s(\omega)n. \qquad (21.3)$$

g_s may be due to a Van Vleck mechanism or a Bloch mechanism (effects of T_2), as stated; most probably in the F-center it is the Bloch mechanism (see Section 18c). Here the angular frequency has been employed in place of the frequency ν, so that the notation in this section will be similar to that of Portis.* For the lattice effect, we may employ a form of Eq. (17.13b) and write

$$\left(\frac{dn}{dt}\right)_{lat} = -\frac{n - n_\theta}{T_1} \qquad (21.4)$$

where n_θ is the thermal equilibrium value of n determined from Boltzmann's statistics. An equilibrium condition can be obtained for a given amount of microwave power by setting the left-hand side of Eq. (21.2) equal to zero. This results in the equation [where Eqs. (17.1) have been used]

$$n = \frac{n_\theta}{1 + \frac{1}{4}\pi\gamma^2 H_1^2 T_1 g_s(\omega - \omega_0)}. \qquad (21.5)$$

The power absorbed from the microwave signal is:

$$P_a = -\frac{1}{2}\hbar\omega\left(\frac{dn}{dt}\right)_{mf} = \frac{1}{2}\omega\chi'' H_1^2$$

$$= \frac{1}{2}\omega\frac{1}{2}\omega_0\frac{\gamma^2 n_\theta \hbar}{2\omega_0}\frac{\pi g_s(\omega)}{1 + \frac{1}{4}\pi\gamma^2 H_1^2 T_1 g_s(\omega)}H_1^2. \qquad (21.6)$$

where Eq. (17.24) has been used (assuming $V_c = 1$).

Hence, using Eq. (21.6) one may write:

$$\chi'' = \frac{1}{2}\chi_0\omega_0\frac{\pi g_s(\omega)}{1 + \frac{1}{4}\pi\gamma^2 H_1^2 T_1 g_s(\omega)}. \qquad (21.7)$$

Equation (21.7) is similar to Eqs. (17.17b), (17.18b), and (18.6) provided g_s is taken to have a proper form. It is more general than these equations since we have not specified the form of g_s. This we shall do shortly. A usual definition is

$$g_s(0) = g_s(\omega_1 - \omega_1) = T_2/\pi. \qquad (21.8)$$

---

* One can introduce the g_s into Eq. (18.5) be several means; they all lead to the same result provided T_2 is defined properly. The method employed here seems simplest. The reader should note that in this section $\int g_s(\omega)\,d\omega = 1$. In general, g_s will be a symmetric function about angular frequency ω_1 so that at times we shall write $g_s(\omega - \omega_1)$. We also note that n changes by 2 for every flip of the spin. g_s is related to T_2. T_1 enters into the problem by means of the second term on the right of Eq. (21.2).

An alternate way of defining T_2 has been suggested by Noble and co-worker (S) for a special form of g_s.

If the centers responsible for the EPR (electron spin resonance), as discussed in Section 20, are in a series of local fields we must modify Eq. (21.7). We introduce a field distribution function h, where $h(\omega_1 - \omega_0)\Delta\omega_1$ is the probability of ω_1 [that is, g_s having the form $g_s(\omega - \omega_1)$] being in the angular frequency interval $\Delta\omega_1$. h has the property

$$\int h(\omega_1 - \omega_0)\,d\omega_1 = 1. \tag{21.9}$$

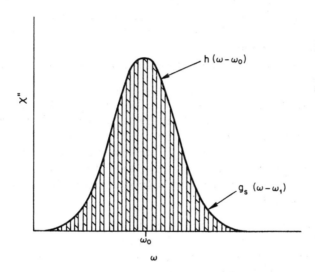

FIG. 21.1. The effect of inhomogeneous broadening. g_s is the shape of the homogeneously broadened lines, while h is the envelope of these lines.

χ'' now has the form

$$\chi''(\omega) = \frac{1}{2}\chi_0 \int_0^\infty \frac{\pi\omega_1 g_s(\omega - \omega_1)}{1 + \frac{1}{4}\pi\gamma^2 H_1^2 T_1 g_s(\omega - \omega_1)} h(\omega_1 - \omega_0)\,d\omega_1, \tag{21.10}$$

which is Portis's equation for the saturation of an inhomogeneously broadened line.

We may illustrate the physics involved in Eq. (21.10) by the use of Fig. 21.1. As shown in Section 20, the F-centers are in various local fields due to the arrangements of the nuclear spins around the negative-ion vacancies which trap electrons to form F-centers. If one considers only the interaction with the six nearest neighbors, there are 19 such lines. The shape of the individual spin—the spin multiplet—is described by $g_s(\omega - \omega_1)$. In our diagram we have assumed that they have a rectangular shape. Actually they may be Lorentzian or Gaussian, depending on the situation. We associate an effective width W (in gauss) with them. For a Lorentzian line, W is proportional to T_2^{-1}. The envelope function due to the various local fields is given by h, referred to as the absorption line [see Eq. (21.13)]. Since the number of possible local fields is large, one would expect that h will approach a random distribution (that is, a Gaussian shape). For the F-center in KCl, we may not resolve the spin multiplet. Note that in Eq. (21.10) the saturation and measurement occur at the same frequency.

Three integrations of (21.10) have been carried through for different g's and h's:

(1) The width of h is assumed to be large compared to g_s, which was assumed to have a Lorentzian form. (This was done by Portis, S.)

(2) The width of h and g_s was assumed to be of the same order; h was Gaussian, while g_s was Lorentzian. (This was done by Castner, S.)

(3) The shape of g_s was assumed to be non-Lorentzian, although the width of h was assumed to be much larger than g_s. (This was done by Noble and co-worker, S.)

At any value of the magnetic field, the total absorption may be considered very roughly as produced by two types of multiplets—that due to absorption near the center, and that due to the absorption in the tails of the multiplets. The saturation of the center of the multiplet goes as H_1^{-2} when $(\frac{1}{4})\pi\gamma^2 H_1^2 T_1 g_s(0) \gg 1$, while the tails are hardly saturated, since the second term in the denominator of (21.10) becomes of the order of unity or less when g_s is small. For narrow multiplets it is this shape and distribution, that is, how close ω is to ω_1, that determines the relative amounts of these two types of saturations and thus the average. This means that the detailed shape of the tail of the multiplet is important.

Consider first Portis's problem (S):

$$\chi''(\omega) = \frac{1}{2}\chi_0\,\omega h(\omega - \omega_0) \int \frac{\pi g_s(\omega - \omega')}{1 + \frac{1}{4}\pi\gamma^2 H_1^2 T_1 g_s(\omega - \omega')}\,d\omega' \quad (21.11)$$

where

$$g_s = \frac{T_2}{\pi}\frac{1}{1 + T_2^2(\omega - \omega')^2} \quad (21.12)$$

The fraction acts like a delta-function. Substituting (21.12) into (21.11) and integrating we obtain

$$\chi''(\omega, H_1) = \frac{\pi}{2}\chi_0\,\omega h(\omega - \omega_0)\frac{1}{[1+\frac{1}{4}\gamma^2 H_1{}^2 T_1 T_2]^{1/2}}. \quad (21.13)$$

Since χ'' is a function of ω and H_1, we have denoted it as a function of the two parameters. The saturation factor S is defined as follows

$$S = \chi''(\omega, H_1)/\chi''(\omega, 0) \quad (21.14)$$

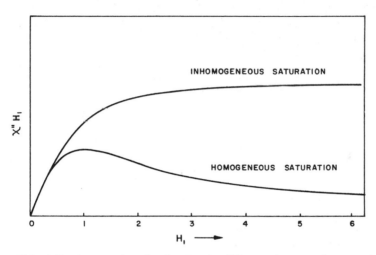

FIG. 21.2. A Portis saturation plot showing the difference between the saturation of a homogeneous and an inhomogeneous line.

where

$$\chi''(\omega, 0) = (\pi/2)\chi_0\,\omega h(\omega - \omega_0). \quad (21.14a)$$

For the Portis case

$$S = \frac{1}{[1+\frac{1}{4}\gamma^2 T_1 T_2 H_1{}^2]^{1/2}}. \quad (21.15)$$

An alternate form of this equation, which we shall find useful, is

$$[(1/S^2)-1] = \tfrac{1}{4}\gamma^2 T_1 T_2 H_1{}^2. \quad (21.15a)$$

One method of presenting the data due to Portis is to plot $\chi'' H_1$ against H_1. This gives a curve shown in Fig. 21.2, where $\frac{1}{4}\gamma^2 T_1 T_2$ has been set equal to unity.

Consider next the Castner case, where g_s again has the form given by Eq. (21.12) and h is assumed Gaussian, namely,

$$h(\omega' - \omega_0) = \pi^{-1/2} \frac{1}{\Delta\omega} \exp\left[-\left(\frac{\omega' - \omega_0}{\Delta\omega}\right)^2\right]. \tag{21.16}$$

Substituting into (21.10) results in

$$\chi''(\omega, H) = \frac{1}{2} \frac{\chi_0}{\pi^{1/2}} \frac{T_2}{\Delta\omega} \int_0^\infty \frac{\omega' \exp\left[-\frac{1}{\Delta\omega^2}(\omega' - \omega_0)^2\right] d\omega'}{1 + T_2^2(\omega - \omega')^2 + \frac{1}{4}\gamma^2 T_1 T_2 H_1^2} \tag{21.17}$$

where χ'' will be evaluated at only one point, the peak of the h curve.

The width of the Lorentzian wave packet is $1/T_2$ and $[T_2 \Delta\omega]^{-1}$ equals the ratio of the width of g to h. We let $a = (1/T_2 \Delta\omega)$. Equation (21.17) now has the form

$$\chi''(\omega_0, H_1) = \frac{1}{2} \frac{1}{\pi^{1/2}} \chi_0 a \int_0^\infty \frac{x' \exp[-a^2(x' - x_0)^2] dx'}{1 + (x' - x_0)^2 + \frac{1}{4}\gamma^2 T_1 T_2 H_1^2} \tag{21.18}$$

where $x = \omega' T_2$. Substituting $y = x' - x_0$, one obtains

$$\chi''(\omega_0, H_1) = \frac{1}{2} \frac{\chi_0}{\pi^{1/2}} a \int_{-\infty}^\infty \frac{(y + x_0) \exp(-a^2 y^2) dy}{t^2 + y^2}. \tag{21.19}$$

$t^2 = 1 + \frac{1}{4}\gamma^2 T_1 T_2 H_1^2$, where t^{-1} is the saturation factor in the Portis case, Eq. (21.14); it will not be the saturation factor in cases (2) and (3). The first term of Eq. (21.19) is odd and drops out. Hence, the integral of Eq. (21.19) must be of the form

$$I(a, t) = 2 \int_0^\infty \frac{e^{-a^2 y^2}}{t^2 + y^2} dy = 2e^{a^2 t^2} \int_0^\infty \frac{e^{-a^2(t^2 + y^2)}}{t^2 + y^2} dy$$

$$= \frac{\pi}{t} e^{a^2 t^2}[1 - \Phi(at)] \tag{21.20}$$

where Φ is the usual error function $(2/\pi^{1/2}) \int_0^{at} e^{-y^2} dy$. The steps in Eq.

(21.20) are slightly involved, but are presented in full detail in Castner's paper. Using (21.20) and (21.19), we obtain Castner's saturation equation.

$$\chi''(\omega_0, H_1) = \frac{1}{2}\chi_0 \pi^{1/2} \frac{\omega_0}{\Delta\omega} \frac{e^{a^2 t^2}}{t}[1 - \Phi(at)]. \tag{21.21}$$

In Fig. 21.3 we have reproduced some curves plotted by Castner. The y-axis is proportional to $\chi'' H_1$; hence, this is a Portis-type plot except that $\log \chi'' H_1$ is plotted instead of $\chi'' H_1$. The reader should note that as a increases, there are deviations from the curves shown in Fig. 21.2. One speaks of the "droop" in the saturation plot.

Finally, we shall consider another deviation from the Portis case, which arises because g_s is not a Lorentzian curve. This calculation is due to Noble (see Noble and Markham, S). There is no good reason for assuming that g_s is Lorentzian. Further, it is known that for the F-center

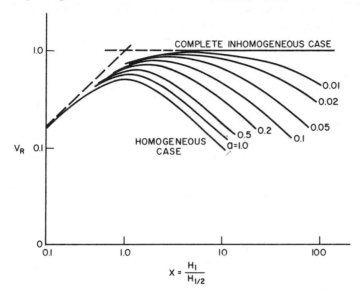

FIG. 21.3. Plots of the saturation for various values of a. The method of Portis is employed (calculations taken from Castner, S); $a = T_2 \Delta \omega$; $V_R \approx \chi'' H_1$, and $x \approx H_1$.

in KCl, a is very small. For this reason Noble integrated Eq. (21.10) by assuming that h can be taken out of the integral, but that g_s has the form

$$g_s(\omega - \omega') = (T_2/\pi) \frac{\sqrt{1+2\epsilon}}{1 + T_2^2(\omega - \omega')^2 + T_2^4 \epsilon^2 (\omega - \omega')^4}. \quad (21.22)$$

In Eq. (21.22) g_s is normalized and a Lorentzian for $\epsilon = 0$.* One should note that $g_s(0) = (T_2/\pi)$ only for $\epsilon = 0$. By selecting the proper value of ϵ, one can make g_s resemble a Gaussian over a range of values of ω. If we

---

* The following integral identity:

$$\int\limits_{-\infty}^{+\infty} \frac{dx}{c^2 + x^2 + \epsilon^2 x^4} = \frac{\pi}{c} (1 + 2\epsilon c)^{-1/2}$$

will be employed. It can be found in a table or proven by contour integration.

set $\epsilon = 1$, it resembles a Gaussian. T_2 is just a scale factor and for the time being can be set equal to unity. Then the normalization factor for (21.22) is just $\sqrt{3}/\pi = 0.551$, while the Gaussian normalization factor is $1/\pi^{1/2} = 0.564$. Hence at $\omega = \omega'$, they are essentially equal and the curves are almost identical for $\omega \ll 1$. The ω dependence can be obtained from the ω^2 term in the expansion and is the same for (21.22), a Gaussian and a Lorentzian. Since they have an identical area, Eq. (21.22) is only slightly narrower than a Gaussian and therefore has more area in the tails. The Lorentzian curve is quite different since its normalization factor is $1/\pi = 0.318$, and for $\omega \ll 1$ they do not approach each other. We may summarize this by writing: Gaussian $g_s(0) = 0.564$; modified Lorentzian $(\epsilon = 1) g_s(0) = 0.571$; and pure Lorentzian $(\epsilon = 0)$, $g_s(0) = 0.318$. By varying ϵ, we may consider the transition in the multiplet shape from a Lorentzian to an approximate Gaussian. The saturated value of χ'' is given by the expression

$$\chi''(H_1, \omega) = \tfrac{1}{2}\chi_0 \omega h(\omega - \omega_0)\sqrt{1+2\epsilon}$$

$$\times \int_{-\infty}^{\infty} \frac{T_2 \, dx}{1 + \tfrac{1}{4}\gamma^2 H_1^2 T_1 T_2 \sqrt{1+2\epsilon} + T_2^2 x^2 + \epsilon^2 T_2^4 x^4}.$$

(21.23)

We have set $x = \omega - \omega'$, since ω' varies from 0 to ∞ and ω is large. We let x vary between $-\infty$ and $+\infty$. Setting $K = \tfrac{1}{4}\gamma^2 H_1^2 T_1 T_2$ and integrating, this becomes

$$\chi''(H_1, \omega) = \tfrac{1}{2}\chi_0 \omega h(\omega - \omega_0) \pi \sqrt{1+2\epsilon}[1 + K\sqrt{1+2\epsilon}]^{-1/2}$$

$$\times \{1 + 2\epsilon[1 + K\sqrt{1+2\epsilon}]^{1/2}\}^{-1/2}. \qquad (21.24)$$

The saturation factor may then be calculated and put in the form we shall use to compare with the data, namely:

$$S^{-2} - 1 = K(1+2\epsilon)^{-1/2} + 2\epsilon(1+2\epsilon)^{-1}\{[1 + K(1+2\epsilon)^{1/2}]^{3/2} - 1\}. \quad (21.25)$$

For very small values of ϵ, this becomes:

$$S^{-2} - 1 = \tfrac{1}{4}\gamma^2 H_1^2 T_1 T_2 + \epsilon[2(K+1)^{3/2} - (K+2)] (\epsilon \ll 1), \quad (21.26)$$

which is very similar to the original equation of Portis (21.15a), but it will not have the $S \sim H_1^{-1}$ dependence at high powers which occurs in Eq. (21.15a). For any ϵ but $K(1+2\epsilon)^{1/2} \ll 1$,

$$\frac{1}{S^2} - 1 = \frac{K}{(1+2\epsilon)^{1/2}} + \frac{3\epsilon}{(1+2\epsilon)^{1/2}} K. \qquad (21.27)$$

Plots of $\chi'' H_1$ against $\log H_1$ are shown in Fig. 21.4. They indicate that a change in the form of g_s can produce a "droop" similar to the ones reported by Castner. This means that one must have an alternate method of deciding whether one is dealing with the Castner or the Noble case.

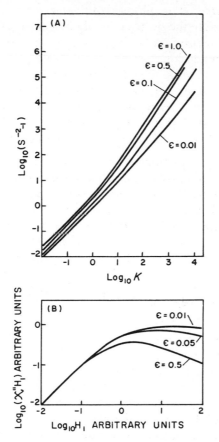

FIG. 21.4. A Noble and a Portis plot of the saturation when the spin packet is assumed to have a non-Lorentzian form; ϵ is defined in Eq. (21.22). (Noble and Markham, S).

This problem will be discussed in full in Section 24c, where the experimental details are considered.

Portis's equation for inhomogeneous broadening has two important consequences:

(1) *The shape.* The shape, that is, the dependence of χ'' on H_0 is given by h, not by Bloch's equation, Eq. (17.17). It is independent of H_1. For

a homogeneously broadened line, Eq. (17.17b) tells us that the center of the line saturates more than the tails. This difference in behavior with increased microwave field is readily observable.

(2) *The saturation.* The physical difference between (17.17b) and (21.15) is connected to the problem of inhomogeneous broadening. If we are studying the saturation of Eq. (17.17b) at a point (value of ω) its behavior depends on ω. The midpoint ($\omega = \omega_0$) saturates as $[1 + \frac{1}{4}\gamma^2 H_1{}^2 T_1 T_2]^{-1}$, while the edges may not be saturated at all. If we study the saturation of Eq. (21.15) it goes as $[1 + \frac{1}{4}\gamma^2 H_1{}^2 T_1 T_2]^{-1/2}$, independent of ω. In a sense, our equipment automatically integrates over g_s and the "area" of g_s saturates as $[1 + \frac{1}{4}\gamma^2 H_1{}^2 T_1 T_2]^{-1/2}$ and, of course, is independent of the frequency of the microwave field.

To test the above equations we may start with the assumption that Portis's equation applies rigorously. One wishes to find a critical manner of presenting the data. H_1 varies over several decades and the Portis plots (Fig. 21.1), though useful, do not indicate whether Eq. (21.14) really applies. A more critical method is to change H_1 by varying the attenuation before and after the cavity, keeping the net attenuation in the line constant. Then if H_{1r} is some reference value and Eq. (21.15a) applies, one obtains

$$\log_{10}(S^{-2} - 1) - \log_{10}(\tfrac{1}{4}\gamma^2 \, H_{1r}^2 \, T_1 T_2) = \log_{10} H_1{}^2 / H_{1r}^2 = \log_{10} P/P_r \tag{21.28}$$

where the right-hand term is simply the attenuation between the signal source and the cavity. If Eq. (21.15a) applies, plots of $\log_{10}(S^{-2} - 1)$ against $\log_{10} P/P_r$ should give straight lines. The intercept $P = P_r$ gives the value of $\log_{10}(\tfrac{1}{4}\gamma^2 H_{1r}^2 T_1 T_2)$ from which $T_1 T_2$ can be calculated. If the above equation applies, the measured *points* must lie on a straight line of *unit* slope. We shall refer to such plots by the name Noble.

To calculate the dispersion, one must return to Eq. (17.22d) and combine it with (21.10). Here we are using a technique developed by Abragam, p. 52. The equation for the dispersion has the form

$$\chi'(\omega_0 + \omega) = [1 + \tfrac{1}{4}\gamma^2 H_1{}^2 T_1 T_2]^{1/2} \frac{1}{\pi} \mathscr{P} \int_{-\infty}^{\infty} \frac{\chi''(\omega_0 + y)\, dy}{y - \omega}. \tag{21.29}$$

Returning to Eq. (21.13) results in:

$$\chi'(\omega_0 + \omega) = \frac{\pi}{2}\chi_0 \omega_0 \frac{1}{\pi} \int_{-\infty}^{\infty} \frac{1}{y - \omega} h(y)\, dy \tag{21.30}$$

where $\omega_0 \mid y$ has been replaced by ω_0 since y is small compared to ω_0. It has been assumed that the Lorentzian factor in (21.11) behaves like a Dirac delta-function.* Equation (21.30) shows that the dispersion is in no way affected by H_1 and hence does not saturate. Expressions for χ' have been derived by Portis (S) and Abragam. They do not agree completely. We have followed Abragam's treatment here.

The question may be asked why we have followed the procedure of adding the χ'' and calculating the χ' from the Kramers-Krönig relation. This is actually the only way one may proceed, since the adding of the χ'' is just summing the energies absorbed in the cavity, which is a linear process [see Eq. (17.24)]. The dispersion, however, can only be calculated indirectly. The fact that χ' and χ'' both saturate in the case of the Bloch equations implies nothing in the case of inhomogeneous broadening such as exists in the F-center. This is a very fundamental point which seems to have been overlooked in the past when the lack of the saturation of χ' came as a surprise. The reader will note that we have used χ and χ_R of Abragam interchangeably.

REFERENCES

N. Bloembergen, E. M. Purcell, and R. V. Pound, *Phys. Rev.* **73**, 679 (1948).
T. G. Castner, *Phys. Rev.* **115**, 1506 (1959).
G. A. Noble and J. J. Markham, *J. Chem. Phys.* **36**, 1340 (1962).
A. M. Portis, *Phys. Rev.* **91**, 1071 (1953).

22. The Electron Nuclear Double Resonance (ENDOR) Technique

In this section we will develop the background for a type of measurement that goes by the name ENDOR (electron nuclear double resonance). This technique gives, among other items, a measure of the F-electron wave function at a nucleus and the symmetry of the function. These are exceptionally important factors if we are to gain a true understanding of the F-center and point imperfections in solids. The technique is based on the hyperfine interaction, Eq. (16.22), and on the electrostatic coupling between the nuclei and the electron, that is, the quadrupole interaction. The major effect arises from Eq. (16.22); hence, the latter will not be considered here.

* For very large H_1 the integral cannot be considered to be a delta-function and our derivation does not apply.

The first three terms of Eq. (16.22) are considered small and for the time being will be omitted,

$$\mathscr{H}(hf) = ag\beta \mathbf{s} \cdot \sum_j \mathbf{i}, \qquad (22.1)$$

we apply it to the simplest wave function considered by Kip, Kittel, Levy, and Portis, namely Eq. (20.2). This means that Hamiltonian (20.8) applies to our system. The associated *exact* wave functions are:

$$\chi_+(i, m) = T_1 \eta_+ \eta(i; m_i) + T_2 \eta_- \eta(i; m_i + 1), \qquad m = m_i + \tfrac{1}{2}; \quad (22.2a)$$

$$\chi_-(i, m) = -T_2 \eta_+ \eta(i; m_i - 1) + T_1 \eta_- \eta(i; m_i), \qquad m = m_i - \tfrac{1}{2}; \quad (22.2b)$$

$$\chi_+(i, m) = T_1 \eta_+ \eta(i; m_i - 1) + T_2 \eta_- \eta(i; m_i). \qquad m = m_i - \tfrac{1}{2}; \quad (22.2c)$$

and

$$\chi_-(i, m) = -T_2 \eta_+ \eta(i; m_i - 2) + T_1 \eta_- \eta(i; m_i - 1), \qquad m = m_i - \tfrac{3}{2}. \quad (22.2d)$$

where $\mathbf{i} = \sum \mathbf{i}^j$ and m_i is the projection of $\mathbf{i}$ along the external magnetic field. The projection of $\mathbf{i}$ and $\mathbf{s}$ along the z-axis is not a good quantum number but $(\mathbf{i} + \mathbf{s})^2$ is a good quantum number. s_z and i_z do not permute with this sum and hence are not good quantum numbers. Equation (22.2) is obtained from (20.12).* η_s has been replaced by η_+ or η_-. The T's are functions of the m's and they can be zero. The corresponding energies to first order are:

$$\epsilon_+(m) = \tfrac{1}{2}g\beta H_0 - g_I \beta_I H_0 (m - \tfrac{1}{2}) + (A/2)(m - \tfrac{1}{2}) \qquad (22.3a)$$

$$\epsilon_-(m) = -\tfrac{1}{2}g\beta H_0 - g_I \beta_I H_0 (m + \tfrac{1}{2}) - (A/2)(m + \tfrac{1}{2}). \qquad (22.3b)$$

If the field given by (17.3) is applied to the crystal, the following time-dependent perturbation is of interest:

$$2g\beta s_x H_1 \cos \omega t - 2g_I \beta_I i_x H_1 \cos \omega t, \qquad (22.4)$$

where i_x is the x component of $\mathbf{i}$. Two types of strong transitions can occur. Both transitions require a change of m by unity according to first-order perturbation theory. The first occurs in the microwave region, where the energy change involved is of the order of $g\beta H_0$, whereas the second involves much less energy, $\tfrac{1}{2}A \pm g_I \beta_I H_0$, and occurs at a lower frequency. As indicated in Section 18, the absorption occurs because $n_\theta \neq 0$, that is, there is a difference in the populations of the two spin levels. The ENDOR technique utilizes this requirement to measure A or

$$a = (8\pi/3)g_I \beta_I |\phi_F(n_j)|^2 \qquad (22.5)$$

* We assume $a\mathbf{s} \cdot \mathbf{i} \gg g_I \beta_I \, i_z H_0$ which applies generally only near the imperfection.

[see Eq. (20.12)], the coupling between the electron and the jth nucleus. Equation (22.4) induces several types of weaker transitions.

To illustrate the problem further, consider P-doped silicon. The nuclear spin of P^{31} is 1/2. The phosphorus atom has an additional electron which behaves very much like a hydrogenic electron in a medium of high dielectric constant [see Kohn (S) or Smith]. For the purpose of illustration we consider only the interaction between this extra electron and the phosphor nucleus; that is, the sum over a in (20.4) or (20.8) reduces to a single term. Since the extra electron is in an s-state relative to the P nucleus (we only have to consider the contact term), the arguments leading up to Eqs. (22.2) apply also to this case, as do the eigenfunctions given by Eqs. (22.2). They now have the form

$$m = 1, \qquad \chi_+(i, \tfrac{1}{2}) = \eta_+ \eta(i, \tfrac{1}{2}); \tag{22.6a}$$

$$m = 0, \qquad \chi_+ = T_1 \eta_+ \eta(i, -\tfrac{1}{2}) + T_2 \eta_- \eta(i, \tfrac{1}{2}); \tag{22.6b}$$

$$m = 0, \qquad \chi_- = -T_2 \eta_+ \eta(i, -\tfrac{1}{2}) + T_1 \eta_- \eta(i, \tfrac{1}{2}); \tag{22.6c}$$

and $\qquad m = -1, \qquad \chi_- = \eta_- \eta(i, -\tfrac{1}{2}). \tag{22.6d}$

There are no off-diagonal terms for $\eta_+ \eta(i, \tfrac{1}{2})$ nor for $\eta_- \eta(i, -\tfrac{1}{2})$ and these functions are eigenfunctions of the Hamiltonian (20.10). The corresponding eigenvalues are:

$$\epsilon_+(1) = \tfrac{1}{2} g \beta H_0 - \tfrac{1}{2} g_I \beta_I H_0 + \tfrac{1}{4} A, \quad \text{for} \quad m = 1 \quad (m_s = \tfrac{1}{2} \text{ and } m_I = \tfrac{1}{2}); \tag{22.7a}$$

$$\epsilon_+(0) = \tfrac{1}{2} g \beta H_0 + \tfrac{1}{2} g_I \beta_I H_0 - \tfrac{1}{4} A, \quad \text{for} \quad m = 0$$
$$(m_s = \tfrac{1}{2}, m_I = -\tfrac{1}{2} \text{ approx.}); \tag{22.7b}$$

$$\epsilon_-(-1) = -\tfrac{1}{2} g \beta H_0 + \tfrac{1}{2} g_I \beta_I H_0 + \tfrac{1}{4} A, \quad \text{for} \quad m = -1$$
$$(m_s = -\tfrac{1}{2}, m_I = -\tfrac{1}{2}); \tag{22.7c}$$

and

$$\epsilon_-(0) = -\tfrac{1}{2} g \beta H_0 - \tfrac{1}{2} g_I \beta_I H_0 - \tfrac{1}{4} A, \quad \text{for} \quad m = 0$$
$$(m_s = -\tfrac{1}{2}, m_I = \tfrac{1}{2} \text{ approx.}). \tag{22.7d}$$

Two high-frequency transitions are obtained from (22.7):

$$\nu_e^{\pm} = \frac{1}{h} \left[g \beta H_0 \pm \frac{A}{2} \right]. \tag{22.8}$$

The low-frequency transitions have the value

$$\nu_I^{\pm} = \frac{1}{h} \left[\frac{A}{2} \pm g_I \beta_I H_0 \right]. \tag{22.9}$$

Here we have assumed that the contact term is larger than the nuclear Zeeman term (see item j, Table 16.1, and Fig. 22.1).

To do the experiment for P-doped silicon, we may first saturate two levels (make their populations equal) by applying a strong high-frequency field [Eq. (22.8)].* Now there is no net absorption signal, since the number of upward and downward transitions is equal. In the actual

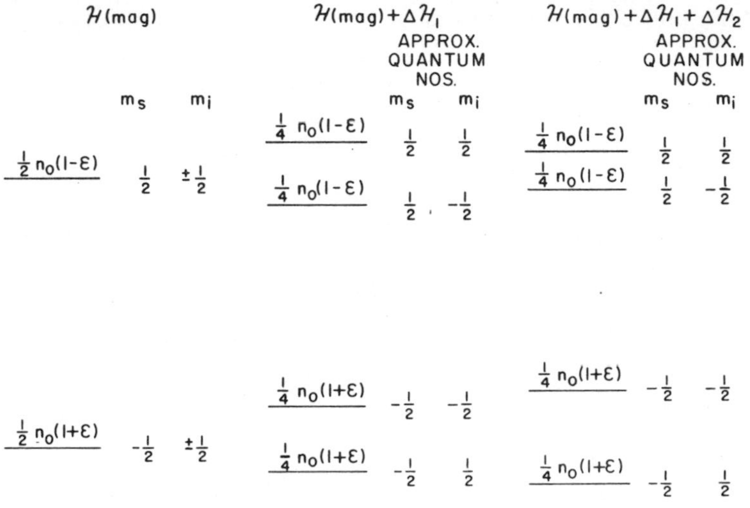

FIG. 22.1. Energy level diagrams for the P atom in silicon when the only hyperfine interaction considered is that between the extra electron and the P nuclei (spin $\frac{1}{2}$). The population of the various levels before the application of any signal is illustrated. The effect of $\Delta\mathcal{H}_1$ and $\Delta\mathcal{H}_2$ is not considered; n_0 is the net number of imperfections. $\Delta\mathcal{H}_1 = ag\beta\mathbf{s}\cdot\mathbf{i}$; $\Delta\mathcal{H}_2 = -\beta_I g_I i_z H_0$.

experiment one keeps ν constant and varies H_0 until relation (22.8) is obtained.

The situation is illustrated in Fig. 22.2, where $\epsilon = g\beta H_0/2k\theta$. The unsaturated populations are given; they depend primarily on the electronic Zeeman energy. In the middle, the population distribution is depicted under a saturation condition. There is still a normal population difference for the case $m_s = \pm\frac{1}{2}$, $m_I = -\frac{1}{2}$, since these levels have not been affected. If a strong radio-frequency field is imposed on the

* Actually, the best results are obtained when one does not completely saturate the EPR signal.

sample at the frequency determined by (22.9), the populations of levels $m_s = \frac{1}{2}$, $m_I = \pm\frac{1}{2}$ are equalized. At that moment, the population distribution is that shown on the right. Now there is a difference between the levels $m_s = \pm\frac{1}{2}$, $m_I = +\frac{1}{2}$ of $\frac{1}{8}n_0\epsilon$, which results in a *microwave* absorption signal. If g_I is known, the measurements give a of (22.5). This in turn determines the wave function at the P nucleus. If g_I is unknown one may obtain two radio-frequency frequencies, one by saturating the upper two levels and the other by saturating the lower two levels. Then, from (22.9) one may calculate both g_I and $\phi^2(0)$.

We have here considered only the possibility of saturating the levels. One may invert the levels by rapid passage, or employ χ' in place of χ''.

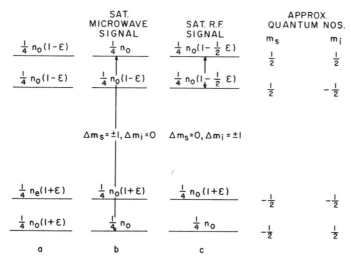

FIG. 22.2. Illustration of what occurs when one saturates the electronic levels and the nuclear levels. The populations are given. This case is the same as in Fig. 22.1, and the same notation is used.

Feher's (1956S) classical experiment was performed on phosphor-doped silicon. He measured χ' and used a rapid passage technique. The temperature was $1.25°$ K; H_0 equaled 3,133 gauss; and ν_e between the $m_I = \frac{1}{2}$ levels were 8,800 mc/sec. The $\nu_{I\alpha}$'s were 53 mc/sec and 11.6 mc/sec, from which Feher calculated a g_I of 2.265 ± 0.004 for P (compared to the accepted values of 2.263) and an a of 0.85 mc, which was in rough agreement with the theoretical calculation.

Equation (22.1) contains only a part of the hyperfine interaction, namely, the contact term. Actually, the other terms should be considered since the electron is not in a pure s-state relative to the surrounding nuclei. We return to Eq. (16.22), label the nuclei by α, to obtain

$$\mathscr{H}(hf) = \beta\beta_I g g_I \left\{ \frac{8\pi}{3} \delta(r_\alpha) \mathbf{s}\cdot\mathbf{i} + \frac{3}{r_\alpha^5}(\mathbf{s}\cdot\mathbf{r}_\alpha)(\mathbf{i}\cdot\mathbf{r}_\alpha) - \frac{1}{r_\alpha^3}\mathbf{s}\cdot\mathbf{i} \right\}. \quad (22.10)$$

$\mathbf{r}_\alpha$ is the distance between the electron and the αth nucleus. The first term has been omitted, since the expectation value of l is zero for real wave functions. This follows since l_z is a pure imaginary operator. If the expectation value of l_z is zero, so is the expectation value of l_x and l_y since one can obtain one from the other by a rotation of an axis. One starts with real wave functions (omit the effects of the magnetic field) and considers terms in the vector potential, $\mathbf{A}$, as a perturbation. The first term of Eq. (22.10) does not depend on the angle, but the second one does. Let us assume that the Zeeman term between $\mathbf{s}$ and the external field is large. This aligns the electron spin along the z-axis. Only the matrix elements $\langle \eta_s | s_z | \eta_s \rangle$ are of importance. It also aligns $\mathbf{i}$ along the external field because the first "isotropic" term is the largest. We omit the small corrections of Section 20 due to Breit and Rabi; hence, the last two terms of (22.10) may be modified by assuming an axis of symmetry for the center, and that $\mathbf{s}$ and $\mathbf{i}$ are along the z-axis. Consider the αth nucleus: let the vector from the center of the imperfection to this nucleus be an axis of rotational symmetry. Let r_α, θ_α, and ϕ_α be the position of the electron relative to this αth nucleus. If the angle between the magnetic field and the axis of symmetry is θ_m and ϕ_m, then

$$\cos\theta = \sin\theta_\alpha \sin\theta_m \cos(\phi_\alpha - \phi_m) + \cos\theta_\alpha \cos\theta_m \quad (22.11)$$

where θ is the angle between $\mathbf{s}$ or $\mathbf{i}$ and $\mathbf{r}_\alpha$. In the square of $\cos\theta$, which arises from $(\mathbf{s}\cdot\mathbf{r})(\mathbf{i}\cdot\mathbf{r})$, in Eq. (22.11) we may average over ϕ_α since it is an axis of symmetry. Hence,

$$\frac{1}{r_\alpha^3}\left\{ \frac{3}{r_\alpha^2}(\mathbf{s}\cdot\mathbf{r}_\alpha)(\mathbf{i}_\alpha\cdot\mathbf{r}_\alpha) - (\mathbf{s}\cdot\mathbf{i}_\alpha) \right\} = s_z i_z(\alpha)(3\cos^2\theta - 1)\frac{1}{r_\alpha^3}$$

$$= \tfrac{1}{2}s_z i_z(\alpha)\{(1 - 3\cos^2\theta_\alpha)(1 - 3\cos^2\theta_m)\}\frac{1}{r_\alpha^3}. \quad (22.12)$$

r_α and θ_α are determined by the position of the electron and the nucleus, and $(1/r_\alpha{}^3)(3\cos^2\theta_\alpha-1)$ must be averaged over the electronic wave function, ϕ. θ_m can be varied by changing the axis of the magnetic field. Hence, the total magnetic Hamiltonian may be written in the approximate form [note $a_\alpha \neq a$ of Eq. (22.5)]

$$\mathscr{H}(\mathrm{mag}) = \beta g H_0 s_z - \sum_a \beta_I g_I H_0 i_z(\alpha)$$

$$+ \sum_a [a_\alpha s_z i_z(\alpha) + s_z i_z(\alpha) b_\alpha (3\cos^2\theta_m - 1)]$$

$$+ \text{quadrupole terms} \tag{22.13}$$

$$a_\alpha = \beta\beta_I g g_I \frac{8\pi}{3} |\phi(\alpha)|^2 \tag{22.13a}$$

$$b_\alpha = \tfrac{1}{2}\beta\beta_I g g_I \left\langle \phi \left| \frac{1}{r_\alpha{}^3}(3\cos^2\theta_\alpha - 1) \right| \phi \right\rangle. \tag{22.13b}$$

$\phi(a)$ is the value of the wave function at the αth nucleus and the expectation value in Eq. (22.13b) is assumed to depend on the nuclear shell but not on the nucleus itself. We are neglecting some small terms in the tensor discussed very briefly in Section 16. These terms have been measured and hence the problem of the hyperfine interaction is somewhat more complicated than presented here. As before, two types of transitions are possible when a high-frequency electromagnetic field is applied at right angles to the z-axis. In the radio-frequency range, $i_z(\alpha)$ can change by unity; s_z changes by unity in the microwave range.

To indicate how this is actually done, assume that the F-center is an electron trapped at a negative-ion vacancy. One saturates only a small portion of the absorption band when applying a microwave signal (at low temperature). This will be discussed more fully in Section 24c. This indicates that only those F-centers where the nuclei are aligned in a particular manner relative to the external field are saturated. Every nucleus about the vacancy can give an ENDOR signal, provided a nuclear flip moves an imperfection from a saturated region of the absorption band to an unsaturated region. The signal from the nearest and next-nearest shell of ions will now be considered.

For this purpose it is useful to use Fig. 22.3, which applies to KCl. In making this figure it was assumed that the ions around V have not been displaced; this is not actually the case. If the electronic wave function ϕ is spherically symmetric, the displacements are radial and the axes of symmetry do not change. This assumption will be made in analyzing the ENDOR results.

There are six nearest neighbors, three of which are shown, and are denoted by K_a, K_b, and K_c. We shall select our axes in such a manner that K_a is at the point $\{1,0,0\}$, K_b is at $\{0,1,0\}$, and K_c is at $\{0,0,1\}$ in units of the distance between nearest neighbors. Vectors of definite length will be denoted by curly brackets, directions by square brackets, and planes by the Miller indices in round brackets. The direction of the external field is given by three direction cosines. H_0 is selected in the $(0,0,1)$ plane (the plane of the ions Cl_A, K_a, Cl_C, and K_b) and one direction cosine is zero. Note that in the case considered here, the z-axis is fixed in the crystal and is not the direction of H_0 or the direction of quantization of the electron spin.

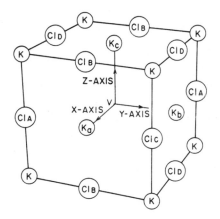

FIG. 22.3. Diagram showing the neighbors of a negative-ion vacancy. No displacement is assumed.

The ENDOR signal can be obtained from Eq. (22.13) by setting $s_z = \pm \frac{1}{2}$, thus the signal due to the αth nucleus is:

$$h\nu_\alpha = \pm \beta_I g_I H_0 + \tfrac{1}{2}a_\alpha + \tfrac{1}{2}b_\alpha(3\cos^2\theta_m - 1) + \text{quadrupole effects.}^*$$

$$(22.14)$$

Every nucleus gives two signals because of the double sign on the first term. Only one will be considered in our analysis, however. The nearest neighbors give three axes of symmetry (a, b, and c), which are the lines joining K_a, K_b, and K_c to the vacancy.

* Quadrupole effects are small and will not be discussed here.

When H_0 is along the x-axis, the angles due to these axes have the values

$$\theta_a = 0, \qquad \theta_b = \pi/2, \qquad \theta_c = \pi/2, \qquad (22.15)$$

and the radio-frequency signals are

$$v_a = \beta_I g_I H_0 + \tfrac{1}{2}a_\alpha + b_\alpha, \qquad v_b = v_c = \beta_I g_I H_0 + \tfrac{1}{2}a_\alpha - \tfrac{1}{2}b_\alpha. \quad (22.16)$$

When the angle between the x-axis and H_0 is θ (in the x-y plane), then

$$\theta_a = 0, \qquad \theta_b = \pi/2 - \theta, \qquad \theta_c = \pi/2 \qquad (22.17)$$

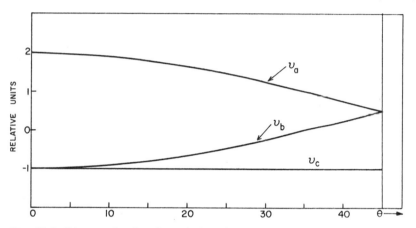

FIG. 22.4. Diagram showing the variation of v_a, v_b, and v_c as a function of θ for the simplest orientation.

and the following three signals are obtained:

$$v_a = \beta_I g_I H_0 + \tfrac{1}{2}a_\alpha + \tfrac{1}{2}b_\alpha(3\cos^2\theta - 1)$$
$$v_b = \beta_I g_I H_0 + \tfrac{1}{2}a_\alpha + \tfrac{1}{2}b_\alpha(3\sin^2\theta - 1)$$
$$v_c = \beta_I g_I H_0 + \tfrac{1}{2}a_\alpha - \tfrac{1}{2}b_\alpha. \qquad (22.18)$$

At the extreme where $\theta = \pi/4$, we again have two signals, since $v_a = v_b$. For $\theta > \pi/4$ the pattern repeats itself (see Fig. 22.4).

When one considers the next-nearest neighbors the problem becomes slightly more complex. We note that 12 nuclei are involved and that there are six axes of symmetry. When H_0 is in the $(0,0,1)$ plane, however, two sets are equivalent and this reduces the number to four. These are the axes that involve Cl_A, Cl_B (twice), Cl_C, and Cl_D (twice) in Fig. 22.3.

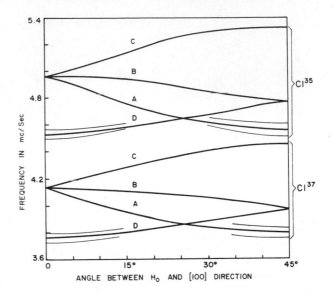

FIG. 22.5. The ENDOR signal as a function of the angle between the [100] and the external magnetic field. The data is for the F-center in KCl (produced by 1-Mev electrons). The secondary lines are due to isotope effects not discussed here (after Feher, 1957S).

The direction cosines of the various axes of symmetry are given by:

Axes	Direction cosines
A	$\dfrac{1}{\sqrt{2}},\ -\dfrac{1}{\sqrt{2}},\ 0$
B	$\dfrac{1}{\sqrt{2}},\ 0,\ \dfrac{1}{\sqrt{2}}$ and $-\dfrac{1}{\sqrt{2}},\ 0,\ \dfrac{1}{\sqrt{2}}$
C	$\dfrac{1}{\sqrt{2}},\ \dfrac{1}{\sqrt{2}},\ 0$
D	$0,\ \dfrac{1}{\sqrt{2}},\ \dfrac{1}{\sqrt{2}}$ or $0,\ -\dfrac{1}{\sqrt{2}},\ \dfrac{1}{\sqrt{2}}.$ (22.19)

When H_0 has the direction cosines 1, 0, 0, and θ_m in Eq. (22.13) has the values

$$\theta_A = \pi/4, \quad \theta_B = \pi/4, \quad \theta_C = \pi/4, \quad \theta_D = \pi/2 \qquad (22.20)$$

two points on the ENDOR pattern appear. If the direction between H_0 and the x-axis is θ, then one obtains the set of equations:

$$\cos^2 \theta_A = \tfrac{1}{2}(\cos \theta - \sin \theta)^2$$
$$\cos^2 \theta_B = \tfrac{1}{2}\cos^2 \theta$$
$$\cos^2 \theta_C = \tfrac{1}{2}(\cos \theta + \sin \theta)^2$$
$$\cos^2 \theta_D = \tfrac{1}{2}\sin^2 \theta. \tag{22.21}$$

Plots obtained from Eq. (22.21) for the F-center in KCl are shown in Fig. 22.5 from the calculation and measurements of Feher (1957S). Two sets are obtained, one for Cl^{35} (75% abundant) and the other for Cl^{37} (25% abundant). The extra lines in curve D are due to quadrupole effects, which have not been discussed.

REFERENCES

G. Feher, *Phys. Rev.* **103**, 834 (1956).
G. Feher, *Phys. Rev.* **105**, 1122 (1957).
W. Kohn, *Solid State Physics* **5**, 257 (1957).

VIII. Experimental Results on the Magnetic Properties of the F-Center

23. THE STATIC PARAMAGNETIC SUSCEPTIBILITY

An uncolored alkali halide is diamagnetic and theory predicts that its susceptibility will be negative and temperature independent (see Fowler and Guggenheim, p. 614). During the coloration, the F-center is introduced into the crystal. As we shall see, the electron is effectively captured in a ground s-state so that there is no orbital paramagnetism. The contribution due to the unpaired spin can be obtained from Eq. (17.1). If one lets $\tanh x = x$, then

$$\chi_0 = \frac{1}{4} n_0 \frac{\beta^2 g^2}{k\theta} = \frac{n_0 \beta^2}{k\theta} \tag{23.1}*$$

where g has been set equal to 2. Thus, a measurement of χ_0 gives a direct means of determining n_0. This measurement can be used with Smakula's equation (Section 4) to evaluate the oscillator strength.

The uncolored KCl has a mass susceptibility of -0.5×10^{-6} emu/gm or -0.97×10^{-6} emu/cm^3 which is temperature independent (Heer and Rauch, S). In a crystal with 10^{18} F-centers, χ_0 increased to -0.38×10^{-6} at $1°$ K; the incremental increase is only 0.059×10^{-6} at $10°$ K. Since the value of the susceptibility of the holder may be many times that of the crystal, colored or uncolored, the measurements are difficult and require great care.

An additional problem is that the crystal has to be handled completely in the dark. If additive coloration is employed, quenching is most important (see Sections 3 and 6). In improperly handled samples, other imperfections occur that do not obey Eq. (23.1). These imperfections may contribute to the optical absorption in the F-region of the spectra, making a simple comparison between Smakula's equation and Eq. (23.1) impossible. Unfortunately, the method of handling the sample was unknown

---

* n_0 of this chapter equals N_0 in Section 3.

at the time when most of the magnetic susceptibilities measurements were made; hence, we do not have completely reliable static measurements.*

The major work in this field has been done by Jensen (S); Scott, Hrostowski, and Bupp (S); Sonders (S); and by Heer and co-workers (S). The most complete study is due to Heer's group, and our material will be drawn from these studies.

The measured additional susceptibility associated with an additively colored sample of KCl is given by

$$\chi_0 = 3 \times 10^{-8} + 1.36 \times 10^{-6}/\theta \qquad \text{in emu/cm}^3. \qquad (23.2)$$

Measurements were made with a Gouy balance between 1° K and 300° K (for details see Bates, S). Heer and Rauch assumed that the second term in Eq. (23.2) arises from Eq. (23.1) and that one may evaluate n_0 by using the known values of β and k in this equation. Using these equations we see that the numerical factor in the second term can be written in the following form:

$$C = \frac{1}{4}\frac{\beta^2 g^2}{k} n_0 = 6.23 \times 10^{-25} n_0. \qquad (23.3)\dagger$$

The experimental range of the validity of Eq. (23.2) is considerable and the data between 1° K and 10° K follow this equation very well. The data of Heer and Rauch have been reproduced in Fig. 23.1.

These researchers believe that the first term in Eq. (23.2) arises from a change in the diamagnetic susceptibility when color centers are present. In additively colored KCl, the change is positive, while in LiF the change is negative. (See Rauch, S.)

Rauch and Heer (S) have established a one-to-one correspondence between n_0 obtained by Smakula's formula and by (23.3). Indeed, by combining the two they have determined f of Eq. (4.14). They worked with a number of additively colored crystals and showed that this approach is self-consistent and gives reasonable values. It is in this manner that parts of Tables 4.1 and 4.2 were obtained.

---

* An example which the author can quote is in the work of Silsbee (S). His source of additively colored crystals was the author, and at the time the crystals were prepared, the author's laboratory did not quench or handle the crystals properly. Hence, some of the samples used by Silsbee did not contain "pure" *F*-centers. Actually Silsbee's measurements were made with an EPR technique, but the same situation must have existed in most (probably all) the static measurements. The additive-coloration procedure of Heer and co-worker as described seems to be satisfactory. See, however, Rauch and Heer (S, Fig. 5), and Konitzer and Markham (S, Fig. 4).

† The actual coefficient used was 6.18×10^{-25}.

The above calculations assume that $g = 2$, which would be expected if the electron were in an s-state. If the electron is in a p-state,* $^2P_{3/2}$, the Lande's g-factor would be 4/3 and the numerical value of (23.3) would decrease to 2.8×10^{-25}. It would be 0.69×10^{-25} if $J = 1/2$, which gives a g-factor of 2/3. For further details see Condon and Shortley, p. 149. This change would be reflected in a marked decrease of f in the tables.

The work of Heer (see Reid, S) indicates that f is identical for additively and for x-ray-colored KCl (result quoted in Bates and Heer, S). The irradiation was done at room temperature. A similar effect was reported

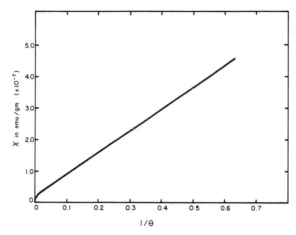

Fig. 23.1. Excess magnetic susceptibility of an additively colored KCl crystal (after Heer and Rauch, S).

by Sonders, who also irradiated his crystals at room temperature. This indicates that no new magnetic centers are introduced during the process of x-irradiation at high temperatures. Since V-centers are produced in addition to the F-centers during x-irradiation (Section 14c), these data show that the V-centers formed at room temperatures are nonparamagnetic.

In view of the recent paramagnetic resonance techniques, one might assume that the static magnetic measurements do not add much to the picture. This is hardly the case, since the work of Heer and his students has rounded out our knowledge of color centers and added an important and beautiful chapter to the field.

One must only hope that someone will repeat the work of Heer and co-workers with crystals that have been handled with greater care. This

* Here we assume that $\mathscr{H}(so)$ is large.

in no way reflects on the work that has been done, since at the time the measurements were made, no one understood the problems of handling crystals.

REFERENCES

L. F. Bates, "Modern Magnetism," p. 115. Cambridge Univ. Press, London and New York, 1951.
R. T. Bates and C. V. Heer, *Phys. Chem. Solids* **7**, 14 (1958).
C. V. Heer and C. Rauch, *Phys. Rev.* **90**, 530 (1953).
P. Jensen, *Ann. Phys.* **34**, 161 (1939).
J. D. Konitzer and J. J. Markham, *J. Chem. Phys.* **32**, 843 (1960).
C. J. Rauch, Ph.D. Thesis, Ohio State University, 1953.
C. J. Rauch and C. V. Heer, *Phys. Rev.* **105**, 914 (1957).
F. J. Reid, M.S.Thesis,Ohio State University, 1957.
A. B. Scott, H. J. Hrostowski, and L. P. Bupp, *Phys. Rev.* **79**, 346 (1950).
R. H. Silsbee, *Phys. Rev.* **103**, 1675 (1956).
E. Sonders, *Phys. Rev.* **125**, 1203 (1962).

24. ELECTRON PARAMAGNETIC RESONANCE

In this section we summarize our experimental knowledge of the EPR properties of the ground state of the *F*-center. Experimental studies currently are being made on the excited state or states; these, however, are too recent to be included here. One might assume that the properties are simple and well known. This is so if one is interested in only the most elementary properties of the center; it is certainly not true if one desires a full understanding of all the physical properties. Here a great deal remains to be done. We are not even sure what the concepts of T_1 and T_2 mean. The saturation properties of χ' and χ'' have been studied primarily in KCl. The effect of optical bleaching on the EPR behavior is also mainly limited to this alkali halide. These limitations have the advantage of enabling one to compare the results of various laboratories. They have the very great disadvantage of limiting our knowledge too much. It is interesting to note that the most detailed studies come from Cornell and the solid state laboratory of Zenith Radio Corporation, although the most basic ideas did not originate at either place.

The EPR properties of the *F*-center have in recent years become a complex and involved field. This section is therefore subdivided into parts, beginning with a general survey of the problem.

a. General Features of Electron Paramagnetic Resonance

One might suspect that electron paramagnetic resonance (EPR) associated with the F-center could be studied in a simple and straightforward fashion. This view motivated much of the early work on EPR of F-centers; there are, however, several experimental problems involved. First, one must establish that the EPR signal does indeed arise from the electrons that produce the optical absorption or the photoconductivity described earlier. Good optical work requires densities of the order of 10^{16} centers/cm^3, whereas the simplest EPR measurements require concentrations of the order of 10^{18} or 10^{19}. Most alkali halides used so far have had magnetic impurities that could give signals comparable to those found in lightly colored crystals (10^{16}), and it requires special care to separate the absorption or dispersion signal of the F-center from the background. Studies of highly colored crystals lead to problems since optical measurements are impossible. One may establish the presence of color centers, but one may not determine the "purity" of the F-centers, since the absorption at the peak of the band is too large to measure. The impurity concentration in alkali halides is unknown. An early report (see Duerig and co-worker, S) suggested it was large. A later report, on the other hand, suggests that the crystals are much purer (see Anderson and co-workers, S). The later results may be more reliable, since Duerig and Markham did not test the impurity in the best Harshaw crystals; on the other hand, the method of analysis may be responsible for the disparate results.

A classic example of the foregoing problem (finding EPR signals that are not related to the F-center) is found in the work of Bleaney and Hayes (S). They irradiated NaF with γ-rays from a Co^{60} source at 40° C. One would suspect that F-centers would be formed during this exposure, and that they could be detected by EPR techniques. Actually the crystal's color is pink after an electron irradiation. Before irradiation there was an EPR signal with $g = 4.28$, whereas after the irradiation there was an isotropic signal at $g = 4.344$. The second absorption line appeared after an electron irradiation plus one with $g = 1.998$. The line was measured at 90° K. The authors suggest that the signal at about $g = 4.3$ is due to an impurity, such as Fe$^+$. They further believed that they did not detect the F-center and that the signal at $g = 1.998$ was due to Cr$^+$ ions in the crystals. The g-factor for the F-center in NaF seems to be very close to the second value they measured. Another illustration of this problem comes from the studies of Noble (1959S) in KI. It will be discussed in detail later.

The first reliable (EPR) measurement on high-concentration samples was made by Hutchison and Noble (S). This study was extended by the very beautiful work of Kip, Kittel, Levy, and Portis (S) and by Portis (S) (the Berkeley group). The first work on dilutely colored samples (optical range) has been done by Noble (1959S). In addition, there have been many other workers.

In Fig. 24.1 the derivative of the absorption signal in slow passage due to *F*-centers in KI is shown. The y-axis is proportional to $d\chi''/dH_0$, while the x-axis is almost exactly proportional to the magnetic field H_0. Exact

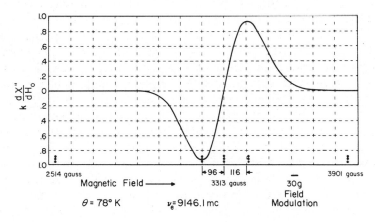

FIG. 24.1. The derivative of the EPR signal (χ'') for the *F*-center in KI (additively colored) taken during slow passage; k is a constant (after Noble, 1959S).

calculations of the field, however, are done from markers, as shown in the figure. The general criterion for rapid adiabatic passage was developed in Section 17. Using Eqs. (17.34) and (17.35) we obtain:

$$\frac{1}{T_2} \ll \frac{1}{H_1}\dot{H}_0 \ll |\gamma H_1|. \tag{24.1}$$

Some typical values for an *F*-center in KCl are:

$$T_2 \approx 10^{-4} \quad \text{sec}; \qquad \dot{H}_0 = 400 \quad \text{gauss/sec};$$

$$H_1 = \text{from } 6 \times 10^{-4} \text{ to } 6 \times 10^{-2} \quad \text{gauss};$$

$$\gamma = 2.80 \times 10^7 \quad (g = 2).$$

A substitution into (24.1) indicates that the first inequality to the left is fulfilled for smaller values of H_1 but the second is not. This really means

TABLE 24.1 ABSORPTION WIDTH AND g OF VARIOUS CRYSTALS

Crystal	Crystal structure	g	Width (gauss)[a]	Reference (S)
LiF	(NaCl)	1.987	Resolved	Wolga and Strandberg
		2.0029	Hyperfine structure	Lord (1957a)
		2.007		Hyde
		2.0014[b]		Holton and Blum
LiCl	(NaCl)	1.9970	67.5	Holton and Blum
NaF	(NaCl)	1.996	Resolved	Wolga and Strandberg
		2.0023	Hyperfine structure	Lord (1957a)
		2.0011		Holton and Blum
NaCl	(NaCl)	1.987	162	Kip et al.
		2.0011	168	Holton and Blum
NaBr	(NaCl)	1.994	353	Holton and Blum
KCl	(NaCl)	1.995	54 ± 2	Kip et al.
Natural		1.995	58	Hutchison and Noble
		1.995		Holton and Blum
93% K^{39}		1.996	54.9	Noble and Markham
7% K^{41}		1.994	58.5	Kawamura and Ishiwatari
		1.996	53	Moran et al.
K^{41}Cl	(NaCl)	1.995	36	Kip et al.
KBr	(NaCl)	1.980	146	Kip et al.
		1.986	146	Noble
		1.980	152	Hyde
		1.986	153	Holton and Blum
KI	(NaCl)	1.970	251	Noble (1959)
RbCl	(NaCl)		Resolved structure	Wolf and Hausser
RbBr	(NaCl)	2 (approx.)	450	Wolf and Hausser
RbI	(NaCl)	2 (approx.)	750	Wolf and Hausser
CsCl	(CsCl)	1.984	800 (approx.) Resolved structure	Hughes and Allard

[a] The ratio between the width to the separation of the points of maximum slope is 1.18 for a Gaussian curve.
[b] Corrected 2.0005.

that we go through the line too rapidly for " rapid passage." This play on words arises because there are two inequalities and the process must be adiabatic in the quantum mechanical sense. In Section 17 we saw that one may go through the absorption by neither rapid nor slow passage.

The reported data are summarized in Table 24.1. The conclusion from the table is that values of the width and *g* are known for KCl, KBr, and KI. Variations of several parts per thousand are to be expected. Noble's study on KI seems sufficiently extensive to warrant our accepting the reliability of his results at present. Differences as large as those reported

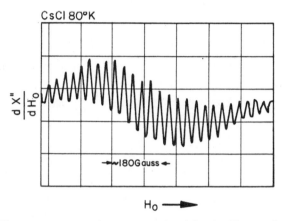

CsCl 80°K

$\dfrac{d\,X''}{d\,H_0}$

←~180Gauss→

H_0 ⟶

FIG. 24.2. Electron paramagnetic resonance signal for the *F*-center in CsCl, during slow passage. *F*-centers formed by electron bombardment (2-Mev electrons). The measurements were made at 80° K (after Hughes and Allard, S).

on NaCl, LiF, and NaF must be ascribed to poor experimental techniques. Probably some of the measurements were made on centers that were not "pure." The most recent measurements and corrections of Holton and Blum (S) seem to resolve this problem. The data of Wolga and Strandberg (S) may be questioned.

When would one expect hyperfine structure? Consider Eq. (20.5), where a_1 refers to the interaction between the trapped electron and the nearest neighbor nuclei; a_2 refers to the next-nearest neighbor, etc. If $a_j = 0$ for $j > 1$, then one would expect to observe 19 lines. According to the calculations of Kittel and Abrahams, one knows that these lines will be narrow. The breadth of these lines must be attributed to nonvanishing values of a_j for $j > 1$ or to a large T_2 which does not come from Van Vleck's theory (see Section 18c). If a_2 is not small, the single lines due to a_1 will be resolved into 37 lines. Here we are assuming that the spin of the nearest twelve negative ions is 3/2, which is approximately true for the alkali halides with a NaCl structure (see Table 16.2). It is interesting to note that one obtains either well-resolved lines or lines that cannot be resolved at all. The best data on a resolved line seem to be those reported by Hughes and Allard (CsCl), shown in Fig. 24.2.

TABLE 24.2. COMPARISON OF CALCULATED EPR ABSORPTION
WIDTH WITH EXPERIMENTAL VALUES

| Crystal | Width (gauss) | |
	Measured	Calculated[a]
LiCl	68	90 (Li[7])
NaCl	165	190
NaBr	353	240
KBr	146	150
KI	251	280
RbBr	450 (natural)	360 (Rb[85])
		750 (Rb[87])
RbI	750 (natural)	440 (Rb[85])
		790 (Rb[87])
CsCl	800 (approx.)	1020

[a] After Kittel (S).

Kip *et al.*, as stated in Section 20, used the values of the width given in Table 24.1 for KCl and K[41]Cl to calculate the a's, assuming that the breadth is due to only the nearest and next-nearest neighbors (Eq. 20.7 and Table 20.2). Subsequently Kittel (S) estimated the a's for other alkali halides by considering the changes of the nuclear charge and the nuclear magnetic moment. Table 24.2 gives some of his calculated widths and compares them with the actual measured values. From this table we conclude that the width can be understood on the basis of the theory developed in Section 20.

Some features of the resonance signal have been established by Noble. These are summarized in Tables 24.3 and 24.4. These data indicate that g is temperature independent. Since $\Delta g = g - g_e$ is the important quantity, these variations require an explanation which, as far as the author knows, has not been given.

It is interesting to note that no one has attempted to establish a one-to-one correspondence between the optical signal and the intensity of the EPR signal. This is a very important point and it has been established

TABLE 24.3. *g* AS A FUNCTION OF TEMPERATURE

Temperature (°K)	*g*-Factor
KI:[a]	
300	1.969 ± 0.001
78	1.970 ± 0.001
5	1.971 ± 0.001
KCl:[b]	
300	1.9964 ± 0.0005
78	1.9964 ± 0.0005

[a] From Noble (1959S).
[b] From Noble and Markham (S).

indirectly. Noble has shown that this is roughly true in KI, and Silsbee (S) has calculated the optical oscillator strength after determining N_0 in Eq. (4.14) (see Table 4.1). There is little question that there is a one-to-one correspondence between the two types of signals.

TABLE 24.4. EFFECT OF NEXT-NEAREST NEIGHBOR OF g^a

Host crystal	*g*-Factor
KCl	1.996
KBr	1.986
KI	1.970

[a] From Noble (1959S).

b. The Saturation at High Temperatures

One of the most interesting features of the EPR of the *F*-center is its saturation. Figure 24.3 shows what happens when more power is applied to the F-center in KI, that is, h_1 of Eq. (17.3) is increased.* The data were taken on an additively colored crystal whose temperature was 4° K. The total attenuation between klystron, which generated h_1, and the recorder was constant. The signal on the left resulted when the total power of the klystron fell on the cavity with the colored crystal (no attenuation between the klystron and the sample). The signals 10, 20, and 30 db correspond to the situation where the signal is attenuated by the respective amounts before it reaches the sample. The figure indicates that at high signal

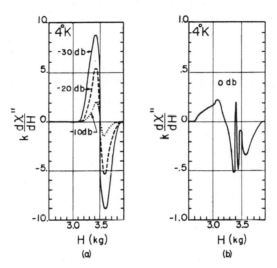

FIG. 24.3. Effects of saturation on the F-center in KI (additively colored). Measurements were made during slow passage at 4° K; k is an arbitrary constant (after Noble, 1959S).

intensity one does not detect F-centers at all, but uncovers another resonance. At low signal intensity a well-resolved and well-formed signal appears.

As stated, Noble (1959S) has been able to show a rough correlation between the EPR signal and the number of F-centers in KI measured optically, thus establishing the fact that the EPR signal shown in Fig. 24.1 indeed comes from the F-centers. If one does not use proper care, the F-center signal might be associated with the resonance on the right. Many

---

* The words "high" and "low" refer to the behavior of the F-center in KCl, since most of the work on saturation has been done on this crystal. KI has a "high" temperature behavior even at 4° K.

electron traps have g values of approximately 2; hence, there is a tendency for EPR signals from different centers to fall on top of each other. The theoretical reason for this is that the ground state of many imperfections is an almost pure s-state or $< |l_z1| > = 0$.

One would naturally like to explore the behavior of χ' and χ'' as a function of h_1 to see how well the theory developed in Section 21 applies. Equation (21.10) assumes that H_0, as well as ω and h_1, are held constant. Unfortunately this is impossible from the experimental point of view, and one must modulate h_1, as was done by Portis (S), or H_0, as was done by Seidel and Wolf (S), Moran, Christensen, and Silsbee (S), and Noble and Markham (S).* Portis modulated h_1 at a moderately high frequency (6 kc/sec); the modulation amplitude was 100%. The two other groups modulated H_0 at low frequency (35 cps with an amplitude of 16 gauss for the Cornell group). Noble used a frequency of 25 cps and varied his amplitude. He also used "square" waves to sweep rapidly over the absorption band.

All the data in the remaining part of this section are for the F-center in KCl.

We have described two solutions of the Bloch equation, one being adiabatic rapid passage (Sections 17*a* and *b*). The criteria (24.1) should inform us if we have the condition of rapid passage or not. In many experiments H_0 is too large (or H_1 is too small), so that the second inequality does not hold. The Cornell group used H_1 as high as 1 gauss, in which case the inequality on the right holds, but the one on the left does not, and again one does not have the condition for rapid passage. Here we are assuming that $T_2 \approx 10^{-4}$ sec and that it is a meaningful or definable quantity; this may not actually be the case.

If (24.1) does not apply, the actual measured energy absorbed is given by first-order perturbation theory or by Eq. (21.3), namely,

$$(dn/dt)_{mf} = -(\pi/4)\gamma^2 H_1{}^2 g_s n(t) \tag{24.2}$$

the appropriate χ'' being obtained from Eq. (17.24). Equation (24.2) is essentially different from the theory in Section 17 in that $n(t)$ is not determined by an equilibrium condition but by the past history of the sample. When T_1 becomes of the order of the frequency of the wobbling magnetic field, then n can be very much dependent on the past history of the sample. This fact was first established and studied by Noble (1960S). His results will now briefly be described.

---

* The second group (Moran *et al.*) will be referred to by the name "Cornell," while the third group will go by the name "Noble."

Figure (24.4a) illustrates the problem of hyperfine broadening. The shape of the individual multiplets is given by g_s with an effective width W. The over-all distribution of the g_s's is given by h (see Section 21).

When no saturation occurs, we should display a portion of h on an oscilloscope, as illustrated in Fig. 24.4b. Actually one most commonly measures $d\chi''/dH_0$ for various values of H_0. It is possible, however, to

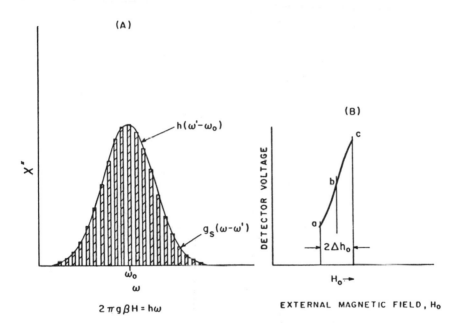

$2\pi g\beta H = h\omega$ EXTERNAL MAGNETIC FIELD, H_0

FIG. 24.4. (A) A schematic diagram showing the line made up of sums of many multiplets. The curve, $h(\omega' - \omega_0)$ is the envelope function or line shape. In the actual case, there are many more multiplets, $g_s(\omega - \omega')$ are distributed continuously and each multiplet is bell-shaped. (B) A schematic representation showing that the detector voltage is proportional to a segment of the χ''-curve (after Noble and Markham, S).

measure χ'' as a function of H_0 for a fixed ω. This is done by observing the output of the intermediate frequency amplifier by means of an oscilloscope. When saturation occurs, one no longer obtains voltages proportional to $d\chi''/dH_0$, since it depends on the past history and care must be employed to obtain the true $h(\omega - \omega_0)$ of Section 21 [$n(t) \neq n$ of (21.5)].

In the first experiments of Noble, a sinusoidal sweep was used and hence, more microwave energy was absorbed by the crystal at the extremes of the sweep at (a) and (c) than at the center (b) (see Fig. 24.4(B)).

The sweep is such that the net external field is of the form

$$H_0 = h_0(t) + \Delta h_0 \sin \Omega t, \qquad (24.3)$$

where $h_0(t)$ is the field on the sample due to the large external magnet, while $\Delta h_0 \sin \Omega t$ is generated by coils. h_0 was varied slowly in a linear fashion. This variation, however, will be ignored. The time a multiplet is in resonance at H_0 is given by

$$\Delta t = \frac{dt}{dH_0} W = \frac{1}{\cos \Omega t_0} \frac{W}{\Delta h_0} \frac{1}{\Omega}. \qquad (24.4)$$

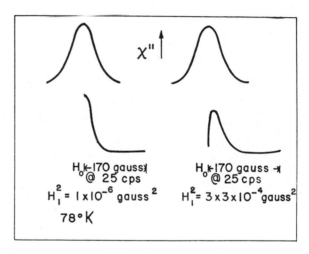

FIG. 24.5. Photographs made of the oscilloscope displays showing χ'' as a function of H_0 for large sinusoidal field modulation. Data taken on the F-center in KCl (additively colored) at 78° K, concentration 3.8×10^{17} cm^{-3} (after Noble and Markham, S).

The values Ωt_0 appropriate to a given set of F-centers are determined by the microwave frequency, the local field, and the external field of the magnet; h_0 must have the values so that the usual frequency condition is obeyed, namely, $\hbar \omega_0 = g\beta H_0$. When $\cos \Omega t_0 = 0$, Δt must be obtained by an integration over W and it is finite. In general, the energy a multiplet receives is proportional to $H_1{}^2$ and the time the field stays at the resonance frequency.

For the F-center, very large saturation can occur in a narrow portion of the resonance, as Fig. 24.5 demonstrates. Here the sweep is large compared to the width of the resonance line. The top tracings were made when the centers of the modulation and the resonance coincided, whereas the bottom ones were obtained with the field shifted to bring an extreme portion of the sweep to the center of the line. The tracings on the left are at low power; those on the right are at high power.

The lower right-hand curve indicates that the slowly changing field at the extremes of the sweep saturates a narrow portion of the line. This proves that the multiplets are narrow and that only a small fraction of the energy diffuses to other imperfections; otherwise the whole resonance would be saturated and the line would not be distorted.* We believe, therefore, that the spin diffusion time is long compared to the sweep time used here.

A further study of the problem was made by changing the field modulation to a trapezoidal waveform with rounded corners. H_0 stayed at each extreme almost all the time. Figure 24.6 shows the plots of the absorption against the field. The time average field was at one of the points of maximum slope of the line. At low powers the tracing is a good representation of a portion of the absorption curve (see Fig. 24.5). At moderate powers the tracings do not overlap and depend on the direction of traverse. As the sweep approaches the low field extreme the spin multiplets are relatively unsaturated but quickly saturate as the field is held on resonance. As the field moves off resonance, the absorption curve is not retraced because the energy has been transferred from saturated spins to some that resonate at a slightly different field.† The same effect occurs at the other extreme of the sweep. The reason a similar displacement of the traces did not occur in the sinusoidal modulation is that the saturation of the extremes was less and the time was too short for "diffusion" to occur. These measurements establish the fact that some energy diffusion occurs away from a saturated region and is evidence of spin diffusion.

In view of these effects, the saturation factor is not constant over the modulated field. The measured susceptibility depends on Δh_0 and Ω, as well as h_0. It seems valid to assume that for the sinusoidal modulation the following conditions apply: (1) there is no energy diffusion into the multiplets from spins that resonate at higher or lower fields; and (2) T_1 is smaller that π/Ω, so that the measured susceptibility does not depend on the past history of the multiplets (that is, the direction of traverse). This is true for the Cornell work, and for that of Noble when he was using a

---

* It is possible that the local field at a given saturated imperfection might change due to nuclear spin-flips.

† Perhaps the nuclear spins flip and the local field changes. We are not sure that actual diffusion takes place.

sinusoidal sweep for measurements above liquid helium temperatures. An entirely new problem occurs at low temperatures; it will be discussed in Section 24c. Moreover, this is restricted to measurements on KCl—the only *F*-center that has been studied in any real detail.

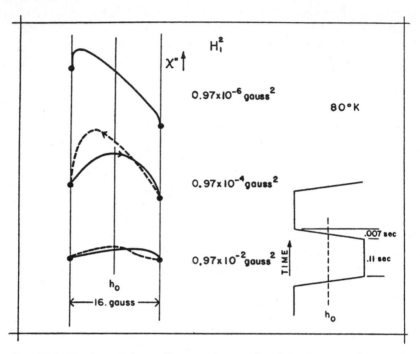

FIG. 24.6. Tracings of the oscilloscope photographs of the detector voltage against linear field modulation. The system was sensitive to the direct-current component and the modulation is shown on the abscissa. The right curve shows the periodic field modulation. Data taken on the *F*-center in KCl (additively colored), concentration 3.8×10^{17} cm^{-3} at 80° K (after Noble and Markham, S).

The energy absorbed by a multiplet as the field passes by is proportional to $H_1{}^2$ multiplied by the time it takes to pass through the multiplet. The time to go from $h_0 - \frac{1}{2}W$ to $h_0 + \frac{1}{2}W$, when $\Omega t = 0$ is determined from the relation

$$\Delta h_0 \sin\left(\tfrac{1}{2}\Omega\Delta t\right) = W/2 \tag{24.5}$$

or

$$\Delta t = W/\Delta h_0 \Omega, \tag{24.5a}$$

since W is small.

At $\Omega t = \pi/2$ the time to go from $h_0 + \Delta h_0 - \frac{1}{2}W$ to $h_0 + \Delta h_0$ and back is determined by the equation

$$h_0 + \Delta h_0 - \tfrac{1}{2}W = h_0 + \Delta h_0 \sin[(\pi/2) - \tfrac{1}{2}\Omega \Delta t]. \qquad (24.6)$$

It is

$$\frac{2}{\Omega}\left[\frac{W}{\Delta h_0}\right]^{1/2}, \qquad (24.6a)$$

since

$$\frac{2}{\Omega}\cos^{-1}\left[1 - \frac{W}{2\,\Delta h_0}\right] = \frac{4}{\Omega}\sin^{-1}\left(\frac{W}{4\,\Delta h_0}\right)^{1/2}. \qquad (24.6b)$$

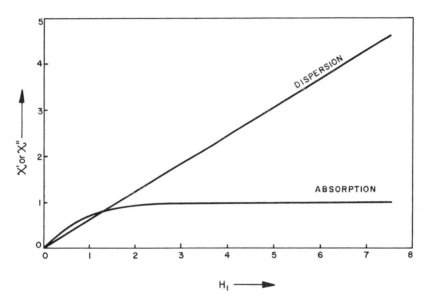

FIG. 24.7. A Portis plot of the saturation of χ' and χ'' for the F-center in KCl. For units, see original paper (after Portis, S).

The important difference between (24.5a) and (24.6a) is that the amount of energy fed into the spins is "linear" at h_0 but not at $h_0 \pm \Delta h_0$. When the sweeps are linear, one would expect that Portis's equation would apply. The first derivative is determined by values of χ'' about h_0, and one would therefore expect that one may measure $d\chi''/dH_0$ by the usual technique of sweeping through the field sinusoidally. Noble's experimental studies of the shape of $d\chi''/dH_0$ as a function of Δh_0 support this view.

What does one measure? At least two possibilities exist: (1) T_1 is short compared to the sweep period and the system completely recovers between the time it absorbs energy; and (2) T_1 is long and the system only partially recovers. The first situation seems to apply for KCl at about $30°$ K and above, for the sweep frequency employed, whereas the second certainly applies at $5°$ K. In the second case, Portis's equation must be employed with caution and a whole set of new phenomena occurs.

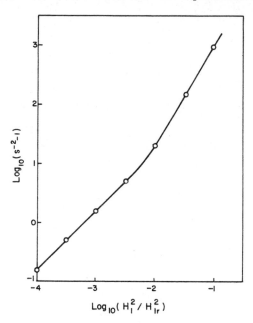

FIG. 24.8a. The saturation curve for *F*-centers in KCl (additively colored) at liquid nitrogen temperature and at a relatively low concentration. Concentration, 4×10^{17}cm^{-3} $H_{1r} = 0.17$ gauss; temperature of measurements, $77°$ K (after Noble and Markham, S).

Three sets of saturation data will now be presented. The first is due to Portis (S) (Fig. 24.7) and indicates that χ'' follows the prediction of Eq. (21.13) and that χ' does not saturate as expected from the discussion of that section. The other data on KCl show a droop in the Portis plot and indicate that the *F*-center does not obey the equation completely. Blumberg (S) studied the saturation in NaCl and showed that Eq. (21.13) applies. The difference between the data may be due to the difference in the methods of detection. Portis and Blumberg, however, studied the saturation over a smaller range of power.

In Figs. 24.8a and b, we present Noble's data on a Noble plot. While it is not evident from a comparison of the data in the literature, because of the different type of plots employed, Noble's data agree quite well with those of the Cornell group. One should note in particular the break in the curve

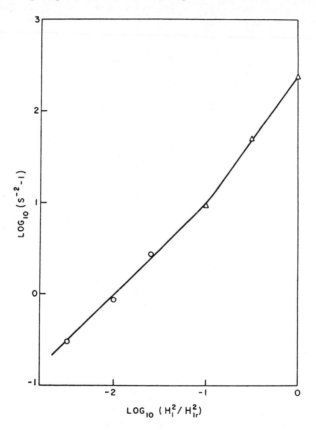

FIG. 24.8b. The saturation plot for the F-centers in KCl (additively colored) at room temperature and at a relatively high concentration. Concentration of F-centers, 4×10^{18} cm^{-3} $H_{1r} = 0.2$ gauss; temperature of measurements, $300°$ K; points indicate different runs (after Noble and Markham, S).

which indicates that Portis's integration applies only approximately. This was the motivation for the analysis under item 3 of Section 21. We believe that the spin-packet is narrow and that the analysis of Castner does not apply. Noble's studies were made at room temperature and below (above $5°$ K, however). Using these plots one may obtain the product $T_1 T_2$,

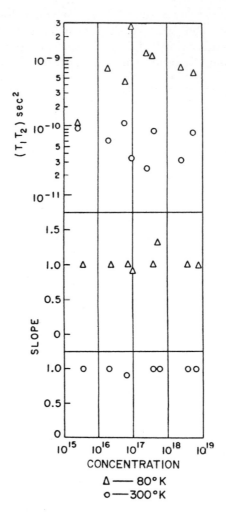

Fig. 24.9. The product of $T_1 T_2$ and the slope on a Noble plot as a function of concentration. The data is for the F-center in KCl (additively colored) (after Noble and Markham, S).

which appears in the various saturation equations. This assumes that the slope for low mf power is unity. A summary of the study of Noble is presented in Fig. 24.9 for measurements at 80° K and 300° K. This product seems to be concentration independent, although the scatter of points is large. This suggests that T_2 is due to some type of Bloch broadening. A fuller discussion must wait until we study the saturation behavior in the liquid helium region.

It is evident that Portis's integration of his equation [i.e., Eq. (21.13)], does not hold for the F-center in KCl at room and liquid nitrogen temperatures. One cannot tell, from the saturation data alone, if Castner's equation or that of Noble and co-worker actually applies. The behavior of the absorption during the sinusoidal and square pulse sweeps indicates that the multiplets are narrow and that the second approach is more appropriate for the F-center in KCl. Actually the saturation is described only approximately by Eq. (21.24) and this is not the final form; further theoretical work is required. From Portis's data one may conclude that χ' behaves as expected: it does not saturate.

c. Saturation at Liquid Helium Temperatures

At liquid helium temperatures the spin-lattice relaxation time for the F-center in KCl approaches the response time of the experimentalist and it is possible to study a new set of problems. They most probably exist at higher temperatures, but would require special equipment that could measure the rapid recovery times.* Two studies have been made, by Ohlsen (S) at Cornell (see also Ohlsen and Holcomb, S) and by Noble (1960S). We shall limit our study to Ohlsen's thesis and Noble's published work. Noble is in the process of making a detailed investigation of these phenomena, but these data will not be included. Further studies are being made at Stuttgart and at Cornell.

From Figs. 24.5 and 24.6 one would suspect that by increasing T_1 (lowering the temperature) one should be able to increase the hole in the diagram to the right of Fig. 24.5 or the middle diagram in Fig. 24.6. This is indeed the case, as was shown first by Noble (1960S) working at 5° K. The essence of Noble's experiment is to modulate in the manner indicated in Fig. 24.10a. Initially the external field is held on H_0 to completely saturate those spins that respond to the frequency γH_0. Then, in a matter of 0.007 sec the sample is swept off resonance and remains there for a length of time τ, after which time the sample is again swept through resonance very rapidly, almost in a linear fashion. This gives a plot of χ'' against H_0 at various times after saturation. The results on two samples are shown in Figs. 24.10b, c. The recovery time is a matter of seconds, depending very strongly on the concentration. The reader should note that at lower

---

* Actually such studies have been made, but will not be described here. It seems to depend only on the response time of the equipment.

MAGNETIC FIELD MODULATION

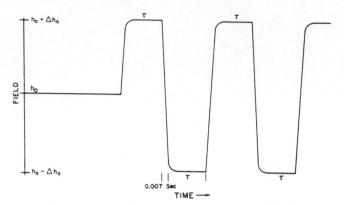

FIG. 24.10a. Method of modulating H_0 used by Noble to burn a hole in the resonance line.

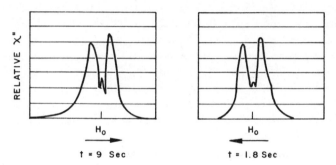

FIG. 24.10b. The absorption after saturating the center of the band at 4°K. The data are on the *F*-center in KCl (additively colored). Concentration, 1.1×10^{17} cm^{-3}. The resonance was displayed on an oscilloscope and photographed. The structure in the center of the hole may or may not be real (after Noble, 1960S).

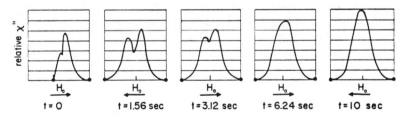

FIG. 24.10c. A sequence of tracings made from a single photograph showing the recovery of the saturation portion of the resonance absorption at 4° K. The data were taken on the *F*-center, in KCl (additively colored); concentration, 4.8×10^{17} cm^{-3} (after Noble, 1960S).

concentration there is a rise in the middle of the hole; this is not observed at higher concentration. It does not always appear in later measurements made by Noble.

A not too successful attempt to measure the recovery time has been made by Markham and Noble (1960S). The importance of this graph is that the recovery takes about 250 sec when the F concentration is as low as 4×10^{16} cm^{-3} (Fig. 24.11). One cannot say from these data if the

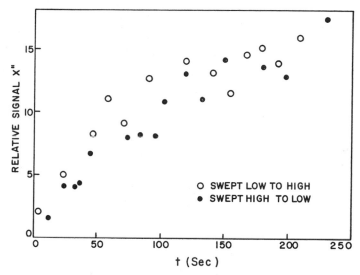

FIG. 24.11. First measurements of the recovery of the hole burnt in the resonance of the F-centers in KCl (additively colored) concentration 4×10^{16} cm^{-3} (after Markham and Noble, S).

recovery is exponential or not. The scatter of the points is large, since the signal is small for such a low concentration. Dr. Noble believes that the scatter of the points is larger than one should expect from the equipment.

Ohlsen's attempt to measure the spin-lattice relaxation time was of a different nature and with radically different results. He saturated the whole resonance line and watched it recover with time. He assumed the data should be of the form

$$M_t = M_\infty(1 - e^{-t/T_1}) \tag{24.7}$$

and plotted $\log(M_\infty - M_t)$ against time.* The result on a densely colored

* This is a solution of Eq. (17.13b), provided $M = 0$ at $t = 0$, which is the case in Ohlsen's measurements.

and on a dilutely colored crystal is shown in Figs. 24.12a, b. Ohlsen's data indicate that T_1 is strongly concentration dependent. Figure 24.12b indicates a slight temperature dependence over a small range. The reader should note that the Ohlsen-type recovery is very much slower than the type studied by Noble. This is particularly evident by comparing Figs. 24.11 and 24.12a. Figure 24.13 is a plot due to Ohlsen showing the

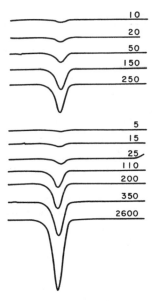

FIG. 24.12a. The recovery of the signal after the entire band has been saturated. The data are for the *F*-center in KCl. Concentration, 8×10^{16} cm^{-3}. The figures denote time in seconds after the band is saturated (after Ohlsen and Holcomb, S).

terminal-recovery slope as a function of concentration. This is roughly a factor of ten longer than the recovery time obtained by burning a hole in the resonance. The energy it must take to burn a hole is more than a tenth of the energy it takes to saturate the whole resonance, as was done by Ohlsen. We conclude this from the relative size of the absorption and the size of the hole.

The theory of Kittel and Abrahams (Section 17) indicates that T_2 depends on the concentration. The width of the individual multiplet (or the reciprocal of T_2) appears in the saturation equation. The fact that this does not show a concentration dependence at high temperatures indicates that some other mechanism broadens the multiplets (probably the Bloch type). This follows from the concentration independence of T_1T_2 at high temperatures. Equations (17.13a) and (17.13b) assume that T_2 cannot be greater than T_1, since the memory of the x and y components of **M** is also destroyed by the lattice vibrations. At 78°K and above there must be some coupling between the spins at the various sites, otherwise one would be able to dig a hole in the signal, as one does at

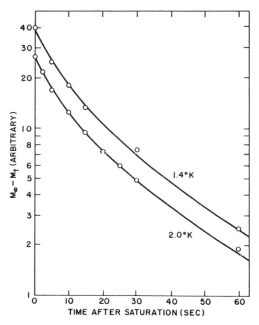

FIG. 24.12b. Recovery curves of the F-center in KCl. Concentration, 3×10^{18} cm^{-3} $H_0 = 3,500$ gauss. The whole resonance was saturated in this case, not a limited region (after Ohlsen and Holcomb, S).

4°K. Since T_2 is concentration independent, the spins must give their energy to the lattice in some manner and it must be relayed rapidly to other F-centers. The relaying mechanism is not influenced by the distance between centers or, stated differently, the mean free path required to destroy the spin energy packet is large compared to the distance between imperfections. At low temperature the relaying mechanism is sensitive to the separation of the centers, since one can only burn a hole in the resonance of dilutely colored samples. The exact temperature at which one may burn a hole depends on the response of the measuring equipment.

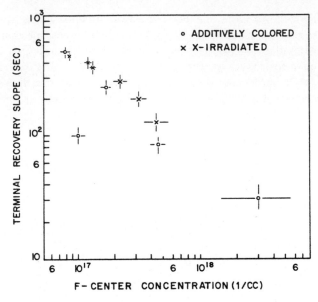

FIG. 24.13. Terminal recovery time for various concentrations of *F*-centers (after Ohlsen S).

TABLE 24.5. VALUES OF T_1 FOR *F*-CENTERS IN KCl

Measured by	T_1 (sec)	Concentration	Temperature (°K)
Markham and Noble (S)	65[a]	4×10^{15}	4
	20[a]	2×10^{17}	4
Noble (1964S)	29–5	2×10^{17}	4
Ohlsen and Holcomb (S)	600	5×10^{16}	2
	250	2×10^{17}	2
	50	10^{18}	2
Holton and Blum (S)	216	5×10^{16}	1.3
	72	2×10^{17}	1.3
	3	10^{18}	1.3
McAvoy *et al.* (S)	1,350	1×10^{16}	2.1

[a] This figure is approximate.

This remark regarding T_2 must also apply to T_1. If the usual spin-lattice theory (see Abragam, Chapters 8 and 9) applies, then both quantities should be insensitive to the concentrations. Experimentally, this is true only at low temperatures.

Some values of T_1 taken at low temperatures are given in Table 24.5 and should be considered preliminary, since it has not even been established that the decay is exponential. A comparison of the various measurements is difficult since they were not taken at the same temperature. The difference between the hole-burning technique (Markham and Noble, as well as Noble) and the saturation of the entire line (Ohlsen and Holcomb, as well as Holton and Blum) may be due to a very strong temperature dependence of T_1. On the other hand, it could be due to the technique of measurement.

TABLE 24.6[a]

	Pure F	Bleached F (B)
g-Factor:	1.9964 ± 0.0005	1.9965 ± 0.0005
Width[b]:	54.9	40.1

[a] After Noble and Markham (S).
[b] Gaussian shape assumed; width indicated in gauss.

d. The EPR Properties of the Bleached F-Center

In Sections 9 and 14b we studied some of the optical properties of F-centers that have been bleached at low and at high temperatures. Here we shall limit our attention to the high-temperature phenomena, that is, the formation of the Molnar-Petroff series of bands. Once again, the study was done at Cornell by Moran, Christensen, and Silsbee (S); in Stuttgart by Gross and Wolf (S); and at Zenith by Noble and Markham (S). In this case we can add the work done at Osaka City University by Kawamura and Ishiwatari (S). The author feels that the work at Cornell and that done by Noble is the most complete, and therefore these studies are used as a basis for this subsection. No one has been able to reproduce the work of Kawamura and Ishiwatari, whereas Gross and Wolf have reported their work in only a preliminary manner. Some studies on this subject have also been done by Bron (S); all are limited to KCl.

Bleaching produces a single EPR absorption band, which is Gaussian and has a g-factor identical to the pure F-center (see Table 24.6). The width and saturation properties, however, are very different. The data will now be summarized. The term "bleached F" will be used for a sample that has had a long exposure to light. As we shall shortly see, an

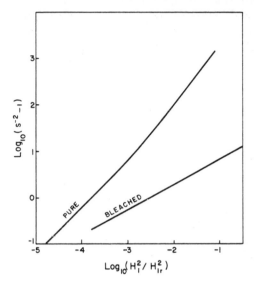

FIG. 24.14. Noble saturation plots for an unbleached and a bleached F-center in KCl (additively colored). Measurement taken at 80° K. Concentration, 7.8×10^{16} cm^{-3}. $H_{1r} = 0.312$ gauss (after Noble and Markham, S).

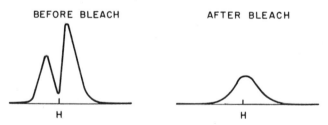

FIG. 24.15. The above diagram illustrates the fact that one cannot burn a hole in the resonance after optical bleaching. The data are for the F-center in KCl (additively colored) (after Noble and Markham, S).

in-between region exists that must be due to a combination of both of these. We shall refer to the well-bleached center as B (see Section 14b).

The general behavior of a well-bleached F-center is shown in Figs. 24.14 and 24.15, which are taken from Noble's work. Figure 24.14 shows that the slope of the graph associated with the B-center does not approach unity, and that its saturation cannot be described by any of the known solutions of Portis's equation (21.10). Under these conditions it is impossible to determine the values of $(T_1 T_2)$ by the method used on the F-center. Figure 24.15 indicates that one cannot burn a hole in the B-center as one can in the F-center. Figures 24.16 and 24.17 illustrate the transition from the "pure" sample to the well-bleached sample. They come from the work at Cornell and use a Portis-type plot. The transition

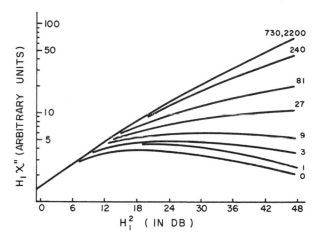

FIG. 24.16. Saturation curves for various bleaching times. The F-center in KCl (additively colored) was employed. The vertical scale was shifted to make the curves coincide at small values of H_1. The numbers on the curve refer to bleaching times in minutes (after Moran et $al.$, S).

between the normal behavior of the "pure" F-center and that of the B-center is evident. Figure 24.17 indicates that the number of magnetic centers is proportional to the optical absorption in the F-region. It was taken from a sample where the F-centers were made from U-centers (see Section 7d, footnote). This type of data has been obtained by Noble in a much more qualitative manner. The Cornell group has some data on F-centers taken on additively colored crystals. The one-to-one correspondence of Fig. 24.17 is much less satisfactory.

The EPR data, as well as the data summarized in Section 14b and Table 24.6, lead to the conclusion that, on bleaching, the F-center is destroyed and that a new center, known as the B-center, is formed. For moderate amounts of bleaching both types of centers may be present, but for prolonged bleaching only the B-center remains. The latter part of the conclusion is based on the powerful technique of "uncovering" an EPR signal by saturating the signal with the longer relaxation time. Thus, in KI that has been additively colored with potassium, one may saturate the F absorption by increasing the microwave power, and "uncover" a second absorption (Fig. 24.3). Since no such phenomenon appears in the bleached case, the author believes that the F-center absorption completely disappears on prolonged bleaching and is replaced by an absorption due to another center.

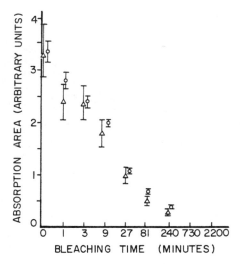

Fig. 24.17. A comparison of the optical absorption and the EPR signal for various amounts of bleaching: △, optical absorption; and ○, EPR signal (after Moran *et al.*, S).

In several respects, the B-center is similar to the F-center; the optical band peak is near the F and the point of maximum EPR absorption occurs at the identical value of the external field. Since the g value is a measure of the symmetry character of the wave function (see Section 20), we must conclude that the general symmetry around the B-center is similar to the F-center. The widths (both the optical absorption and the EPR signal), however, have changed. This is a personal opinion of the author, not generally accepted. There are connections between the absorption in the F-region and in the Molnar-Petroff region. The relations between the EPR behavior and these connections are not clear at present. They may modify the above ideas.

e. Information from the ENDOR Technique

In this subsection we present details regarding the ENDOR measurements that have been made on the F-center. The experimental work was done by Feher (S), Lord (S), Seidel (S), Seidel and Wolf (S), Holton and

TABLE 24.7. HYPERFINE CONSTANTS

Shell and direction	Nucleus	a_α (mc/sec)	b_α (mc/sec)	$|\phi_F|^2$ (cm^{-3} × 10^{21})	$\langle(3\cos^2\theta_\alpha - 1)/r_\alpha^3\rangle_{av}$ (cm^{-3} × 10^{21})
			Sodium Fluoride[a]		
1 [100]	Na^{23}	105.6 ± 0.8		603	
2 [110]	F^{19}	61.6		99	
3 [111]	Na^{23}	1.28 ± 0.04	0.68 ± 0.08	7.3	6.5
4 [200]	F^{19}	0.9 ± 0.1	0.63 ± 0.1	1.5	1.7
5 [210]	Na^{23}				
6 [211]	F^{19}	0.94		< 1.5	
8 [220]	F^{19}	0.9 ± 0.04	0.65 ± 0.02	1.5	1.8
			Sodium Fluoride[c]		
1 [100]	Na^{23}	107.0	5.3		
2 [110]	F^{19}	96.8	9.8		
3 [111]	Na^{23}	3.1	0.3		
4 [200]	F^{19}	6.5	1.3		
5 [210]	Na^{23}	0.8	0.2		
6 [211]	F^{19}	1.5	0.5		
8 [220]	Na^{23}	0.7	0.3		
9A [300]	F^{19}	0.8	0.2		
9B [221]	F^{19}				
10 [310]	Na^{23}				
11 [311]	F^{19}				
12 [222]	Na^{23}				
13 [320]	F^{19}	0.8	0.2		
14 [321]	Na^{23}				
16 [400]	F^{19}	0.1	0.2		
			Sodium Chloride[a]		
1 [100]	Na^{23}	61.5 ± 0.5	3.1 ± 0.3	351	30
2 [110]	Cl^{35}	12.5 ± 0.01	0.96 ± 0.01	193	25
			Sodium Chloride[b]		
1 [100]	Na^{23}	62.4	3.01		
2 [110]	Cl^{35}	12.53	1.06		
3 [111]	Na	0.340	0.170		
4 [200]	Cl	0.460	0.068		
5 [210]	Na	0.614			

TABLE 24.7 *continued*

Shell and direction	Nucleus	a_α (mc/sec)	b_α (mc/sec)	$|\phi_F|^2$ (cm$^{-3} \times 10^{21}$)	$\langle (3\cos^2\theta_\alpha -1)/r_\alpha \rangle_{av}$ (cm$^{-3} \times 10^{21}$)
			Lithium Fluoride[a]		
1 [100]	Li^7	39.06 ± 0.02	3.20 ± 0.01	152	21
2 [110]	F^{19}	105.94 ± 0.02	14.96 ± 0.02	169	40
3 [111]	Li^7	0.5 ± 0.01	0.68 ± 0.02	1.94	4.43
4 [200]	F^{19}	0.48 ± 0.01	1.12 ± 0.01	0.77	3.01
5 [210]	Li^7	0.27 ± 0.01	0.28 ± 0.01	1.05	1.82
6 [211]	F^{19}	0.88 ± 0.01	0.69 ± 0.01	1.41	1.86
8 [220]	F^{19}	1.34 ± 0.01	0.56 ± 0.01	2.15	1.51
			Lithium Chloride[a]		
1 [100]	Li^7	19.1 ± 0.1	1.72 ± 0.06	74	11.2
2 [110]	Cl^{35}	11.24 ± 0.15	0.90 ± 0.05	173	23.3
3 [111]	Li^7	2.1 ± 0.1	2.1 ± 0.1	8.2	13.7
4 [200]	Cl^{35}	0.5	0.057	7.7	1.5
5 [210]	Li^7	< 0.2		< 0.78	
6 [211]	Cl^{35}	0.2	< 0.03	3.1	0.8
			Potassium Chloride[a]		
1 [100]	K^{39}	20.6	0.91	667	49.4
2 [110]	Cl^{35}	6.9	0.50	106.4	12.9
3 [111]	K^{39}	0.31	0.032	10.0	1.74
4 [200]	Cl^{35}	1.06	0.11	16.4	2.8
6 [211]	Cl^{35}	0.10	0.03	1.5	0.78
			Potassium Bromide[b]		
1 [100]	K^{39}	18.56	0.75		
2 [110]	Br^{81}	43.2	2.7		
3 [111]	K	0.27	0.022		
4 [200]	Br	5.76	0.40		
5 [210]	K	0.16	0.02		
6 [211]	Br	0.84			
8 [220]	Br	0.54	0.07		

[a] Holton and Blum (S).   [b] Seidel (S).   [c] Doyle (S).

Blum (S), and Doyle (S). The most detailed study was that of Holton and Blum; hence, this subsection is based primarily on their paper. As stated previously (Section 22), detailed studies by the ENDOR technique can measure the Fermi contact term a_α of Eq. (22.13a), the anisotropic term b_α of Eq. (22.13b), and the quadrupole coupling terms, which we have not discussed. Feher measured the quadrupole terms and found them small compared to a and b, but not an order of magnitude smaller than b. Holton and Blum do not give any values for this term and, to keep the discussion reasonably simple, we shall not consider them here.

The essential method of the ENDOR technique is to identify the low-frequency absorption due to transitions from various nuclei that surround the point imperfection. This is done by rotating the crystal in the magnetic field so that θ_α of Eq. (22.13b) changes. All the nuclei do not have the same axis of symmetry, and by the association of a set of nuclei with the behavior of a line or lines under rotation, it is possible to find the relation between the signal and the nuclei and, in turn, to evaluate a_α and b_α. The method in which this is done has been described in Section 22, hence only the data are presented here (Table 24.7). The meaning of the data will be discussed briefly at the end of Section 28. Some actual data on the F-center in KCl were given earlier. A second type of data measurements (from a recorder) are shown in Fig. 24.18. The reader will note that the interactions at the various types of nuclei can be obtained, at least in the nearby shells. One should compare Tables 20.2 and 24.7.

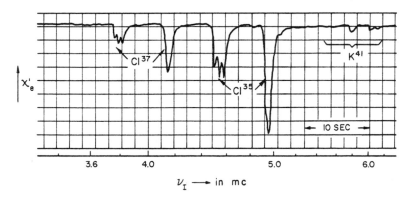

FIG. 24.18. Actual ENDOR data where the rapid passage technique is used. The centers were produced by electron bombardment. The temperature was 1.2° K, the angle θ equaled zero, and the external magnetic field was such that frequency associated with the electron's flip was 9,150 mc/sec (after Feher, S).

REFERENCES

S. Anderson, J. S. Wiley, and L. J. Hendricks, *J. Chem. Phys.* **32**, 949 (1960).
B. Bleaney and W. Hayes, *Proc. Phys. Soc.* (*London*) **B70**, 626 (1957).
W. E. Blumberg, *Phys. Rev.* **119**, 1842 (1960).
W. E. Bron, *Phys. Rev.* **125**, 509 (1962).
W. T. Doyle, *Phys. Rev.* **126**, 1421 (1962).
W. H. Duerig and J. J. Markham, *Phys. Rev.* **88**, 1043 (1952).
G. Feher, *Phys. Rev.* **105**, 1122 (1957).
A. Gross and H. C. Wolf, *Naturwissenschaften* **48**, 299 (1961).
W. C. Holton and H. Blum, *Phys. Rev.* **125**, 89 (1962).
F. Hughes and J. G. Allard, *Phys. Rev.* **125**, 173 (1962).
C. A. Hutchinson and G. A. Noble, *Phys. Rev.* **87**, 1125 (1952).
J. S. Hyde, *Phys. Rev.* **119**, 1483 (1960).
H. Kawamura and K. Ishiwatari, *J. Phys. Soc. Japan* **13**, 574 (1958).
C. Kittel, Conference on *Defects in Crystalline Solids* (Physical Society, London, 1955) p. 33.
A. F. Kip, C. Kittel, R. A. Levy, and A. M. Portis, *Phys. Rev.* **91**, 1066 (1953).
N. W. Lord, *Phys. Rev. Letters* **1**, 170 (1958).
N. W. Lord, *Phys. Rev.* **105**, 756 (1957a).
N. W. Lord, *Phys. Rev.* **106**, 1100 (1957b).
J. J. Markham and G. A. Noble, *Proc. Semiconductor Conf.* (*Prague*) p. 711 (1960).
B. R. McAvoy, D. W. Feldman, J. G. Castle, and R. W. Warren, *Phys. Rev. Letters* **6**, 618 (1961).
P. R. Moran, S. H. Christensen, and R. H. Silsbee, *Phys. Rev.* **124**, 442 (1961).
G. A. Noble, *J. Phys. Chem.* **31**, 931 (1959).
G. A. Noble, *Phys. Rev.* **118**, 1028 (1960).
G. A. Noble, Unpublished data (1964).
G. A. Noble and J. J. Markham, *J. Chem. Phys.* **36**, 1340 (1962).
W. D. Ohlsen, Ph.D. thesis, Cornell University, 1961.
W. D. Ohlsen and D. F. Holcomb, *Phys. Rev.* **126**, 1953 (1962).
A. M. Portis, *Phys. Rev.* **91**, 1071 (1953).
H. Seidel, *Z. Physik* **165**, 218, 239 (1961).
H. Seidel and H. C. Wolf, *Naturwissenschaften* **46**, 597 (1959).
R. H. Silsbee, *Phys. Rev.* **103**, 1675 (1956).
H. C. Wolf and K. H. Hausser, *Naturwissenschaften* **46**, 646 (1959).
G. J. Wolga and M. W. P. Strandberg, *Phys. Chem. Solids* **9**, 309 (1959).

IX. The Theory of the *F*-Center Wave Functions

25. INTRODUCTION: THE MODEL*

We have described the properties of a center; now a model is suggested. A microscopic model of an imperfection is almost always subject to revision. Only in some extremely unusual situations can one make sufficiently detailed and accurate calculations to completely confirm a model and remove all doubts. For most items this is not the case here, since the theoretical calculations are not completely accurate and leave much to be desired. Indeed, many of the measurable parameters have never been computed. For the model now suggested, it will be indicated that all the experimental results and theoretical calculations tend to support it. The agreements, however, are such that it is conceivable that an alternate model would give as good results, with one exception, the ENDOR experiments. These results have been described. They remove any real doubt one might have regarding the model.

In view of the fact that *F*-centers can be formed by the injection of electrons and by additive coloration with a metal, it is natural to assume that the center consists of an electron trapped at an imperfection.

Historically, three models have been proposed:

(1) a neutral metal atom at a regular lattice site; the self-trapped electron;

(2) a neutral metal atom at an interstitial position, i.e., an electron trapped at an interstitial positive ion; and

(3) a negative-ion vacancy that has trapped an electron.

For model (1) to have any stability one must assume that the ions surrounding the atom are displaced in such a manner as to form a potential well. The required displacements are illustrated in Fig. 25.1. Such displacements might be stable because of the long time it takes the ions to relax. The positions of the surrounding ions are determined by the potential due to the *average* distribution of the extra charge and not to its instantaneous value. The potential energy of the electron at time t is

---

* The notation for the *F*-center wave functions is not the same in this chapter as used previously, because more details are considered here.

determined by the instantaneous position of the electron. One may assume that the positive ion makes no charge contribution to the imperfection because it is at its normal site. This model corresponds to the self-trapped electron, self-trapped because the extra electron itself causes the trapping potential. This model was proposed by Landau (S) in 1933. In many of the early Göttingen papers the *F*-center was attributed to a nonionized metal, that is, Na or K. No reference was made to the ionic displacements (as far as the author knows); these are required for stability.

In recent years the concept of self-trapping has been associated with an electron at the bottom of the conduction band in an ionic solid, that is,

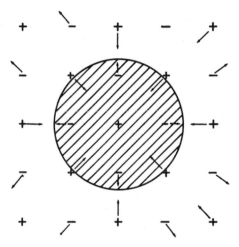

FIG. 25.1. The cross-hatched area represents the location of the self-trapped electron. The arrows represent the displacement of the ions due to the trapped extra charge.

the polaron. Some rather detailed calculations indicate that this system does not have enough thermal binding energy to be stable even at moderate temperature; nor are the optical energies sufficient to explain the absorption of the *F*-band. The data in Fig. 6.1 are due to a reaction of the type

$$\text{Free electron} \rightleftarrows F\text{-center.} \tag{25.1}$$

If the *F*-center is a self-trapped electron, then a positive ion must enter the crystal with the electron or a negative-ion vacancy must be formed. This is required to keep the crystal neutral. In either case, relation (25.1) breaks down and the measurements cannot be explained.

Further, an F'-center forms when a second electron is trapped at an F-center. This model suggests that one may have two self-trapped electrons, which is most difficult to conceive. The problem of F-center formation by x-irradiation would be greatly simplified if this model could be accepted.

We may visualize the electron trapped at an interstitial as a metal at a $\{\frac{1}{2}; \frac{1}{2}; \frac{1}{2}\}$ site. It is surrounded by four negative and four positive ions. Figure 25.2 indicates the difference in symmetry between a negative-ion

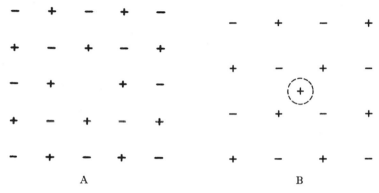

A   B

FIG. 25.2A. Symmetry of the negative-ion vacancy. Note the fourfold axis.
FIG. 25.2B. Symmetry of a negative ion at a $\frac{1}{2}$; $\frac{1}{2}$ site. Note the twofold axis.

vacancy and an interstitial metal ion for a two-dimensional crystal. The figure is more complex in three dimensions. The interstitial model has a much lower symmetry. This most probably would lead to a measurable asymmetry in the optical and magnetic properties of the F-center. Returning to Eq. (4.3) we note that for polarized light one must replace $\frac{1}{3}|\langle\psi_2|r|\psi_1\rangle|^2$ by $|\langle\psi_2|x|\psi_1\rangle|^2$ where x is the direction of the electric vector associated with the light which excites the center. If we select x along the lines which join negative ions or along the lines which join positive ions, the matrix elements should not be equal, since the positive and negative ions will distort the F-center wave function differently. This should lead to dichroic bleaching effects. These have not been observed, hence this is a good argument against the interstitial model. Seitz (1946) has made estimates of the ratio of negative-ion vacancies to interstitial ions. The ratio is at least 1 to 100 in favor of the vacancies. In Section 5a, the work of Smakula seems to indicate that there are initially imperfections within a crystal and that they trap electrons to form F-centers; we may also use this argument against the interstitial model.

The de Boer Model. The de Boer or negative-ion vacancy model seems to be capable of explaining the observed phenomena. We shall now consider this model in detail.

(1) *Symmetry properties.* The symmetry properties of the *F*-center can be determined by bleaching with polarized light; by measuring the asymmetric properties of the *g*-factor; and by means of the electron nuclear double resonance techniques. No detailed studies exist in the literature on the first two because the results are negative. The data in Section 24 establish the third point without any doubt. We must conclude that the high degree of symmetry supports this model.

(2) *Expansion properties.* The fact that a crystal expands when it is colored (Section 5*e*) tends to support the idea that the radiation produces negative-ion vacancies which decrease the density of the material, thus causing it to expand. The order of magnitude of the expansion indicates that for heavy irradiation one negative-ion vacancy is produced per *F*-center formed. Perhaps a positive-ion vacancy is produced as well. For light irradiation this is not the case; here electrons seem to fill up negative-ion vacancies which are initially present. Many questions regarding the expansion during irradiation remain to be solved. No final conclusion can be arrived at regarding this point at the time of the writing of this book.

(3) *Additive coloration.* The equation of Mott and Gurney (Section 6) used in analyzing the additive coloration data employs the ideas of de Boer. The experiments support this model.

(4) *The F'-center.* In Section 9 we discussed the properties of the *F'*-center. It involved an *F*-center that has trapped a second electron. The de Boer model implies that the *F*-center is a "neutral" imperfection whereas an *F'*-center has a negative charge. The charges are calculated relative to a negative ion and resemble an H^- ion. The stability of such ions occur because on the average, the two electrons are nearer the positive nucleus than they are to each other. They have very few bound states, usually only one. Hence, it is natural to expect a single bound state for the *F'*-center. The breadth of the *F'*-band arises from transitions between this single state and the conduction bands.

(5) *Growth rates and negative-ion vacancies.* There are several experiments which indicate that one can make *F*-centers more readily if one has more initial negative-ion vacancies. This vacancy may be produced by doping or by plastic deformation. Unfortunately, at present, we do not know how to control the negative-ion vacancies and this evidence is weak.

The major problem related to the de Boer model is the production of negative-ion vacancies. If we assume that 25 ev of energy are required to knock an ion out of the lattice, it is very difficult to see how low-energy electrons or photons can impart that much energy to a heavy ion if the laws of conservation of energy and momentum in a two-body collision are to be obeyed. In the author's opinion, no completely satisfactory mechanism has been suggested for the coloration process during irradiation so far. This problem is certainly one of major interest in the field of radiation damage and in the field of color centers. Even if the value 25 ev is too large, the fundamental problem remains.

REFERENCE

L. Landau, *Physik. Z. Sowjetunion* **3**, 664 (1933).

26. THE AIM OF THE THEORY

The theory of the F-center is one of the biggest challenges which the solid state theorist faces today. One may measure over a dozen quantities which involve the electron wave function as well as the vibrations of the ions about the vacancy. Carefully designed experiments have given or are giving these quantities to a few percent accuracy, far better than one may hope to obtain from any theory in the near future. Not all these quantities are known; many experiments remain to be performed. Theoretical calculations have been done on only a few of them. Even crude first-order calculations of many of the quantities have not been made to date. Refined calculations of some quantities are required for us to have a true understanding of the problems involved.

We start this section by listing the quantities which are known or should be known regarding the F-center. Anyone making such a list realizes that it will be out of date in a few years, when the attention of workers in the field will focus on other quantities. Nevertheless, such a list has value, for it orients the thinking of the reader; there are, moreover, many quantities that have been known for a great many years on which detailed calculations have not, but ought to have, been made. Here we list the quantities and refer to some of the calculations. This list is not complete at the time of writing, and it will become less so with the passage of time; it should be noted, moreover, that it does not aim at enumerating all the calculations that have been made.

(1) $\epsilon_m(a)$—the optical activation energy for the absorption of a photon when a center is excited from its ground to its first excited state; ϵ_m corresponds to the maximum absorption (the most probable transition). These values are known to a few percent for most alkali halides. The variation with the crystal temperature and pressure has also been measured. Many theories which are not completely equivalent exist. One cannot at present decide which theory is the most correct. The temperature variation of ϵ_m has not been explained satisfactorily (see Section 3).

(2) $\epsilon_m(e)$—the optical activation energy for the spontaneous emission of a photon during a transition from the first excited state to the ground state; preliminary data exist on several alkali halides. Detailed measurements of $\epsilon_m(e)$ as a function of temperature for KCl have been reported by Lüty and Gebhardt (S). No theoretical calculation of this quantity has been reported (in press). The problem of ionic and lattice polarization is a major one in all these calculations (see Section 8).*

(3) $\epsilon_t(0)$—the thermal activation energy for the ground state to release an electron to the conduction band (see Section 11). To obtain the actual value of $\epsilon_t(0)$ from the measurements requires a detailed calculation, as has been indicated. Some preliminary progress on the calculation of this quantity has been made.

(4) $\epsilon_t(1)$—the thermal activation energy for the first excited state to release an electron to the conduction band; this quantity has been determined for many alkali halides by measuring the photoconductivity from the *F*-center at various temperatures (see Section 7).

To understand the next three items one must refer to $H(\theta)$, H at temperature θ. As we shall see (Section 31), if the broadening is caused by a single effective phonon frequency, $\nu_{\rm eff}$, then the following equation applies to first order:

$$H^2(\theta) = H^2(0)\coth\left\{\frac{1}{2}\frac{h}{k\theta}\nu_{\rm eff}\right\} \tag{26.1}$$

Experiments indicate that this holds approximately for the absorption in most alkali halides. It holds for both the absorption and the emission in KCl.

(5) *The calculation of $H(0)$ for absorption.* The exact form of $H(0)$ has been given in terms of the electronic wave functions associated with the ground and the excited states as well as the properties of the normal modes (see Section 31). No exact calculations of $H(0)$ have been made. Several have been reported but they are known to be unrealistic, since the

* Some calculations will have appeared before this book is published.

correct normal modes were not considered. A correction studied by McCombie and co-workers (S) as well as by Casselman and the author (S) has to be taken carefully into account.

(6) $H(0)$ *for emission*. This quantity is known for several alkali halides. Lemos and the author (S) have made detailed calculations in the strong coupling case (see Section 30) where the electron interacts only with the six nearest neighbors. These calculations apply both to absorption and to emission.

(7) ν_{eff}(*absorption*) *and* ν_{eff}(*emission*). These are two quantities that are known experimentally but have been explained theoretically only in a very qualitative manner. Their very concept of an *effective frequency* requires an explanation.

(8) *The shape of the absorption curve*. This factor has been explained satisfactorily at low temperatures (see Section 31) but there is no rigorous, completely quantum mechanical explanation for the lack of symmetry of the absorption or the emission bands at higher temperatures. Hence, there are correction terms to be added to Eq. (26.1) and to the present theory.

(9) *The oscillator strength f for absorption and the local field*. Many years ago Smakula derived his famous equation relating the density of imperfections to the absorption (Section 4). In such a calculation it is necessary to obtain an expression for the local field, that is, the actual field at the imperfection. At present no reliable theory exists. Only after this problem has been solved can one obtain a true theoretical estimate of the f-factor [see Eq. (4.3)]. Several sets of measurements of this quantity exist, but no reliable comparison between the theoretical and the experimental values can be made until we have a better understanding of the local field at a negative-ion vacancy. This item is really two quantities, the local field and f (absorption).

(10) *f for emission and the lifetime of the excited state*. f enters into expressions for the emission of light by an imperfection as well as for the absorption of light from this imperfection. Recently, measurements have been made of the lifetime of the excited state (Section 8). This has not been explained satisfactorily at present, although work on this subject has been done by Fowler and Dexter (S) as well as by the author (S). One would like to know if f is frequency dependent and what changes occur in the excited and ground-state wave function due to ionic displacements. Since f contains ν explicitly, one might suspect a frequency dependence. This may not be true, however, since the matrix element may also have such a dependence. Pekar and Perlin (S) have calculated this quantity

using Pekar's (S) theory of the F-center. The theory does not seem to take the electron-phonon interaction into account in a proper manner, hence their value is subject to question although it agrees very well with experimental data.

(11) *Higher excited states associated with the F-center*. A careful theoretical investigation of the question " Can higher states exist beyond the first excited one in a negative-ion vacancy ?" is of major importance.

The foregoing eleven items arise from the optical and electrical properties of F-centers (photoconductivity or thermal conductivity). Several additional ones are obtained when the magnetic measurements on this imperfection are included. The most important of these are the following.

(12) *The g-factor*. We know experimentally that this factor is influenced by the next-nearest neighbors, as was shown by the measurements of Noble (see Section 24, Table 24.4). Several calculations of this factor exist; they were discussed in Section 18. The theories explain why the g-factor is less than $g_e = 2.0023$, the value for a free electron, or a pure s-state. They do not, however, explain the importance of the next-nearest neighbors and the variation between different salts. At present, we know a great deal regarding the ground-state wave function of the electron trapped at a negative-ion vacancy due to ENDOR experiments. With this knowledge and some further theoretical work it should be possible to explain the variation shown in Table 24.4.

(13) *Hyperfine interactions with the nearby nuclei*. The ENDOR technique has been used to obtain the wave function of the electron at the nearby nuclei, sometimes going out to the eighth shell. Several calculations of these coefficients have been made, and these will be discussed shortly. The ultimate aim of the theory must be to put the calculation of wave functions at a nucleus on a rigorous, systematic basis. This problem is directly related to the shape of the electron spin resonance absorption band obtained from an F-center, since it is due to the hyperfine interactions between the excess electron and the nuclei in the surrounding shells.

(14) *Relaxation times*. The problem of the relaxation times of the F-center is twofold: what is the actual meaning of T_1 and T_2 (that is, their definition for an inhomogeneously broadened line); and how one is to calculate these quantities. T_1 has been calculated under certain limited assumptions. A great deal more work remains to be done, however, since there is no over-all agreement with the experimental results.

Other quantities exist, such as higher order magnetic effects, which we are just beginning to understand. Important studies are being made on the excited state and further quantities to be measured and calculated are appearing from them. Various interactions between imperfections, which include the F-center, are of interest and could have been included in this list. In a sense, the theory has a lot of catching up to do if future fruitful progress is to be made in this field.

We now proceed to develop the theory, making the required approximations.

REFERENCES

T. N. Casselman and J. J. Markham, *Phys. Chem. Solids* **24**, 669 (1963).

W. B. Fowler and D. L. Dexter, *Phys. Rev.* **128**, 2154 (1962).

A. Lemos and J. J. Markham, *Phys. Chem. Solids* **26**, 1837 (1965).

F. Lüty and W. Gebhart *Z. Physik* **169**, 475 (1962).

J. J. Markham, *Z. Physik* **188**, 139 (1965).

C. W. McCombie, J. A. D. Matthews, and A. M. Murray, *J. Appl. Phys.* **33**, 359 (1962).

S. I. Pekar and Yu. E. Perlin, *JETP (English)* **16**, 782 (1963).

S. I. Pekar, "Research in Electron Theory of Crystals." M.S., A.E.C. tr-5575. U.S. Dept. of Commerce.

27. FUNDAMENTAL ASSUMPTIONS REGARDING THE CALCULATION OF WAVE FUNCTIONS AT POINT IMPERFECTIONS

The most calculated quantity regarding the F-center is $E_1(a) - E_0(a)$. It is assumed that this quantity equals ϵ_m for absorption. The small temperature variation of ϵ_m is ignored.

The calculations on the F-center are based primarily on the ideas of N. F. Mott, although details of the calculations were carried through by his students or co-workers.*

The first serious attack on this problem is the extremely fundamental paper of Tibbs (S). It laid the foundation for most of the later calculations. Several simplifications and modifications were made by Simpson (S) and by Krumhansl and Schwartz (S). In recent years, a new calculation has been made by Smith (S), who used the concepts of Simpson. He calculated the electronic wave functions for many of the alkali halides. More recently, Gourary and Adrian (S) have carried through some

* Exceptions, of course, occur in the treatments of the Japanese school, the work of Pekar (S), and of Gourary and Adrian (S).

further calculations. Although the Gourary-Adrian formulation seems quite different from the approach of Tibbs and Simpson, there are many similarities and we shall be able to present their calculations within the framework of the Tibbs-Simpson theory. The fundamental concept of the method has been examined and completely modified by Slater (S) and by Koster and Slater (S). The importance of Slater's development is that it gives a correct treatment of the problem in principle and shows how far short the present developments fall.

This very brief summary completely omits many detailed and important calculations. Some readers may feel that the calculations of Tibbs, Simpson, and Krumhansl and Schwartz are contradictory and represent essentially different approaches. They may also feel that the approaches used by various Japanese and Russian schools deserve a place in this book. Without a doubt they do, and some of the contributions are extremely important. Nevertheless, in an attempt to make this book finite, many treatments have had to be omitted. The author hopes that by discussing certain theories in detail, he will be able to show the unity of the field. The theories presented here show satisfactory agreement with experiments, usually better than the ones omitted; it is also felt that those included have a greater potential for giving us the required feeling for the problem which we do not have at present. The final calculations will, beyond a question of doubt, be much more complex and involve machine calculations. One example of this is the important work of Wood and co-workers (S).

One must actually admit that our knowledge of calculating a wave function at a point imperfection in a polar solid is extremely limited. The effective mass approximation to be presented breaks down and cannot be applied to the *F*-center with any feeling of security. The polarization effects are extremely important but very hard to handle. We lack an overall theory regarding point imperfections which can be used as a guide. The concept of considering the imperfection as a molecule may be very important in the development of the theory although it is not discussed here in any detail.

The treatment starts with a consideration of the properties of Wannier functions and their relations to wave functions in imperfect crystals. The problem of the vibration of the ions will be postponed until the next chapter. Our treatment follows the development of Slater (S), Slater and Koster (S), and Smith. Then, the development will be adapted to the calculation of energy levels on an electron trapped at a negative-ion vacancy.

a. Wannier's Function in a Perfect Crystal

The Bloch functions can be used in principle for any solid, although they are commonly developed for monatomic ones. When an alkali metal atom approaches a halogen atom at a certain distance, the nonfilled outer p electron on the halogen acquires less energy than an outer s electron on a metal. At this distance, the p shells get filled up. The first empty level may be thought of as electrons in outer s-states of the metal. The electronic conductivity occurs by a "jumping" from one metal ion to another. This will be a useful concept for us to maintain in the following development. Thus, we shall assume that the Wannier functions have their maximum values on the metal ion and are small on halide ions.[*]

First consider wave functions in perfect crystals. Let $b(n; \mathbf{k})$ be a Bloch function corresponding to the energy $E_\mathbf{k}$.[†] The wave function satisfies the following equation:

$$\mathcal{H}_0 b(n, \mathbf{k}; \mathbf{r}) = E(n, \mathbf{k}) b(n, \mathbf{k}; \mathbf{r}) \tag{27.1}$$

where

$$b(n, \mathbf{k}; \mathbf{r}) = e^{i\mathbf{k} \cdot \mathbf{r}} u_{n, \mathbf{k}}(\mathbf{r}) \tag{27.2}$$

$\mathcal{H}_0$ is the Hamiltonian for the perfect crystal, $u_{n, \mathbf{k}}$ is a function which has the periodicity of the lattice, and $\mathbf{k}$ is the wave number vector associated with the lattice (the quasi-momentum). The b's form a complete set. Here we assume one atom per cell. This can be readily generalized. We shall use the Born-von Kármàn cyclical boundary conditions (Seitz, 1940).

$$\mathbf{k} = \frac{2\pi}{N_1} h_1 \mathbf{b}_1 + \frac{2\pi}{N_2} h_2 \mathbf{b}_2 + \frac{2\pi}{N_3} h_3 \mathbf{b}_3 = 2\pi(\eta_1 \mathbf{b}_1 + \eta_2 \mathbf{b}_2 + \eta_3 \mathbf{b}_3)$$

where

$$\mathbf{b}_1 = \frac{1}{\mathbf{a}_1 \cdot (\mathbf{a}_2 \times \mathbf{a}_3)} \mathbf{a}_2 \times \mathbf{a}_3 \quad \text{etc.} \tag{27.2a}$$

[*] Tibbs (S) attempted to calculate the electron wave function at the bottom of the conduction band of NaCl, and found that the electron did not necessarily reside on the metal ion, but spent equal time on both types of ions. The reason for this is that only at large distances from a negative ion is the potential negative. At short distances, the potential is positive. The potential right near a Na nucleus is $11e/r$, whereas near a Cl nucleus it must be $17e/r$; e is the electronic charge and r is the distance from the nucleus.

[†] The Bloch function will be denoted by $b(n, \mathbf{k}; \mathbf{r})$, $b(n, \mathbf{k})$ or $b(\mathbf{k})$, depending on the situation. If it is clear, the variables n and $\mathbf{r}$ will not be written out explicitly; n denotes the band. Also, $E(n; \mathbf{k})$, $E(\mathbf{k})$, and E_k will be used.

The h's are integers and $N_1 N_2 N_3 = N$ are the number of cells in the crystal. The b's are normalized over the crystal. $\mathbf{a}_1$, $\mathbf{a}_2$, and $\mathbf{a}_3$ define the unit cell.

We wish to build up linear combinations of the b's which will concentrate electrons in particular cells (atoms or ions) of the crystals. These linear combinations will no longer be eigenfunctions of the wave equation, although they have some extremely interesting and useful properties. For this purpose, Wannier defined the function (Wannier function):

$$a_n(\mathbf{r} - \mathbf{R}_j) = a\,(n, j) = \frac{1}{N^{1/2}} \sum_{\mathbf{k}} b(n, \mathbf{k}; \mathbf{r})\, e^{-i\mathbf{k}\cdot\mathbf{R}_j} \tag{27.3}$$

$$= \frac{1}{N^{1/2}} \sum_{\mathbf{k}} u_{n\mathbf{k}}(\mathbf{r})\, e^{i\mathbf{k}\cdot(\mathbf{r}-\mathbf{R}_j)}. \tag{27.3a}$$

$\mathbf{R}_j$ is a vector from the origin to the jth cell, namely:

$$\mathbf{R}_j = l_1 \mathbf{a}_1 + l_2 \mathbf{a}_2 + l_3 \mathbf{a}_3. \tag{27.4}$$

In Eq. (27.3a) $\mathbf{k}$ is summed over all the wave vectors. Because of the form of the b's the Wannier functions add on the jth cell [the terms in the exponentials of (27.3a) are zero] and interfere with each other on cells any distance from $\mathbf{R}_j$. The a's are an orthonormal set. We may prove this easily by using the relation (Born-Huang, p. 296).

which
$$\frac{1}{N} \sum_{l_1, l_2, l_3} \exp\,\{2\pi i(\eta_1 l_1 + \eta_2 l_2 + \eta_3 l_3)\}$$

$$= 1 \quad \text{for} \quad \eta_1 = \eta_2 = \eta_3 = 0$$

and

$$= 0 \quad \text{otherwise.} \tag{27.4a}*$$

In (27.4a) the η's are parameters defined above, and the l's are integers. The proof of (27.4a) is elementary when one recognizes that one is dealing with a geometric series. It is equivalent to

$$\frac{1}{N} \sum e^{i\mathbf{k}\cdot\mathbf{R}_j} = 1 \quad \text{for} \quad \mathbf{R}_j = 0$$

$$= 0 \quad \text{otherwise.} \tag{27.5}$$

Using (27.5) one may express the b's as an expansion of the Wannier functions and further prove the orthonormal relation between the a's.

---

* This relation actually holds at any zone boundary in k-space where $\eta_i l_i$ are integers.

One proceeds as follows:

$$\sum_j \exp(i\mathbf{k}\cdot\mathbf{R}_j)\,a_n(\mathbf{r}-\mathbf{R}_j) = \frac{1}{N^{1/2}}\sum_{j,\mathbf{k}'} b(\mathbf{k}')\exp[i(\mathbf{k}-\mathbf{k}')\cdot\mathbf{R}_j]$$

$$= \frac{1}{N^{1/2}}\sum_{\mathbf{k}'} b(\mathbf{k}')\sum_j \exp[i(\mathbf{k}-\mathbf{k}')\cdot\mathbf{R}_j] \qquad (27.6)$$

$$= \frac{1}{N^{1/2}}\sum_{\mathbf{k}'} N\delta_{kk'}\,b(\mathbf{k}') \qquad (27.6a)*$$

or

$$b(n,\mathbf{k};\mathbf{r}) = \frac{1}{N^{1/2}}\sum_j a_n(\mathbf{r}-\mathbf{R}_j)\exp(i\mathbf{k}\cdot\mathbf{R}_j). \qquad (27.7)$$

Using Eqs. (27.3a) and (27.7) we can write the symmetric equations

$$a_n(\mathbf{r}-\mathbf{R}_j) = a(n,j) = \frac{1}{N^{1/2}}\sum_k b(n,\mathbf{k})\,e^{-i\mathbf{k}\cdot\mathbf{R}_j} \qquad (27.8a)$$

and

$$b(n,\mathbf{k}) = \frac{1}{N^{1/2}}\sum_j a(n,j)\,e^{i\mathbf{k}\cdot\mathbf{R}_j}. \qquad (27.8b)$$

They behave like Fourier transforms of one another. The orthonormal relations now follow:

$$\int a^*(n,i;\mathbf{r})\,a(m,j;\mathbf{r})\,d\tau_r = \frac{1}{N}\sum_{\mathbf{k},\mathbf{k}'} \exp\{i[\mathbf{k}'\cdot\mathbf{R}_i - \mathbf{k}\cdot\mathbf{R}_j]\}$$

$$\times \int b^*(n,\mathbf{k}';\mathbf{r})\,b(m,\mathbf{k};\mathbf{r})\,d\tau_r$$

$$= \frac{1}{N}\delta_{nm}\sum_k \exp\{i\mathbf{k}\cdot(\mathbf{R}_i-\mathbf{R}_j)\} = \delta_{nm}\delta_{ij}. \qquad (27.9)$$

The fact that the b's are orthonormal has been employed.

The a's are "nice" functions, but they are not eigenfunctions of $\mathcal{H}_0$ as are the Bloch functions. To derive the equations for the a's one proceeds as follows:

$$\mathcal{H}_0\,a_n(\mathbf{r}-\mathbf{R}_j) = \frac{1}{N^{1/2}}\sum_k e^{-i\mathbf{k}\cdot\mathbf{R}_j}E(n,\mathbf{k})\,b(n,\mathbf{k};\mathbf{r})$$

$$= \frac{1}{N}\sum_{\mathbf{k},i} E(n,\mathbf{k})\,e^{i\mathbf{k}\cdot(\mathbf{R}_i-\mathbf{R}_j)}a(n,i)$$

$$= \sum_i \epsilon_n(\mathbf{R}_i-\mathbf{R}_j)\,a(n,i) \qquad (27.10)$$

* $\mathbf{k}-\mathbf{k}'$ is assumed to be within a single Brillouin zone.

where

$$\epsilon_n(\mathbf{R}_i - \mathbf{R}_j) = \int a^*(n, i)\, \mathcal{H}_0\, a(n, j)\, d\tau_r = \frac{1}{N} \sum_{\mathbf{k}} E(n, \mathbf{k})\, e^{i\mathbf{k}\cdot(\mathbf{R}_i - \mathbf{R}_j)}. \quad (27.11)$$

Here we have used (27.8a) and operated on $b(n, \mathbf{k})$ with $\mathcal{H}_0$. Equation (27.10) indicates that $\mathcal{H}_0 a(n,j)$ can be expanded in terms of the Wannier functions associated with the nth band.

b. Wannier's Functions and the Point Imperfection

Next, consider what happens in Eq. (27.10) when an imperfection is introduced into the crystal. The imperfection is a negative-ion vacancy. Around the vacancy the perturbation is large and one cannot consider only the first few terms in an expansion. Nevertheless, it is instructive to start our study by considering only a slight imperfection and thus see which terms have been neglected. Let the Hamiltonian in this case be $\mathcal{H}_0 + \mathcal{H}_1$. At the center of the negative-ion vacancy the potential changes from $(Ze/r) \to \infty$ to a finite positive value. Outside the vacancy $\mathcal{H}_1$ arises from the missing negative ion as well as from the displacements and the polarization of the surrounding ions. $\mathcal{H}_1$ may be considered small at moderate distances from the vacancy. Now, $\mathcal{H}_0$ is replaced by $\mathcal{H}_0 + \mathcal{H}_1$.* The wave functions associated with $\mathcal{H}_1$ are now written in the form:

$$\Psi_I = \sum_{n,j} U_n(\mathbf{R}_j)\, a(n,j). \quad (27.12)$$

The $b(n, \mathbf{k})$'s form a complete set provided one sums both over the n's and the $\mathbf{k}$'s. Also the $a(j)$'s form a complete set provided one includes all the n's. For Ψ_I to be normalized we require that

$$\langle \Psi_I | \Psi_I \rangle = \sum_{m,n,i,j} U_m^*(\mathbf{R}_i)\, U_n(\mathbf{R}_j) \int a_m^*(\mathbf{r} - \mathbf{R}_i)\, a_n(\mathbf{r} - \mathbf{R}_j)\, d\tau_r$$

$$= \sum_{m,n,i,j} U_m^*(\mathbf{R}_i)\, U_n(\mathbf{R}_j)\, \delta_{mn} \delta_{ij}$$

$$= \sum_{m,i} |U_m(\mathbf{R}_i)|^2 = 1. \quad (27.12a)$$

If only one band is used, then

$$\sum_i |U_m(\mathbf{R}_i)|^2 = 1. \quad (27.12b)$$

If two functions of the type (27.12) are employed, they should be orthogonal; hence

* $\mathcal{H}_0$ defines the a's and the b's.

$$\langle \Psi_I(A)|\Psi_I(B)\rangle = \sum_{m,n,i,j} U_m^*(\mathbf{R}_i)\, U_n'(\mathbf{R}_j) \int a_m^*(\mathbf{r}-\mathbf{R}_i)\, a_n(\mathbf{r}-\mathbf{R}_j)\, d\tau_r$$

$$= \sum_{m,n,i,j} U_m^*(\mathbf{R}_j)\, U_n'(\mathbf{R}_i)\, \delta_{nm}\, \delta_{ij}$$

$$= \sum_{m,i} U_m^*(\mathbf{R}_i)\, U_m'(\mathbf{R}_i) = 0, \qquad (27.12c)$$

or
$$\langle \Psi_I(A)|\Psi_I(B)\rangle = \sum_i U_m^*(\mathbf{R}_i)\, U_m'(\mathbf{R}_i) = \delta_{AB} \qquad (27.12d)$$

when a single electronic band can be used.

Combining (27.12) with $\mathcal{H}_0 + \mathcal{H}_1$ results in

$$\sum_{m,j} [\epsilon_n(\mathbf{R}_i - \mathbf{R}_j)\,\delta_{nm} + V_{nm}(\mathbf{R}_i,\mathbf{R}_j)]\, U_m(\mathbf{R}_j) = E_T U_n(\mathbf{R}_i), \qquad (27.13)$$

E_T in Eq. (27.13) is the eigenvalue associated with $\mathcal{H}_0 + \mathcal{H}_1$ and

$$V_{n,m}(\mathbf{R}_i,\mathbf{R}_j) = \int a^*(n,i)\, \mathcal{H}_1\, a(m,j)\, d\tau_r . \qquad (27.13a)$$

To obtain (27.13) an eigenfunction equation has been assumed which determines Ψ_I and we have used (27.11) to obtain the first term of (27.13). We have written $a(n,i)$ for $a_n(\mathbf{r}-\mathbf{R}_i)$. If $\mathcal{H}_1$ varies slowly over a unit cell, the following equation can be obtained:

$$\int a^*(n,i)\, \mathcal{H}_1\, a(m,j)\, d\tau_r$$

$$= \mathcal{H}_1(\mathbf{R}_j) \int a^*(n,i)\, a(m,j)\, d\tau_r$$

$$= \mathcal{H}_1(\mathbf{R}_j)\, \delta_{ji}\, \delta_{nm}. \qquad (27.14)$$

The second step can be justified if $\mathcal{H}_1$ varies only a small amount over the jth cell, since $a_m(\mathbf{r}-\mathbf{R}_j)$ approaches zero unless r is inside the jth cell. This approximation holds near a vacancy but not at it. Hence, $V_{nm}(\mathbf{R}_i,\mathbf{R}_j)$ is simply the perturbation potential at $\mathbf{R}_j$. We would like to write $\sum_{mj}\epsilon_n(\mathbf{R}_i-\mathbf{R}_j)\, U_m(\mathbf{R}_j)\,\delta_{nm}$ in an alternate form so that $\mathbf{k}$ can play the role of a momentum operator. Slater (S) has shown that this can be done as follows:

$$\sum_{m,j} U_m(\mathbf{R}_j)\, \epsilon_n(\mathbf{R}_i - \mathbf{R}_j)\,\delta_{nm}$$

$$= \sum_j U_n(\mathbf{R}_j) \int a^*(n,i)\, \mathcal{H}_0\, a(n,j)\, d\tau_r$$

$$= \frac{1}{N} \sum_{j,\mathbf{k},\mathbf{k}'} U_n(\mathbf{R}_j) \int b^*(n,\mathbf{k})\, e^{i\mathbf{k}\cdot\mathbf{R}_i}\, \mathcal{H}_0\, b(n,\mathbf{k}')\, e^{-i\mathbf{k}'\cdot\mathbf{R}_j}\, d\tau_r$$

$$= \frac{1}{N} \sum_{j,\mathbf{k}} U_n(\mathbf{R}_j)\, E_n(\mathbf{k})\, \exp[-i\mathbf{k}\cdot(\mathbf{R}_j-\mathbf{R}_i)] \qquad (27.15)$$

where (27.1) has been used.

Let us now write the eigenvalue for the perfect crystal $E(\mathbf{k})$ (a function of $\mathbf{k}$) in a Fourier expansion:

$$E(n, \mathbf{k}) = E_n(\mathbf{k}) = \sum_j A_n(\mathbf{R}_j) e^{-i\mathbf{k}\cdot\mathbf{R}_j}. \qquad (27.16)$$

Hence, using (27.15),

$$\sum_{m,j} U_m(\mathbf{R}_j)\,\epsilon_n(\mathbf{R}_i-\mathbf{R}_j)\,\delta_{nm}$$

$$= \frac{1}{N}\sum_{kj} E(n, \mathbf{k})\,U_n(\mathbf{R}_j)\exp[i\mathbf{k}\cdot(\mathbf{R}_i-\mathbf{R}_j)]$$

$$= \frac{1}{N}\sum_{k,j,j'} A_n(\mathbf{R}_i-\mathbf{R}_{j'})\,U_n(\mathbf{R}_j)\exp\{i\mathbf{k}\cdot[(\mathbf{R}_i-\mathbf{R}_j)-(\mathbf{R}_i-\mathbf{R}_{j'})]\}$$

$$= \sum_j A_n(\mathbf{R}_i-\mathbf{R}_j)\,U_n(\mathbf{R}_j) = \sum_s A_n(\mathbf{R}_s)\,U_n(\mathbf{R}_i-\mathbf{R}_s) \qquad (27.17)$$

where (27.4a) has again been used. We may further write:

$$U_n(\mathbf{R}_j-\mathbf{R}_s) = [U_n(\mathbf{R})]_{\mathbf{R}_j} - \left[\frac{d}{dR}U_n(\mathbf{R})\right]_{\mathbf{R}_j}\mathbf{R}_s + \frac{1}{2}\left[\frac{d^2}{dR^2}U_n(\mathbf{R})\right]_{\mathbf{R}_j}\mathbf{R}_s{}^2$$

$$= [e^{-\mathbf{R}_s\cdot\nabla}U_n(\mathbf{r})]_{\mathbf{R}_j}. \qquad (27.18)$$

The first line is symbolic and applies to the one-dimensional case. The correct three-dimensional expression arises from the expansion of the last line. The coefficient U_n as defined by (27.12) is not a continuous function of the variable $\mathbf{r}$. They have been replaced by a continuous function which equals $U_m(\mathbf{R}_j)$ at $\mathbf{r}=\mathbf{R}_j$. The reason small $\mathbf{r}$ is introduced here is that we shall talk of an envelope function which in the limit of small perturbations varies little over a cell. Using the foregoing two equations results in

$$\sum_j U_n(\mathbf{R}_j)\,\epsilon_n(\mathbf{R}_i-\mathbf{R}_j) =$$

$$\sum_s A(\mathbf{R}_s)\,e^{-\mathbf{R}_s\cdot\nabla}\,U_n(\mathbf{r}) = E_n\!\left(\frac{1}{i}\nabla\right)U_n. \qquad (27.19)$$

In (27.19) we have replaced $\mathbf{k}$ by $(-i\nabla)$. Hence, (27.13) takes the form

$$E_n(-i\nabla)\,U_n(\mathbf{r}) + \sum_{m,j} V_{nm}(\mathbf{R}_i,\mathbf{R}_j)\,U_m(\mathbf{r}) = E_T\,U_n(\mathbf{r}). \qquad (27.20)$$

This is a "Schrödinger" equation in the sense that the quasimomentum $\hbar\mathbf{k}$ is replaced by the operator $(\hbar/i)\nabla$. In (27.20) we consider $E_n(-i\nabla)$ to be the eigenvalue associated with the perfect lattice. It is essentially "exact" since no approximations have been made. The only change is that the first term has been written in operator form. Now we make the approximations

$$V_{nm} = 0 \qquad \text{for} \qquad n \neq m$$

or to obtain a *differential* equation:

$$V_{nn}(\mathbf{R}_i, \mathbf{R}_j) = \mathscr{H}_1(\mathbf{r}) \qquad \text{for} \qquad i = j$$
$$= 0 \qquad \text{for} \qquad i \neq j. \tag{27.21}$$

Then

$$[E_0(-i\nabla) + \mathscr{H}_1(\mathbf{r})] U(\mathbf{r}) = E_T U(\mathbf{r}). \tag{27.21a}$$

If $E_0(\mathbf{k})$ has a maximum or a minimum in $\mathbf{k}$ space, one may write (27.21a) in an alternate form by expanding about such a point, $\mathbf{k}_0$, $k_x(0)$, $k_y(0)$, and $k_z(0)$, namely

$$E_0(\mathbf{k}) = E_0 + \frac{1}{2}\left(\frac{\partial^2 E_0}{\partial k_x^2}\right)_0 [(k_x - k_x(0)]^2 + \frac{1}{2}\left(\frac{\partial^2 E_0}{\partial k_y^2}\right)_0 [(k_y - k_y(0)]^2$$
$$+ \frac{1}{2}\left(\frac{\partial^2 E_0}{\partial k_z^2}\right)_0 [(k_z - k_z(0)]^2 + \cdots \tag{27.22}$$

where E_0 is evaluated at $\mathbf{k}_0$ and the axis of the $\mathbf{k}$ vector has been chosen in such a manner that terms in $(k_x - k_x(0))(k_y - k_y(0))$ do not appear. It is an advantage to replace U_n by a "normalized" function hence the substitution

$$U_n = n^{-1/2} w(\mathbf{r}) e^{i\mathbf{k}_0 \cdot \mathbf{r}}. \tag{27.23}$$

The factor $n^{-1/2} = (V/N)^{-1/2}$ (where V is the volume) is necessary to normalize w. The phase factor appears because the energy minimum in k-space is at $\mathbf{k}_0$. To show the orthogonality condition we return to Eqs. (27.12b) and (27.12c) and write

$$\sum_i |U(\mathbf{R}_i)|^2 \to \frac{n}{n}\int w^2 \, d\tau_r = 1 \tag{27.23a}$$

because $\Delta N = (N/V)\Delta V$. Further,

$$\sum_i U^*(\mathbf{R}_i) U'(\mathbf{R}_i) = \langle w | w' \rangle = 0 \tag{27.23b}$$

for two different Ψ_I's. Returning to Eq. (27.21), the following Schrödinger equation is obtained (the *effective mass* approximation):

$$-\frac{\hbar^2}{2}\left[\frac{1}{m_x}\frac{\partial^2}{\partial x^2} + \frac{1}{m_y}\frac{\partial^2}{\partial y^2} + \frac{1}{m_z}\frac{\partial^2}{\partial z^2}\right] w(\mathbf{r}) + [E_0 + \mathscr{H}_1(\mathbf{r})] w(\mathbf{r})$$
$$= E_T w(\mathbf{r}). \tag{27.24}$$

The effective mass is defined by the relation

$$\frac{1}{m_x} = \frac{1}{\hbar^2} \frac{\partial^2 E_0(\mathbf{k})}{\partial k_x^2}.$$ (27.24a)

An alternate useful form of (27.24) is

$$-\frac{\hbar^2}{2}\left[\frac{1}{m_x}\frac{\partial^2 w}{\partial x^2} + \frac{1}{m_y}\frac{\partial^2 w}{\partial y^2} + \frac{1}{m_z}\frac{\partial^2 w}{\partial z^2}\right] + \mathscr{H}_1 w = (E_T - E_0) w.$$ (27.25)

The subscript n on w implies that there may be more than one solution of Eq. (27.25). In obtaining (27.24) the major approximation made is that U_n is determined only from V_{nn}, that is, Eq. (27.21a). This involves two approximations: (1) only Bloch functions associated with a single band were employed, and (2) that V_{nn} varied only a small amount over a cell. Returning to Eqs. (27.12) and (27.23) one obtains:

$$\Psi_I = \frac{1}{n^{1/2}} \sum_j w(\mathbf{R}_j) \exp(i\mathbf{k}_0 \cdot \mathbf{R}_j) a_n(\mathbf{r} - \mathbf{R}_j).$$ (27.26)

Equation (27.26) shows that Ψ_I is a sum of Wannier functions which are associated with various atoms surrounding the imperfection. w gives the amplitude of the function and $\exp(i\mathbf{k}_0 \cdot \mathbf{r})$ gives the phase factor.

Perhaps the simplest possible example one can obtain is to assume *ad hoc* that $a_n(\mathbf{r} - \mathbf{R}_j)$ is approximated by a function which has the following properties

$$a_n(\mathbf{r}) = v^{-1/2} \qquad \text{for} \qquad r < \tfrac{1}{2}a$$
$$= 0 \qquad \text{for} \qquad r > \tfrac{1}{2}a;$$ (27.27)

a is the interionic distance, not to be confused with a_n, while $v = (\pi/6)a^3$. This, of course, is a very crude assumption. Equation (27.27) distributes the electron uniformly on the ion located on the site at $\mathbf{R}_j$. It ignores the void spaces when one has close-packed spheres and the fact that the Wannier functions can overlap. Equation (27.9) does not assure one that there is no overlap, but only that the integral of the overlap is zero. Returning to (27.25) the following approximate form for Ψ_I is obtained:

$$\Psi_I = \frac{1}{(vn)^{1/2}} w(\mathbf{r}) e^{i\mathbf{k}_0 \cdot \mathbf{r}}.$$ (27.28)

Equation (27.25) tells one how to obtain w provided the approximations made in obtaining it are justifiable. These approximations should apply at a moderate distance from a negative-ion vacancy. They cannot be justified at the negative-ion vacancy itself where $\mathscr{H}_1$ and $V_{nm}(\mathbf{R}_i, \mathbf{R}_j)$ are certainly large. To obtain the actual wave function at a point within a cell, one must use (27.26).

Two very basic properties of Wannier functions have been proven by Smith (Chapter 11). Let us write the wave function associated with the imperfection in the form

$$\Psi_I = \frac{1}{n^{1/2}} \sum_j e^{i\mathbf{k}_0 \cdot \mathbf{R}_j} w(\mathbf{R}_j) a(\mathbf{r} - \mathbf{R}_j) \qquad (27.29)$$

where the subscript n is dropped. We stress that w is associated with a *band* and a *solution* of (27.25). Now, using Eq. (27.8a) results in:

$$\Psi_I = n^{-1/2} \sum_j e^{i\mathbf{k}_0 \cdot \mathbf{R}_j} w(\mathbf{R}_j) N^{-1/2} \sum_{\mathbf{k}} e^{-i\mathbf{k} \cdot \mathbf{R}_j} b(\mathbf{k})$$

$$= n^{-1/2} \sum_{\mathbf{k}} \left\{ N^{-1/2} \sum_j w(\mathbf{R}_j) e^{i(\mathbf{k}_0 - \mathbf{k}) \cdot \mathbf{R}_j} \right\} b(\mathbf{k})$$

$$= n^{-1/2} \sum_{\mathbf{k}} g(\mathbf{k}) b(\mathbf{k}). \qquad (27.30)$$

Likewise,

$$\Psi_I = n^{-1/2} \sum_{\mathbf{k},j} g(\mathbf{k}) N^{-1/2} e^{i\mathbf{k} \cdot \mathbf{R}_j} a(\mathbf{R}_j)$$

$$= n^{-1/2} \sum_j e^{i\mathbf{k}_0 \cdot \mathbf{R}_j} \left\{ N^{-1/2} \sum_{\mathbf{k}} e^{i(\mathbf{k} - \mathbf{k}_0) \cdot \mathbf{R}_j} g(\mathbf{k}) \right\} a(\mathbf{R}_j). \qquad (27.31)$$

Hence, the following important relations are obtained:

$$g(\mathbf{k}) = N^{-1/2} \sum_j e^{i(\mathbf{k}_0 - \mathbf{k}) \cdot \mathbf{R}_j} w(\mathbf{R}_j), \qquad (27.30a)$$

$$w(\mathbf{r}) = N^{-1/2} \sum_{\mathbf{k}} g(\mathbf{k}) e^{i(\mathbf{k} - \mathbf{k}_0) \cdot \mathbf{r}} \qquad (27.31a)$$

where we have replaced $\mathbf{R}_j$ by $\mathbf{r}$.

If the major contribution to Ψ_I comes from around the minimum then we may approximate it by the form

$$\Psi_I = n^{-1/2} \sum_{\mathbf{k}} g(\mathbf{k}) e^{i\mathbf{k} \cdot \mathbf{r}} u(\mathbf{k}_0)$$

where Eq. (27.2) has been used and $u_{\mathbf{k}}(\mathbf{r}) \to u(\mathbf{k}_0)$. Then

$$\Psi_I = n^{-1/2} u(\mathbf{k}_0) e^{i\mathbf{k}_0 \cdot \mathbf{r}} \left\{ \sum_{\mathbf{k}} e^{i(\mathbf{k} - \mathbf{k}_0) \cdot \mathbf{r}} g(\mathbf{k}) \right\}$$

$$= V^{1/2} b_{\mathbf{k}_0} w(\mathbf{r}). \qquad (27.32)$$

The dimensions of the b's and the w's are $V^{-1/2}$, hence one must expect a factor of $V^{1/2}$ when one combines the w's and the b's to form Ψ_I as is done in (27.32).

Consider next the fraction of an electron within the volume ΔV.

$$|\Psi_I|^2 \Delta V = \frac{1}{n} \int_{\Delta V} \sum_{j,j'} w^*(\mathbf{R}_{j'}) w(\mathbf{R}_j) a_n{}^*(\mathbf{r}-\mathbf{R}_{j'}) a_n(\mathbf{r}-\mathbf{R}_j) d\tau_v. \quad (27.33)$$

If the major portion of the a's are concentrated in ΔV then the integral over ΔV is almost the same as over V and

$$|\Psi_I|^2 \Delta V = (V/N) \sum_{j,j'}^{\Delta V} w^*(\mathbf{R}_{j'}) w(\mathbf{R}_j) \delta_{jj'}. \quad (27.34)$$

The sum over the j's in (27.34) gives the number of cells within ΔV or $(N/V)\Delta V$ which results in the very important equation

$$|\Psi_I|^2 \Delta V = |w(\mathbf{R}_j)|^2 \Delta V$$

or

$$|\Psi_I|^2 dV = |w(\mathbf{r})|^2 d\tau_v. \quad (27.35)$$

This times the electronic charge is the average charge over many cells. To find the *exact* charge at a point $\mathbf{r}$ we must use an *exact* expression for Ψ_I.

c. The Approximation of Tibbs

An alternate approach in part due to Tibbs (S) is useful. It will now be outlined, not exactly in the manner given by Tibbs, however. Ψ_I is written in the form

$$\Psi_I = \phi(\mathbf{r}) b(\mathbf{k}_0) \quad (27.36)$$

where $\mathbf{k}_0$ is a minimum energy point in $\mathbf{k}$ space. The Schrödinger operator is taken in the form

$$-\frac{\hbar^2}{2m} \nabla^2 + V_p + \mathscr{H}_1 \quad (27.37)$$

where V_p is the potential energy for the perfect crystal. $\mathscr{H}_0$ equals the first two terms of (27.37). Operating on Ψ_I one obtains

$$b(\mathbf{k}_0) \left[-\frac{\hbar^2}{2m} \nabla^2 \phi + \mathscr{H}_1 \phi \right] - \frac{\hbar^2}{m} \nabla \phi \cdot \nabla b(\mathbf{k}_0)$$

$$= (E_T - E_0) \phi b(\mathbf{k}_0). \quad (27.38)$$

We now assume that the last term on the left averages to zero because the

$b(\mathbf{k}_0)$ oscillate rapidly within the solid. This is justified at large distances from the negative-ion vacancy where the variation in $\mathscr{H}_1$ is small, but is hard to justify within the vacancy. This is Tibbs' equation; note the true mass is used.

We stress that the first method uses Wannier functions and introduces an *effective* mass. Since Slater's method applies rigorously to shallow traps, we must assume that the $\nabla\phi\cdot\nabla b$ term in (27.38) need not be small and cannot, in general, be neglected. It is the term which introduces the effective mass in Section 27b. Equation (27.32)* is identical to (27.36) with ϕ replaced by $V^{1/2} w(r)$. The differential equation which determines w approximately is (27.24). Both approaches have approximations which cannot be justified rigorously for the F-center.

Within the vacancy itself (associated with the F-center) there is no need to introduce either the Bloch or the Wannier functions and one can, in principle, solve for the wave function directly. To calculate the field in the vacancy, we may consider the ions as point charges and use some standard summation techniques. Unfortunately, this does not give us the eigenfunction outside the vacancy. To calculate the potential rigorously one must determine the displacements and the polarization of the ions around the imperfection. Further, at the edge of the vacancy the wave functions must join smoothly. This assumes that a boundary exists between the crystal and the vacancy, which is, of course, pure fiction.

REFERENCES

B. S. Gourary and F. J. Adrian, *Solid State Physics* **10**, 127 (1960).
G. F. Koster and J. C. Slater, *Phys. Rev.* **96**, 1208 (1954).
J. A. Krumhansl and N. Schwartz, *Phys. Rev.* **89**, 1154 (1953).
S. I. Pekar, "Research in Electron Theory of Crystals." M.S., A.E.C. tr-5575. U.S. Dept. of Commerce.
J. H. Simpson, *Proc. Roy. Soc.* **A197**, 269 (1949).
J. C. Slater, *Phys. Rev.* **76**, 1592 (1949).
S. R. Tibbs, *Trans. Faraday Soc.* **35**, 1971 (1939).
R. F. Wood and H. W. Joy, *Phys. Rev.* **136**, A451 (1964).
R. F. Wood and J. Korringa, *Phys. Rev.* **123**, 1138 (1961).

28. THE F-CENTER CALCULATIONS

a. The Simplifying Assumptions

Utilizing a concept due to W. Jost (see Mott and Gurney, p. 56), one divides the crystal into two parts. The vacancy is considered to be a

---

* Note that $w(\mathbf{r})$ is normalized over the crystal.

vacuum (it is assumed spherical) and the dielectric around it is considered as a continuum or as a semicontinuum depending on the problem under consideration. Within the vacancy there is no crystal and the Schrödinger equation has the simple form

$$\left[-\frac{\hbar^2}{2m}\nabla^2 + V(\mathbf{r})\right]\Psi_I = E_T\Psi_I \qquad (28.1)$$

where m is the *true* electron mass and $V(r)$ is the potential in the vacuum due to the charge distribution in the crystal (outside the vacuum). In a perfect crystal the Schrödinger equation is again given by (28.1) provided $V(r)$ is the actual potential at $\mathbf{r}$. It is composed of the ion core potential V_c and the potential due to the surrounding charges V_m (Madelung). Detailed calculations indicate that the variation in the Madelung potential over an ion is small. Hence, for the sake of simplicity, we may assume that V_m is a constant over an ion, its value being $\pm \alpha e/a$. α is Madelung's constant (1.746 for the NaCl lattice) and a is the distance between nearest neighbors. When we consider the effects of the missing negative ion and the distortion surrounding it, a third term has to be added to the potential, namely V_I, the distortion potential. V_I occurs because (1) there is a missing ion; this creates a field since the crystal, without the electron, is no longer neutral; (2) the ions are slightly displaced from their equilibrium positions, and (3) they are polarized.*

Since V_I is reasonably small away from the vacancy one may assume that (27.24) applies and $\mathscr{H}_1(\mathbf{r}) = V_I(\mathbf{r})$, hence

$$\left[-\frac{\hbar^2}{2m^*}\nabla^2 + V_I(\mathbf{r})\right]w = (E_T - E_0)\,w. \qquad (28.2)$$

In Eq. (28.2), m^* is the effective scalar mass. To obtain Ψ_I, w has to be multiplied by the phase factors [see Eq. (27.23)], a Wannier function and then summed—Eq. (27.12).

If Tibbs' approximation is used, Eq. (28.2) takes the form

$$-\frac{\hbar^2}{2m}\nabla^2\phi + V_I\phi - \frac{\hbar^2}{m}\frac{1}{b(\mathbf{k}_0)}\nabla b(\mathbf{k}_0)\cdot\nabla\phi = (E_T - E_0)\phi \qquad (28.3a)$$

where now the complete wave function has the form

$$\Psi = \phi b(\mathbf{k}_0). \qquad (28.3b)$$

We stress that in reality two types of Schrödinger equations exist, one

---

* Strictly speaking, V_c is changed because the ions are displaced from their positions in a perfect crystal. To simplify the problem, one assumes that this can all be taken care of in V_I.

inside and another outside the Jost sphere. Note that the total eigenvalue appears in (28.1) while the difference in two eigenvalues appears in (28.2) and (28.3). At the surface of the sphere, the usual quantum mechanical requirements of continuity apply.

The foregoing treatment is completely rigorous provided one may evaluate $V_I(\mathbf{r})$. The idea of using two equations was employed by Tibbs and by Krumhansl and Schwartz (S). This approach seems, to the author, to be the most correct one given so far. It leads to lengthy and complex calculations. We shall present the simplifications made by Simpson (S), who assumed that Eq. (28.1) or Eq. (27.32) applies throughout the crystal.*

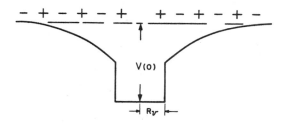

FIG. 28.1. Potential well used for a simplified calculation of the F-center.

This is equivalent to assuming that: (1) m^* of (28.2) equals m, or that the term $-(\hbar^2/m)[1/b(k_0)]\nabla b(k_0)\cdot\nabla\phi$ of (28.3a) averages to zero, and (2) that one refers the energy to the bottom of the conduction band. Item (2) may or may not be a real limitation since one is making calculations in a polar material; it neglects the electron affinity.

Thus a single Schrödinger equation is employed, although it has two parts since V is calculated by two different methods inside and outside the Jost sphere. Inside the sphere a constant potential will be assumed. Its depth is determined from the potential at the center of the Jost sphere. The sides of the well will be approximated by a Coulomb field with corrections which account for the ionic displacements (see Fig. 28.1). The radius of the well is set equal to the Mott-Littleton value. These concepts will now be described in detail.

b. The Polarization

One of the central problems in calculating V_I is the handling of the polarization of the solid. This problem enters into the calculation and has

---

* One calculates $V_I(\mathbf{r})$ relative to an average $V_m + V_c$ instead of $V_m(\mathbf{r}) + V_c(\mathbf{r})$ as one should.

a major result on the eigenvalues associated with the trapped electron. This problem is therefore considered in detail.

When an electron is placed near an ion, the system's energy may be computed by making a series of approximations. Some of these are:

(1) One may completely ignore the interactions between the free electron and the bound electrons.

(2) One may take the electron-electron interaction into account by averaging the potential energy over the positions of the bound and free electrons, while ignoring the Pauli exclusion principle (Hartree's approximation).

(3) One may repeat (2) but include the Pauli exclusion principle (Fock's approximation).

(4) One may assume that the free electron influences the position of the bound electrons and vice versa to the extent that the one electron approximation breaks down.

The crudest method of considering item (4) is to assume that we are dealing with polarizable ions which respond instantaneously to the position of the free electron. If the electron vibrates in such a manner that it sets up a field

$$E_0 + E_1(e^{i\omega t} + e^{-i\omega t}) \qquad (28.4\text{a})$$

at the ion; then one may show that the ionic polarization (Born and Huang, p. 189) has the form

$$\text{const}\left\{\frac{1}{\omega_r + \omega} + \frac{1}{\omega_r - \omega}\right\}. \qquad (28.4\text{b})$$

$\hbar\omega_r$ is the difference in energy between the ground and the first excited states. ω is the angular frequency of the polarizing field; it equals zero for E_0 and ω for E_1. In (28.4b) if one neglects the last term one returns to the Hartree-Fock approximation.* For a bound electron, ω_r approximately equals the electronic binding energy divided by $\hbar$. For an ion, $\hbar\omega_r$ is the binding energy to the ion and is of the order of the frequency associated with the energy it takes for an electron to go from the valence to the conduction band. Since the binding energy of an electron in a negative-ion vacancy is much smaller than the binding energy of the electrons in the ions, one may neglect ω in (28.4b).

This approach is a crude attempt to go beyond the Hartree-Fock approximation, because it makes the bound electrons respond to the

---

* The first term gives very little polarization since $\omega_r + \omega$ is large. Actually ω is not very much smaller than ω_r and these approximations are not completely justified.

instantaneous position of the extra electron, which moves more slowly (having less binding and less kinetic energy). Perhaps the crudeness of this approach introduces a large error; although it probably does, it is nevertheless a step in the right direction. We shall shortly see that the polarization introduces large corrections and that it has to be included.

Equation (28.4b) also applies to the polarization that arises from the displacements of the ions. Here ω_r is of the order of the ionic vibrations, i.e., $10^{13} \sec^{-1}$ and $\omega_r \ll \omega$. The ions see only the first term of (28.4a) which arises from the *average* electron distribution.

These arguments suggest that the ion core electrons follow the motion of the trapped electron adiabatically, while the displacement polarization arises from the average field of the trapped electron. This must be taken into account in calculating V_I. These differences in the response times of the two types of polarization are the bases of the low- and high-frequency dielectric constant. An elementary way to achieve this is based on the work of Jost and is discussed in detail by Mott and Gurney. The author doubts that this method is rigorous or that it gives the correct polarization to better than a factor of two. He favors an alternate approach suggested by Mott and Littleton (S) (see also Markham and Seitz, S).*

Consider first the extremely simple case. We start by placing an electron on an ion at the origin O in a continuous dielectric with high- and low-frequency dielectric constants of κ_∞ and κ_0, respectively. Since the extra electron is loosely bound, the ionic polarizability responds adiabatically to its presence, while the displacement polarization only responds to E_0 of (28.4a). To calculate the energy of the ionic polarization, we assume that a spherical hole of radius R_i exists in the dielectric.† If a

---

* Gouray and Adrian (S) have adopted an alternate point of view and ignore the polarization in the first approximation. They believe that the problem is similar to the Hartree-Fock procedure used in atomic calculations where the polarization of the inner, more closely bound electrons is not considered. Further, the electron in the ground state is within the vacancy. In the author's opinion, the polarization problem is a primary factor in calculating the energy difference between the bound states of the *F*-center. Figure 12.1 shows the large difference between $h\nu(e)$ and $h\nu(a)$. This must be accounted for in a fundamental manner and must arise from the polarization. This the author believes is a weakness in the point-ion lattice method. Also, it cannot treat the ionic field problem rigorously unless it falls back on the treatment of Slater or Tibbs.

† This hole is not the negative-ion vacancy but is introduced in a fictitious manner to take account of the polarization that an extra charge introduces in an alkali halide. It also should not be confused with a semiconductor "hole", that is, an electron vacancy in the valence band. We here assume a *point* electron.

charge q is placed at the center of the hole, the electric displacement at a distance $\mathbf{r}$ beyond R_i is

$$\mathbf{D(r)} = (q/r^3)\mathbf{r}, \tag{28.5a}$$

while the electric field is

$$\mathbf{E(r)} = (1/\kappa)(q/r^3)\mathbf{r}. \tag{28.5b}$$

Hence, the net field due to the polarization is $-(q/r^3)[1-(1/\kappa)]\mathbf{r}$. The net polarization charge on the surface of the sphere is $-q[1-(1/\kappa)]$. This produces a potential

$$-\frac{q}{R_i}\left(1-\frac{1}{\kappa}\right) \tag{28.6}$$

at the center of the sphere. If we add a charge dq to the sphere, the work done against the polarization is

$$-\frac{q}{R_i}\left(1-\frac{1}{\kappa}\right)dq. \tag{28.7}$$

The total work to bring an electron from outside arising from polarization is

$$V_p = -\int_0^e \frac{1}{R_i}\left(1-\frac{1}{\kappa}\right)q\,dq = -\frac{1}{2}\frac{e^2}{R_i}\left(1-\frac{1}{\kappa}\right). \tag{28.8}$$

Since the electron cannot be localized on a particular ion in the crystal, only the high-frequency dielectric constant enters into this problem and we set $\kappa=\kappa_\infty$.* The reader will recall that when one calculates $b(\mathbf{k})$ in metals, employing the method developed by Wigner and Seitz (or a modification of it), one deals with *neutral* cells which make up the solid. In our case one does not have neutral cells and corrections are required. Tibbs attempted to calculate $b(\mathbf{k})$ for an electron in the conduction band. Actually a $b(\mathbf{k})$ does not localize the electron but wave packets made from $b(\mathbf{k})$'s do and one actually deals with this situation. The electron will probably localize itself since this will lower its energy. If the electron remained in the conduction band, this effect would not be important since it would be a constant; however, when we take it from the conduction band and place it in a negative-ion vacancy, these terms must be considered. The introduction of R_i is *certainly* very artificial but it seems to be the best available approach at present.

---

* The polaron problem will not be considered. We shall immediately place the electron into a vacancy.

The potential at the center of a negative-ion vacancy is composed of two terms. One is the Madelung term

$$\alpha e/a. \tag{28.9}$$

A second term arises from a term similar to (28.6), that is,

$$-\frac{e}{R_v}\left(1-\frac{1}{\kappa_0}\right) \tag{28.10}$$

where R_v is the radius of the vacancy and κ_0 is the static dielectric constant. Equation (28.10) accounts for the contribution of the polarization of the lattice. To actually determine R_v one must make some rather detailed and involved calculations. The basic step in this direction has been made by Mott and Littleton (S). They actually calculated the potential at the center of a negative-ion vacancy and evaluated R_v using (28.10) and known values of κ_0. The discrete nature of the lattice was included. The first calculation assumed that the ions were held at their equilibrium positions, κ_0 is replaced by κ_∞ and the potential due to ion core polarization is (from Mott and Littleton, S)

$$3.0 \text{ ev} \qquad \text{(for NaCl)}. \tag{28.11a}$$

If we let the ions move ($\kappa = \kappa_0$) the foregoing value changes to

$$6.0 \text{ ev} \qquad \text{(for NaCl)} \tag{28.11b}$$

(from Mott and Littleton). Equation (28.11b) includes the Born-Mayer repulsive term which would push the nearest neighbors into the vacancy. Actually the ionic displacements are outward when one considers the coulomb and repulsive forces. The value for the Madelung term is

$$9.0 \text{ ev} \qquad \text{(for NaCl)}. \tag{28.11c}$$

It is hence of the same order as the various polarization effects, provided one has a total electric charge equal to e (the electronic charge) in the vacancy.

The value of R_v is not $(3/4\pi)^{1/3}a$, as one might expect, but is very much larger; a is the distance between nearest neighbors. The calculation of Mott and Littleton indicates it to be $0.95a$ for a negative-ion vacancy in NaCl. The preceding figures are certainly only approximate and superior ones could be obtained from more elaborate calculations, some of which may be in the literature. The figures are presented to indicate the order of magnitude of the effects.

The potential at the center of the vacancy is

$$\frac{\alpha e}{a} - \frac{e}{R_v}\left(1 - \frac{1}{\kappa_0}\right) \tag{28.12}$$

provided there is no electron there. If we put an electron into the center of the negative-ion vacancy, its potential will decrease to $-\alpha e^2/a$ since the center is now neutral and there is no surrounding polarization. The repulsive Born-Mayer force is ignored. The energy involved is

$$
\begin{aligned}
E_v &= -\frac{\alpha e^2}{a} + \int_0^e \frac{1}{R_v}\left(1 - \frac{1}{\kappa_0}\right)(e - q)\,dq \\
&= -\frac{\alpha e^2}{a} + \frac{1}{2}\frac{e^2}{R_v}\left(1 - \frac{1}{\kappa_0}\right).
\end{aligned}
\tag{28.13}
$$

Equation (28.13) takes into account the energy change which occurs in the environment. It considers a truly adiabatic process (infinitely slow) and κ_0 is the low-frequency dielectric constant. The expression can be written in the form

$$E_v = -\frac{\alpha e^2}{a} + \frac{1}{2}\frac{e^2}{R_v}\left(1 - \frac{1}{\kappa_\infty}\right) + \frac{1}{2}\frac{e^2}{R_v}\left(\frac{1}{\kappa_\infty} - \frac{1}{\kappa_0}\right). \tag{28.13a}$$

The first term of (28.13a) is due to the Madelung energy, the second arises from the polarization of the ions, and the third is due to the ionic displacements. The $\frac{1}{2}$ in the second and third term arises because we consider an adiabatic process. Since the electronic processes are fast compared to the readjustment times of the ions, the displacements must be determined in a more careful manner. Hence (28.13a) can be written as follows

$$E_v = -\frac{\alpha e^2}{a} + \frac{1}{2}\frac{e^2}{R_v}\left(1 - \frac{1}{\kappa_\infty}\right) + V_d \tag{28.13b}$$

where V_d is the energy due to the displacement of the ions.

If the electron is taken from a point within the crystal the energy given by Eq. (28.8) must be subtracted from (28.13b). $E(n,\mathbf{k})$ is neglected since we are only interested in the differences in energy—see Eq. (27.24a). Note that the only energy term which changes and which is not taken into account in Eq. (27.1) is term (28.6). It is for this reason that it should appear in (28.13a). Thus, the net potential energy is

$$V(0) = -\frac{\alpha e^2}{a} + \frac{1}{2}\frac{e^2}{R_v}\left(1 - \frac{1}{\kappa_\infty}\right) + \frac{1}{2}\frac{e^2}{R_i}\left(1 - \frac{1}{\kappa_\infty}\right) + V_d. \tag{28.14}$$

In view of the crudeness of the calculation, we set $R_v - R_i$ and obtain the expression originally given by Tibbs, namely

$$V(0) = -\frac{\alpha e^2}{a} + \frac{e^2}{R_v}\left(1 - \frac{1}{\kappa_\infty}\right) \qquad (28.15)$$

provided V_d is omitted in (28.15) since the electron is confined to the vacancy and the average effective charge seen from a point outside the vacancy is almost zero.*

To understand the physics of the situation, we remind the reader that the second and third terms of (28.14) arise for two different reasons. The second term appears because an electron is in a medium which has been polarized by a fictitious *positive* charge. The third term arises because the electron is taken from a point in the crystal where the polarization is due to itself, that is, a *negative* charge. This change from negative to positive charges accounts for the double terms and justifies Tibbs's expression.

Equation (28.15) will be discussed further, but let us examine V_d in some detail. The electron is not actually confined to the vacancy. The following definition is now made:

$$p(r) = \int_0^r 4\pi w^2 r^2 \, dr. \qquad (28.16)$$

Consider the ionic displacements outside the vacancy. Due to (27.34), $p(r)$ is the average charge contained within a sphere of radius r. If w is an s-function, or if one may use only a spherically symmetric part, then the average static field at r is

$$\frac{1}{\kappa_0}[1 - p(r)]\frac{e}{r^2}. \qquad (28.17)$$

Hence

$$-\left(1 - \frac{1}{\kappa_0}\right)[1 - p(r)]\,(e/r^2) \qquad (28.18a)$$

arises from the polarization while

$$[1 - p(r)]\,(e/r^2) \qquad (28.18b)$$

is due to the charge within r. The vacancy is assumed to have unit charge. These add to give (28.17). The polarization effects due to the susceptibility of the ions is given by

$$-\left(1 - \frac{1}{\kappa_\infty}\right)[1 - p(r)]\,(e/r^2). \qquad (28.19)$$

* Krumhansl and Schwartz (S) have suggested that one use Eq. (28.13) without considering the correction due to (28.8).

The difference between (28.18a) and (28.19), namely

$$\mathbf{F}_d(r) = -\left(\frac{1}{\kappa_\infty} - \frac{1}{\kappa_0}\right)[1 - p(r)]\,(e/r^3)\,\mathbf{r} \tag{28.20}$$

can be described as the field produced by the ionic displacements. They make the following

$$V_d = -\int_\infty^r eF_d(r)\,dr \tag{28.21}$$

contribution to the potential. V_d is a function of the wave function w associated with the trapped electron. Hence, w is required to evaluate the potential term in the Schrödinger equation. This means that V_d must be calculated in a self-consistent manner. We assume that the w wave function has the form

$$w_s(\mu) = w_\mu = (\mu^3/\pi)^{1/2}\,e^{-\mu r}. \tag{28.22a}*$$

We then obtain:

$$p(r) = 1 - e^{-2\mu r}(2\mu^2 r^2 + 2\mu r + 1) \tag{28.22b}$$

and

$$V_d(r) = V_\mu(r) = \frac{e^2}{r}\left(\frac{1}{\kappa_\infty} - \frac{1}{\kappa_0}\right)(1 + \mu r)\,e^{-2\mu r}. \tag{28.22c}$$

The potential due to the displacements at the center of the Jost sphere is $V_d(R_v)$ while outside it is given by $V_d(r)$. If μ is large so that $\mu R_v \gg 1$, the electron is concentrated within the vacancy and $p(R_v)$ approaches 1 while $V_d(R_v)$ approaches zero. In general, the electron will not be concentrated entirely within the vacancy and $V_d(R_v)$ of (28.22c) is not zero.

A reasonably simple form of $\mathscr{H}_I$ can be obtained if we calculate the depth at the center of the vacancy using Eq. (28.15) and approximate the potential by a sawed-off coulomb well. The depth of the well is given by $V(0)$, Eq. (28.15), while the sides $r > R_v$ are obtained from the expression

$$V(r) = -\frac{e^2}{\kappa_\infty r} + V_d(r), \tag{28.23}$$

see Fig. 28.1. This technique, due to Simpson, does the following: It raises the potential at the center of the vacancy by an amount equal to the "self-energy of the electron" which arises from the core polarization and ignores this energy outside the vacancy. The procedure is not completely logical and one might proceed as follows:

---

* s is the ground state of Eq. (27.25).

(1) Ignore the effects of the polarization of the ions. This is equivalent to assuming that V_p, Eq. (28.8), is always present and that it is a constant included in E_0 of Eq. (27.24a). The fact that there is no polarization within the negative-ion vacancy is ignored.

(2) The polarization effect due to the ionic displacements should include $p(r)$ arising from the charge within the vacancy as well as outside it. The ion at a distance r *sees* a charge of $e[1-p(r)]$, not simply e as assumed earlier. This process ignores the third term of Eq. (28.14) but considers that V_d is an important term.

The foregoing technique has its shortcomings, as has the method presented earlier. A complete understanding of the F-center problem requires that one resolve these questions, and they are far from being resolved at this time.

Actually, Eq. (28.15) has two unknowns, $V(0)$ and R_v. $V(0)$, however, has the form one would obtain from the concepts of the Jost sphere. The development leading up to Eq. (28.15) was necessary to justify the use of this equation for the F-center problem. Actually $V(0)$ without the Madelung term is calculated directly by the method of Mott and Littleton, and its actual value [in Eq. (28.15)] is used to evaluate R_v.

The sides of the well, given by (28.23) depend on w. Since V_d has its maximum value inside the vacancy one cannot justify this procedure. If μ is small, the complete shielding suggested by Simpson's approach requires a re-examination. Equation (28.11) indicates that the second term of (28.15) makes a sizable contribution. For NaCl, the Madelung depth is 9 ev, whereas the second term (28.15) gives 6 ev. If we assume that the ions around the vacancy do not readjust their positions, the hole depth would be only 3 ev. From these crude arguments, we see that the ion readjustment energies are of the order of volts and are of the correct *magnitude* to explain the Stokes's shift (see Fig. 12.1).

c. Some Calculations on the F-Center Wave Functions

To calculate the ground state, we use the variational principle. The energy is given by $(m^* = m)$

$$E_0(a) = E_T - E_0 = W_s(\lambda, \mu) = -\frac{\hbar^2}{2m} \int_0^\infty w_\lambda \nabla^2 w_\lambda \, d\tau_r + \int_0^{R_v} V_0 w_\lambda^2 \, d\tau_r$$

$$- e^2 \int_{R_v}^\infty \frac{1}{r\kappa_\infty} w_\lambda^2 \, d\tau_r + \int_{R_v}^\infty V_\mu w_\lambda^2 \, d\tau_r \qquad (28.24)$$

since the wave function (28.22a) is normalized. The third term arises from the vacancy which at large distances acts like a positive charge. The variation is taken in terms of λ, the parameter that enters directly into the wave function. The variation is not taken in terms of the potential V_μ. It is evaluated for the value of $\lambda=\mu$, which gives the minimum value of $W_s(\lambda,\mu)$ or $E_0(a)$, using the notation of Section 12. This procedure means that the potential associated with the vacancy is not altered during the variation procedure.

Two procedures have been used in applying the variational principle: One is due to Pekar (S); (for the other see Markham and Seitz, S).* The Born-Oppenheimer techniques require that one is at an absolute minimum with respect to the displacements of the ions (see Section 30a). This is really an expression of Newton's second law, that is, that at equilibrium there is no force on the ions (or nuclei). We may employ this and require that the W of Eq. (28.24) be an absolute minimum with respect to a variational parameter where λ has been set equal to μ before the variation. On the other hand, one may vary only the parameter which appears in the wave function and then set λ equal to μ, after the differentiation. In the second procedure one may have to require that the net forces on the ions are zero (that is, self-consistent), and some of these forces arise from electron-ion interactions and include the electronic wave function. Further work remains to be done to see the association of Pekar's method with the Born-Oppenheimer technique. The second approach can be very lengthy.

The excited state is calculated by using a p-function of the form

$$w_p = (\beta^5/\pi)^{1/2}\, r\, e^{-\beta r}\cos\theta. \tag{28.25}$$

The angular dependence means larger kinetic energy.† The total energy is given by

$$E_1(a) = W_p(\beta,\mu) = W(1s, 2p) = -\frac{\hbar^2}{2m}\int_0^\infty w_p\nabla^2 w_p\, d\tau_r + \int_0^{R_v} V_0 w_p{}^2\, d\tau_r$$

$$+ \int_{R_v}^\infty V_\mu w_p{}^2\, d\tau_r - e^2\int_{R_v}^\infty \frac{1}{r\kappa_\infty} w_p{}^2\, d\tau_r \tag{28.26}$$

where the second term is the potential energy for the electron in the Jost sphere while the last two terms are the contribution from outside. V_0 and

---

* Also see Simpson (S).

† To simplify the problem, Simpson assumed that a linear combination of p-functions existed which is spherically symmetrical.

V_μ have not changed because we assume that the Franck Condon principle applies, and that the ions are not displaced during the absorption process (see (Section 30). To stress this fact the level is denoted by the symbol $W(1s; 2p)$; β is evaluated by minimizing $W(1s; 2p)$.

Smith (S) has carried through an elaborate calculation of the parameters which enter into Simpson's calculation. Some representative values are given in Table 28.1. The following items should be noted.

TABLE 28.1. CALCULATIONS OF $\epsilon_m(a)$ BY THE METHOD OF SIMPSON

Crystal	a (Å)	$\alpha e^2/a^a$ (ev)	$V(0)^b$ (ev)	R_v (Å)	$E_0(a)=$ $W(1s)^c$ (ev)	$E_1(a)=$ $W(1s;2p)^c$ (ev)	$\epsilon_m(a)$ (ev)^e	$\epsilon_m(a)$ (ev)^d
LiF	2.01	12.5	8.9	1.9	-4.61	-0.97	3.64	5.10
NaCl	2.81	8.9	5.9	2.6	-3.29	-1.01	2.28	2.75
KCl	3.14	8.0	5.1	2.6	-2.80	-0.85	1.95	2.30
KBr	3.29	7.6	4.7	2.8	-2.63	-0.81	1.82	2.06
KI	3.53	7.1	4.3	3.2	-2.40	-0.76	1.64	1.86

[a] Madelung potential.

[b] Depth of the potential well including the polarization (method of Mott and Littleton).

[c] By Smith (S), using the method just described. It should be noted that only the $W(1s)$ as opposed to the $W(1s; 2p)$ are those calculated by Smith. The author believes Smith's values of $W(1s; 2p)$ to be in error. The values of $W(1s; 2p)$ that appear are due to R. Gilbert and we believe these are the values that follow from the theory. Gilbert has been able to reproduce Smith's $W(1s; 2p)$ upon use of W_{2p} as it appears on page 50 of Smith (S). It should be noted that as it stands there, W_{2p} contains a dimensionally incorrect term (R has been omitted from the denominator of the expectation values of the ionic polarization potential energy). Calculation of W_{2p} with this correction has yielded the $W(1s; 2p)$ listed here. Further, $\epsilon_m(a)$ for NaCl now agrees with Simpson's value.

[d] Measured from Table 3.2a.

[e] Calculated.

(1) The Jost sphere has a radius approximately equal to a_0, the distance between nearest neighbors, and is larger than the Goldschmidt radii. The radius of the vacancy is, therefore, larger than the removed ion.

(2) The polarization potential is a sizable fraction of the Madelung

energy. If we allowed the ion to be displaced there would be a further correction to V_0 of the order of 1 ev. This would raise both $W(1s)$ and $W(1s;2p)$. One would *suspect* that $W(1s)$ would be raised more, making $W(1s;2p) - W(1s)$ smaller.

(3) $W(1s;2p)[E_1(a)]$ is large compared to $\epsilon_t(1)$, which is of the order of 0.1 ev. This suggests that the ion readjustment energy is of the order of $W(1s;2p)$ (half an electron volt). This is not an unreasonable value in view of (28.11).

(4) $W(1s)[E_0(a)]$ should be compared to $\epsilon_t(0)$; again a sizable readjustment energy is required.

(5) The optical transition energies calculated by Smith are moderately good. We note from Table 28.2 that other theories give equally good agreement with the measured absorption peak. Thus, this criterion alone is not a sufficient reason for accepting a theory. As stated previously there are a great many other parameters which the theory has to explain.

In Table 28.1 we have included the measured values of $W(1s;2p) - W(1s)$, or ϵ_m. The values were those measured at $0°$ K. The parameters used by Smith were obtained at room temperature, and this comparison may be questioned. At the present limited state of our knowledge, we do not fully understand the reason for the shift in ϵ_m with temperature. Most probably, however, this shift is not included in Simpson's theory, and the best procedure is to ignore it and assume that all the parameters used by Smith are valid at $0°$ K. Smith attempted to see if a change in these parameters would influence ϵ_m. His conclusion is that the temperature change in the parameters would influence ϵ_m only a small amount. In one case, it was in the wrong direction.

In Table 28.2 we have included the results of several other calculations. The calculations of Gourary and Adrian (S) in essence ignore the polarization problem entirely (in their first-order calculations), and determine the depth of the well from the Madelung term alone. Since these calculations are based on a point-lattice model, the depth of the well should be given to a good approximation by the Madelung term [see Eq. (28.11c)] and is deeper than calculated by the approach of Mott and Littleton. They take the width of the well to be a which approximately equals the Jost radius R_v of Table 28.1. The sides of the Gourary-Adrian* wells are different from Simpson's but the integrated potential is probably not

---

* Although the Gourary-Adrian approach seems quite different from Simpson's, in essence the only difference is the polarization term of (28.15), although the problems of exchange, or orthogonality, and of second-order polarization effects make the Gourary-Adrian approach seem quite different.

influenced to a major extent by these small differences. The trial wave functions in both theories are similar. Gourary and Adrian also employed some more complex functions which only cause a minor variation in the eigenvalues.

TABLE 28.2. SOME OTHER CALCULATIONS OF $E_0(a)$ AND $E_1(a)$

Crystal	Gourary and Adrian			Krumhansl and Schwartz			Observed
	$E_0(a)$ (ev)	$E_1(a)$ (ev)	$\epsilon m(a)$ (ev)	$E_0(a)$ (ev)	$E_1(a)$ (ev)	$\epsilon m(a)$ (ev)	$\epsilon m(a)$ (ev)
LiF	−8.0	−4.1	3.9				5.1
NaCl	−6.5	−4.1	2.4	−3.8	−1.2	2.6	2.7
KCl	−5.9	−4.0	1.9	−3.2	−0.8	2.4	2.3

TABLE 28.2a. GOLDSCHMIDT RADII FOR
NEGATIVE IONS

Ion	Radii (Å)
F⁻	1.33
Cl⁻	1.81
Br⁻	1.96
I⁻	2.20

Experimentally, we know that $\epsilon_t(1)$ is of the order of 0.1 ev, while $\epsilon_t(0)$ is of the order of 2 ev in KCl. This means that the polarization energy in the $W(1s)$ state must be of the order of 4 ev; the adjustment energy for the $W(2p;2p)$ must be of the same order, if the approach of Gourary and Adrian applies. One wonders why such large polarization energies enter into $\epsilon_t(0)$ and $\epsilon_t(1)$ while they do not affect $W(1s)$ and $W(1s;2p)$. The author feels that the polarization effects are a vital point in the F-center problem, and that correct calculations must include it *a priori*. Probably Simpson's approach is *slightly* naïve, but it is a very fundamental one in that it makes an extremely complex problem sufficiently simple to handle.

In Table 28.2, some of the calculations of Krumhansl and Schwartz are included. The values agree roughly with those obtained by Smith. We have not by any means included *all* the calculations made on ϵ_m of F-centers, nor have we attempted to discuss all the various techniques.

In summarizing the results of the calculations on ϵ_m we must say that there are many nonequivalent ways to calculate this value. The results can easily be made to agree approximately with the measured values. All these calculations fall short from a theoretical viewpoint, however, since they are not based on a rigorous theory such as given by Slater and Wannier or by Tibbs, and they are full of crude approximations. Nevertheless, they give a fair value of ϵ_m. The utility of a theory must, therefore, be judged by its ability to handle the other measurable quantities listed in Section 26. Some of these problems will be considered in the next chapter. We wish to very briefly outline some alternate approaches to the theory.

d. Some Refinements to the Wave Function Calculations

Many refinements have been made to the theory just outlined. Only a few of these will be considered here. Essentially, two problems will be of interest: One is the calculation of the actual wave function at a nucleus; the other is the molecular approach. The imperfection is considered as a large molecule and Ψ_I is built up from various atomic orbital functions associated with the surrounding ions.

TABLE 28.3. WAVE FUNCTION AT NEIGHBORING IONS

Ion	Theory of Dexter ($\times 10^{21}$ cm^{-3})	ENDOR measurement[a] ($\times 10^{21}$ cm^{-3})
$\lvert\phi(\text{Na}^+)\rvert^2 a\{1,0,0\}$	610	351
$\lvert\phi(\text{Cl}^-)\rvert^2 a\{1,1,0\}$	450	193

[a] See Section 24e. The notation of this section is used.

The first problem can be treated by two methods: one due to Dexter (S) and Krumhansl (S), and the other is due to Gourary and Adrian (S).

The value of the wave function at a nucleus can be obtained from the width of the resonance line and from ENDOR experiments. Dexter used Eq. (27.32) with $V = 1$.* He calculated the contact term for NaCl using

---

* This is not stated, but is assumed by the writer. See also Eq. (27.36).

the wave function for the electron in the conduction band obtained by Tibbs and the envelope function obtained by Simpson. Using these values, Dexter estimates that $b_{k_0}(\text{Na}^+) = 2.7 \times 10^2$ cm^{-3} and that $b_{k_0}(\text{Cl}^-) = 8.5 \times 10^2$ cm^{-3}. These are crude estimates since our knowledge of b_k for the conduction band is very limited. Using Simpson's wave function, Dexter obtained the following values: $w(\text{Na}^+) = 2.3 \times 10^{21}$ cm^{-3} and $w(\text{Cl}^-) = 5.3 \times 10^{20}$ cm^{-3}. The two results are combined in Table 28.3. The theoretical values are only approximate and, in view of this, Dexter's calculations are most remarkable. The experimental measurements were made years after the calculation. They suggest that refinements in the calculations of both w and b would probably lead to correct results.

An alternate approach to the problem has been made by Gourary and Adrian. They attempted to build a Slater determinant from a set of orthogonal wave functions associated with the electrons in the ions which surround the imperfection $\phi_{i\alpha}$'s and the w. The effects of the b's and the a's do not play a role here. Further, the fact that w is an envelope function is not considered. To arive at an orthogonal set which includes Ψ_I, Gourary and Adrian define the function

$$\Psi_I' = \left\{ w - \sum_{i,\alpha} \langle F|i,\alpha \rangle \phi_{i\alpha} \right\} \left\{ 1 - \sum_{i,\alpha} \langle F|i,\alpha \rangle^2 \right\}^{-1/2} \tag{28.27}$$

where

$$\langle F|i,\alpha \rangle = \int w\phi_{i,\alpha} d\tau_r . \tag{28.27a}$$

The wave functions are real and Ψ_I' is orthogonal to the ϕ_n's. Equation (28.27) has the effect of amplifying the wave function near a nucleus (since ϕ is large there) as do the b and a functions and the calculated total wave function at a nucleus is much larger for Ψ_I' than when one just uses w. Holton and Blum (S) as well as Seidel (S) have compared their measured wave function (by ENDOR) to the wave function given by Eq. (28.27) and the agreement is only fair. Using (28.27) we may write the wave function as follows

$$|\Psi_I'(\alpha)|^2 = N^2 \left\{ w - \sum_{\alpha,i} \phi(i,\alpha) \langle F|i,\alpha \rangle \right\}^2 \approx N^2 \sum_{\alpha,i} \phi^2(i,\alpha) \langle F|i,\alpha \rangle^2 \tag{28.28}$$

where α refers to a given ion, i refers to an orbital in that ion and N is the normalizing factor of Eq. (28.27). At a nucleus the first term is small compared to the second as is indicated by Dexter's calculation of b at the nucleus. Since the ϕ's are normalized $\langle F|i,\alpha \rangle$ is a type of average of w and

$\phi(i, \alpha)$ is the value of the orbital at the nucleus. For an inner electron the ϕ's around a nucleus behave in a manner similar to the b's and expression (28.28) resembles the one used before. One may approximate Eq. (28.28) by the following expression

$$|\Psi'_I(\alpha)|^2 = \sum_{i,\alpha} \left\{ \frac{\phi(i, \alpha) \langle F|i, \alpha \rangle}{w(\alpha)} \right\}^2 w^2(\alpha) = A w^2(\alpha). \quad (28.29)$$

Actual calculation indicates that the quantity in parentheses is independent of the position of the nucleus; this justifies the last step. In Fig. (28.3) we show Seidel's plots of $a^3 w^2$ as well as the measured value obtained from ENDOR experiments. Attempts to calculate A from the "exact" form given in the second term of Eq. (28.28), show a good agreement according to Seidel; but only an order-of-magnitude agreement according to Holton and Blum, who used a different type of plot and determined the A's by curve fitting. One must stress that Fig. (28.3) is quite remarkable,

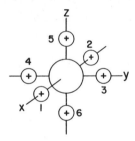

FIG. 28.2. Various atomic orbitals used in the molecular approach to the *F*-center wave function (after Kojima, S).

especially when one considers that one may not expect good agreement from one- or two-parameter wave functions at large distances from the vacancy.

Around an imperfection it is known that Bloch functions can be damped and that Ψ_I is large. This will be discussed in some detail in the next chapter, where the vibrations of an imperfect lattice will be considered. It therefore seems natural to approach the *F*-center problem from an entirely different point of view, namely, to consider the imperfection as a big molecule. (This approach was employed in Section 19 when we considered the g-shift.) In this calculation one includes some excited states, in addition to s-functions, since such functions must be involved.

Kojima (S) considered the negative-ion vacancy as a large molecule with six ions, as shown in Fig. 28.2. In the ground state the functions employed in addition to s-functions are given in Table 19.1. The relation between the notation in the figure and the table is

$$p_x(\mathbf{R}_1) \rightarrow a\{1,0,0\}, \quad p_x(\mathbf{R}_2) \rightarrow a\{-1,0,0\}, \quad p_y(\mathbf{R}_3) \rightarrow a\{0,1,0\},$$
$$p_y(\mathbf{R}_4) \rightarrow a\{(0,-1,0\}, \quad p_z(\mathbf{R}_5) \rightarrow a\{0,0,1\}, \quad p_z(\mathbf{R}_6) \rightarrow a\{0,0,-1\}$$

(28.30)

where the functions are located on the various ions and distances are measured from their nuclei. Kojima assumed the ground-state wave function to have the form

$$\psi_g = a_1 \sum_{k=1}^{6} s(\mathbf{R}_k) + a_2\{p_x(\mathbf{R}_1) - p_x(\mathbf{R}_2) + p_y(\mathbf{R}_3) - p_y(\mathbf{R}_4)$$
$$+ p_z(\mathbf{R}_5) - p_z(\mathbf{R}_6)\}.$$

(28.31)

This gives *one* adjustable parameter, since ψ_g has to be normalized. The following form is assumed for the excited state

$$\psi_e = b_1\{s(\mathbf{R}_5) - s(\mathbf{R}_6)\} + b_2 \sum_{1}^{4} p_z(\mathbf{R}_i) + b_3[p_z(\mathbf{R}_5) + p_z(\mathbf{R}_6)]. \quad (28.32)$$

It also has *one* independent variable since it must be normalized and made orthogonal to ψ_g. ψ_e resembles a p-function along the z-axis. Kojima thus considered a $1s$ to $2p$ transition. The actual Hamiltonian involved is very complex since he attempted to include the potential field within the ions, the polarizations (due to the ionic shell as well as that due to the displacements of the ions), and the effects of exchange. The problem requires machine calculations. The result for LiF is $\epsilon_m(a) = 3.5$ ev compared to measured values of 5.10 ev (see Table 3.2a). Wood and Korringa (S) carried through a similar calculation on LiCl and obtained a value of 2.4 ev compared to a measured one of 3.2 (room temperature). Wood and Korringa made calculations using a linear combination of atomic orbitals as well as central functions. A central function is an envelope function, namely our w. The agreement when the calculations are limited to $\epsilon_m(a)$ is fairly good. The most remarkable item is that all the calculations when limited in this manner give satisfactory results. The functions can give reasonable values of $|\psi_g(0)|^2$ at the nearby nuclei. The difficulty occurs when one attempts to obtain the other quantities listed at the beginning of this chapter. The basic reason for this is unknown.

Wood and Korringa made an extremely fundamental assumption regarding the F-center which has not been completely justified but which is of major importance. This may not be obvious at first but becomes so

when one considers the details. The point group symmetry of the undistorted lattice is O_h, which allows s- and p-state central functions. We
may call them s- or p-functions but could use the more complex notation
of group theory. Wood and Korringa assume that for an equilibrium

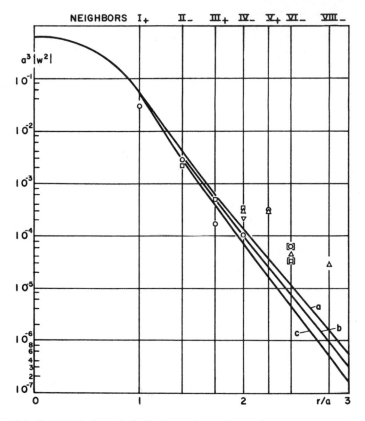

Fig. 28.3. Seidel (S) plots of $a^3|w|^2$ where a is the distance between nearest neighbors.
To determine w one must know A of Eq. (28.29); it depends on the ion. w was assumed
to have the form $(1/r)e^{-\eta r/a}$ for $r > a$, one of the types used by Gourary and Adrian (S).

		a (Å)	η	A_+	A_-	Curve
+	KF	2.76	2.3	650	350	a
○	NaCl	2.81		260	1,500	
□	KCl	3.14	2.45	650	1,500	b
△	KBr	3.29		650	4,000	
▽	KI	3.52	2.6	650	7,500	c

p-state the displacement of surrounding ions is not equal, four being displaced differently from the two others depending on the direction of the *p*-state. This changes the symmetry from an O_h to a D_{4h}. The point group allows an *s*-state function but splits the *p*-states since it does not have an irreducible representation of dimensions greater than two. Some of the details of the splitting have been worked out by Griffith; unfortunately not enough of these arguments have been applied to the *F*-center.

We end this section by stating that we have only covered a limited number of calculations and that many details of great value have been omitted.

REFERENCES

D. L. Dexter, *Phys. Rev.* **93**, 244 (1954).
B. S. Gourary and F. J. Adrian, *Solid State Physics* **10**, 127 (1960).
W. C. Holton and H. Blum, *Phys. Rev.* **125,** 89 (1962).
T. Kojima, *J. Phys. Soc. Japan* **12**, 908, 918 (1957).
J A. Krumhansl, *Phys. Rev.* **93**, 245 (1954).
J. A. Krumhansl and N. Swartz, *Phys. Rev.* **89**, 1154 (1953).
J. J. Markham and F. Seitz, *Phys. Rev.* **74**, 1014 (1948).
N. F. Mott and J. J. Littleton, *Trans. Faraday Soc.* **34**, 485 (1938).
S. I. Pekar, "Research in Electron Theory of Crystals," M.S., A.E.C. tr-5575. U.S. Dept. of Commerce.
H. Seidel, *Z. Physik* **165**, 218 (1961).
J. H. Simpson, *Proc. Roy. Soc.* **A197**, 269 (1949).
W. A. Smith, Jr., G. E. Rept. KAPL-1720 (Knoll Atomic Power Lab.).
R. F. Wood and J. Korringa, *Phys. Rev.* **123**, 1138 (1961).

X. Strong Electron-Phonon Interactions

The object of this chapter is to consider the case of strong electron-phonon interactions. It is best to define these concepts after an understanding of a phonon has been developed. Hence, we proceed by discussing phonons and their interactions with trapped electrons.

29. CRYSTAL AND LOCAL MODES

The object of this section is to develop a feeling for the normal modes of vibrations of a solid. This is a very old subject, dating back to the last century. The first major interest in this field was in relation to the problem of the specific heats of solids, where the considerations of Dulong and Petit, of Einstein, of Debye, and of Born and von Kármàn played an important role. With the development of the theory of solids, these vibrations entered into the problem of the mobility of an electron and the thermal broadening of x-ray lines. In recent years, the problem of the modes has been related to the breadth of the absorption bands in solids, such as the F-band, and to the problem of spin-lattice relaxation. The first effect, of an electrostatic character, comes about because of the scalar potential set up by the longitudinal lattice vibrations. The second is related to the vector potentials, which are produced by the transverse vibrations of the lattice.

A complete treatment of this problem is extremely involved and thus is beyond the scope of this book. We shall simply consider the vibrations of the linear chain in some detail. The author hopes that this will give the reader a feeling for the problems involved. This treatment will introduce the crystal and local modes, as well as the normal coordinates.

Consider first the vibrations of a chain made of three types of particles whose masses are m, m', and M (Fig. 29.1). The assumption is made that $m < M$. The particles, which will be denoted by the letter n, are attached to each other by springs with a constant, γ. Only the interaction between the nearest neighbors will be considered. There is only one particle of mass m', and it is located at the origin ($n = 0$). The particles of mass M are at the odd sites, while those of mass m are located at even sites. We shall assume that there are $2N$ light and $2N$ heavy particles, and, to make the problem concrete, the two particles at $\pm 2N$ will be restrained so that they are not displaced. Thus, our system has only $4N - 1$ degrees of freedom and the same number of normal modes.

If $u(n)$ is the displacement of the nth particle, the total potential energy has the form

$$V = \tfrac{1}{2} \sum_{-2N+1}^{2N} \gamma[u(n) - u(n-1)]^2 \tag{29.1}$$

where the sum of $4N$ terms includes the zeroth particle. The kinetic energy of the chain is a sum of terms which is quadratic in the linear momentum of the particles. One introduces coordinates that make the

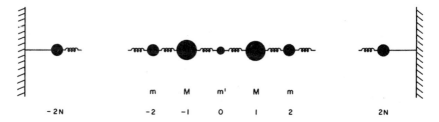

Fig. 29.1. Diatomic linear chain with a point imperfection at $n = 0$.

potential energy a sum of terms quadratic in the displacements but does not introduce cross terms in the kinetic energy. Under these conditions, the net Hamiltonian is a sum of Hamiltonians, each associated with an individual mode (simple harmonic oscillators). Certain limitations are imposed on the transformation which make the normal modes unique, provided they are nondegenerate (do not have the identical frequency).

We shall therefore associate a normal mode with a frequency. In principle, it is relatively easy to find the required transformation and to introduce the modes. In practice, this leads to involved algebra, and it is not possible to carry through the details except in extremely simple cases. Here, the modes will be found without introducing the coordinates. Later it will be indicated how these coordinates are introduced into the problem by considering a monatomic chain (Section 29b).

a. The Crystal Modes

First, let $m' = m$, and the equations of motion for a particle are:

$$m \frac{d^2 u(n)}{dt^2} = \gamma[u(n+1) - 2u(n) + u(n-1)] \qquad n \text{ even (including zero),}$$

$$\tag{29.2a}$$

$$M \frac{d^2 u(n)}{dt^2} = \gamma[u(n+1) - 2u(n) + u(n-1)] \qquad n \text{ odd.} \tag{29.2b}$$

Our boundary conditions state that

$$u(2N) = u(-2N) = 0. \tag{29.2c}$$

Equations (29.2a, b, c) are sufficient to determine the frequencies and the wavelength of the modes.

The standing wave solutions of these equations are:

$$u_j(n) = A_j \exp(i\omega_j t) \sin(2N+n)\phi_j \qquad n \text{ even,} \qquad (29.3a)$$

$$u_j(n) = B_j \exp(i\omega_j t) \sin(2N+n)\phi_j \qquad n \text{ odd,} \qquad (29.3b)$$

$$\phi_j = j\pi/4N \tag{29.3c}$$

where j is an integer. The $A_j \exp(i\omega_j t)$ and $B_j \exp(i\omega_j t)$ are proportional to the normal mode of frequency ω_j. In a pure quantum mechanical calculation, time may or may not enter in explicitly. In this section the problem is solved purely classically, since our interest is in the frequency distribution and the appearance of the localized modes. Here, A and B are determined from the initial conditions.

On substituting (29.3) into (29.2), the following equations are obtained:

$$(m\omega_j^2 - 2\gamma) A_j + 2\gamma B_j \cos \phi_j = 0 \tag{29.4a}$$

and

$$2\gamma A_j \cos \phi_j + (M\omega_j^2 - 2\gamma) B_j = 0. \tag{29.4b}$$

The requirement that the A's and the B's be nonzero determines the frequency. It is given by the relation

$$\frac{mM}{\gamma} \omega_{j\pm}^2 = m + M \pm [m^2 + M^2 + 2mM \cos 2\phi_j]^{1/2}. \tag{29.5}$$

To obtain Eq. (29.5) we employ only (29.2a) and (29.2b), and not the boundary condition (29.2c). This condition is contained in the value ϕ_j selected. The selection given by (29.3c) assures one that condition (29.2c) is fulfilled. When (29.5) is satisfied, one obtains

$$\frac{A_j}{B_j} = \frac{2\gamma - M\omega_j^2}{2\gamma \cos \phi_j}. \tag{29.6}$$

The modes obtained from the foregoing analysis can be divided into two branches, "optical" with the positive sign in (29.5), and "acoustical" with the negative sign in (29.5). In the optical modes, neighboring particles vibrate out of phase and generate dipoles if the masses are charged ions. Further, these modes can be classified into symmetric (S) and antisymmetric (A). For a symmetric mode, the displacement of the nth particle is the same as the $-n$th particle, while for an antisymmetric mode, the displacements are 180 degrees out of phase. We thus may form the following table:

Optical branch

$$\omega_j{}^2 = \frac{\gamma}{mM}\{m+M+[m^2+M^2+2mM\cos 2\phi_j]^{1/2}\};\tag{29.7a}$$

$$\phi_j = \frac{j\pi}{4N}\quad\text{for}\quad j=1,3,\cdots 2N-1\quad\text{symmetric};\tag{29.8a}$$

$$\phi_j = \frac{j\pi}{4N}\quad\text{for}\quad j=2,4,\cdots 2N-2\quad\text{antisymmetric};\tag{29.9a}$$

and

$$\frac{A_j}{B_j} = -\frac{M}{m}\quad\text{for}\quad \phi_j\to 0\tag{29.10a}$$

$$= (-)\infty\quad\text{for}\quad \phi_j\to\pi/2.\tag{29.11a}$$

Acoustical branch

$$\omega_j{}^2 = \frac{\gamma}{mM}\{m+M-[m^2+M^2+2mM\cos 2\phi_j]^{1/2}\};\tag{29.7b}$$

$$\phi_j = \frac{j\pi}{4N}\quad\text{for}\quad j=1,3,\cdots 2N-1\quad\text{symmetric};\tag{29.8b}$$

$$\phi_j = \frac{j\pi}{4N}\quad\text{for}\quad j=2,4,\cdots 2N-2\quad\text{antisymmetric};\tag{29.9b}$$

and

$$\frac{A_j}{B_j} = 1\quad\text{for}\quad \phi_j\to 0\tag{29.10b}$$

$$= 0\quad\text{for}\quad \phi_j\to\frac{\pi}{2}.\tag{29.11b}$$

We have listed $4N-2$ modes above; hence, we have to add one more mode. We choose to add the one at the top of the acoustical branch, where only the lighter particles are displaced. The situation is illustrated in Fig. 29.2. An examination of the modes omitted indicates that they really do

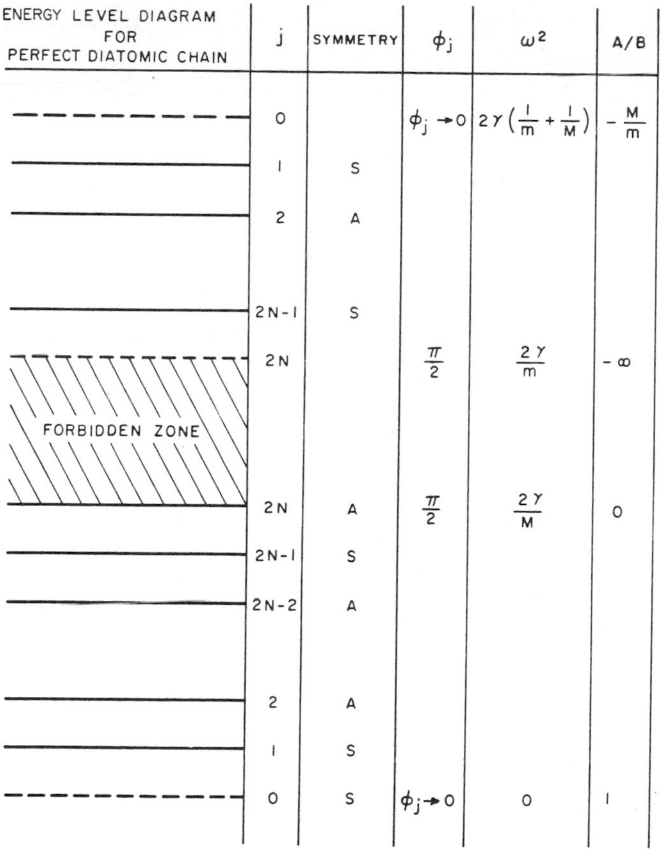

ENERGY LEVEL DIAGRAM FOR PERFECT DIATOMIC CHAIN	j	SYMMETRY	ϕ_j	ω^2	A/B
	0		$\phi_j \to 0$	$2\gamma\left(\dfrac{1}{m}+\dfrac{1}{M}\right)$	$-\dfrac{M}{m}$
	1	S			
	2	A			
	2N-1	S			
	2N		$\dfrac{\pi}{2}$	$\dfrac{2\gamma}{m}$	$-\infty$
FORBIDDEN ZONE					
	2N	A	$\dfrac{\pi}{2}$	$\dfrac{2\gamma}{M}$	0
	2N-1	S			
	2N-2	A			
	2	A			
	1	S			
	0	S	$\phi_j \to 0$	0	1

Fig. 29.2. Distribution of the normal modes for the perfect diatomic chain. A/B is ratio of the displacement of the even (lighter) to the odd (heavier) particles. The minus sign means that the particles are out of phase. The symmetry results from the particular geometry employed.

not cause a displacement of the particles. For example, the mode at the bottom of the optical branch does not displace the particles, since $B_j = 0$ from (29.11a), and u (even) is zero because of the value of the sine in Eq. (29.3a).

The reader should note that one has pure acoustical modes only when ϕ is zero. By "pure acoustical," we mean that neighboring particles are displaced an equal amount in phase. As ϕ approaches $\pi/2$, the character of the modes changes and, in the limit, only the lighter particles are displaced.

The solution given here is based on (29.4) or (29.5), and on the boundary condition, that is, the requirement that the 2Nth particles be stationary. Essentially the same results would have been obtained if we had used the Born-von Kármàn boundary conditions (see Seitz, 1940, p. 117).

We now consider the frequency distribution of the modes. To avoid mathematical complexities, which would add little to the understanding of the problem, let us set $m = m' = M$. Then, (29.5) takes the particularly simple form

$$\frac{m^2 \omega_j^2}{\gamma} = 2m(1 \pm \cos \phi_j) = 4m \begin{cases} \cos^2 \dfrac{\phi_j}{2} = 4m \sin^2 \left(\dfrac{\phi_j}{2} + \dfrac{\pi}{2} \right) \\[2ex] \sin^2 \dfrac{\phi_j}{2}. \end{cases} \tag{29.12}$$

The top form of (29.12) may be used by extending the range of ϕ to π. Thus, Eqs. (29.8) and (29.9) are replaced by

$$\phi_j = j \frac{\pi}{4N} (j = 1, 2, 3, \cdots 4N - 1). \tag{29.13}$$

The "top" mode $j = 4N$ is omitted. Under these conditions, there is only one branch, the acoustical. From (29.12), we may obtain the relation

$$\nu = \frac{1}{\pi} \left(\frac{\gamma}{m} \right)^{1/2} \sin \frac{\phi_j}{2} = \nu_0 \sin \frac{\phi_j}{2}. \tag{29.14}$$

At the limit of small ϕ, this reduces to

$$\nu = \left(\frac{\gamma}{m} \right)^{1/2} \frac{j}{8N} = \left(\frac{\gamma}{m} \right)^{1/2} \frac{1}{\lambda} \tag{29.14a}$$

where $\lambda = 8N/j$* is the wavelength associated with the mode, while $(\gamma/m)^{1/2}$ is the phase velocity of the long wavelength modes. The density of the modes—that is, the number of modes between the frequencies ν and $\nu + d\nu$—is given by $\delta(\nu)$. This function can be calculated from (29.14a). The result is

$$\delta(\nu) = \frac{dj}{d\nu} = 8N \left(\frac{m}{\gamma} \right)^{1/2} (\phi_j \to 0). \tag{29.15}$$

* From Eq. (29.3a), $\lambda\phi_j = 2\pi$, where λ is in units of a, the distance between nearest particles.

When (29.14) is employed, the following distribution is obtained:

$$\delta(\nu) = \left(\frac{m}{\gamma}\right)^{1/2} \frac{8N}{\cos \phi_j/2} \qquad (29.15a)$$

$$= \frac{8N}{\pi[\nu_0{}^2 - \nu^2]^{1/2}}. \qquad (29.15b)$$

In Fig. 29.3a the frequency is plotted against the "wave number". We have also plotted δ against ν in Fig. 29.3b for both the exact and approximate relations. In the exact relation the frequencies bunch up strongly

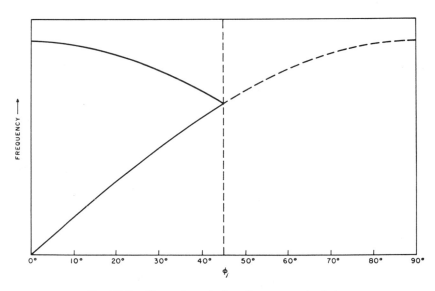

Fig. 29.3a. Dispersion relation of a monatomic chain.

about the point ν_0. If an insensitive means of measuring the distributions were used, one might conclude that the chain vibrates at a single frequency, approximately ν_0. This, of course, depends on the means of detection employed.

The division of modes into symmetric and antisymmetric made here is possible because an impurity will be placed *exactly* in the middle of the chain, and we have used fixed boundary conditions (see Section 29d). The reflection symmetry introduces a "parity" in the modes. In general, this division is not possible if one places the impurity at any site in the chain. The division has no meaning when the cyclic or Born-von Kármàn

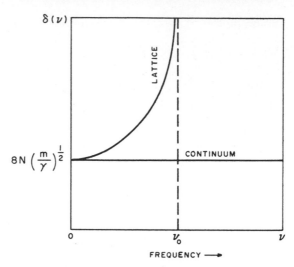

FIG. 29.3b. Distribution of modes for a monatomic chain. Note difference between the distribution in a real chain and the infinitely long wave approximation "continuum" ($\phi_j \to 0$).

boundary conditions are used. It is nevertheless a useful concept for the introduction of the normal modes, and is probably approximately obeyed.

b. The Normal Coordinates for the Monatomic Chain

The foregoing treatment serves to introduce the crystal modes for a monatomic chain. It determines the frequencies of the modes but does not introduce the normal coordinates themselves. When one is dealing with electron-phonon interactions, a knowledge of the modes themselves is required. In principle, one can obtain them directly from (29.1) by a very general method (see Born and Huang, p. 173). In practice, the steps are involved and difficult to carry through.

To gain an understanding of this problem, consider again the chain with $m' = m = M$ [Wilson (S), p. 137]. The problem will be slightly simplified by introducing the cyclic boundary conditions. The $\pm 2N$ particle, which has been held fixed, is now eliminated. We add $4N - 1$ particles on both sides of the chain and assume that the fictitious particles vibrate in exactly the same manner as the real chain. Thus, the motion of the $-(2N-1)$th particle is identical to that of the $+2N$th particle. The displacement will be assumed to have the form

$$u(n) = [2(4N-1)]^{-1/2} \sum_j (\alpha_j e^{in\eta_j} + \alpha_j^* e^{-in\eta_j}). \qquad (29.16)$$

α is a complex number that depends on time when the problem is solved classically. Here, η_j (sometimes denoted by η) has replaced ϕ_j, since an alternate boundary condition is employed. η_j has the values

$$\eta_j = \frac{2\pi j}{(4N-1)} (j = 0, 1, 2, 3, \cdots 2N-1). \tag{29.17}$$

Note that $\eta \geqslant 0$. This gives the correct number of modes, since for $\eta = 0$, only one mode exists, while for all other values of j, two degenerate modes appear, corresponding to α and α^*. The distribution given by (29.17) is slightly different from that described by (29.8) and (29.9) or by (29.13); however, the number of modes per increment of ϕ or η is the same, provided N is large. The relation between the frequency distribution and the boundary condition has been discussed in detail by Born (S). Quantum mechanically, $\dot{\alpha}$ (time derivative of α) is related to an operator that will be introduced shortly. The normal modes are not the α_j's, but they may be obtained as follows: the kinetic energy has the form

$$T = \frac{1}{2}m \sum_n \left[\frac{du(n)}{dt}\right]^2$$

$$= \frac{m}{4(4N-1)} \sum_{\eta,\eta'} \sum_n \{\dot{\alpha}_j \dot{\alpha}_{j'} e^{in(\eta+\eta')} + \dot{\alpha}_j \dot{\alpha}_{j'}{}^* e^{in(\eta-\eta')}$$

$$+ \dot{\alpha}_j{}^* \dot{\alpha}_{j'} e^{-in(\eta-\eta')} + \dot{\alpha}_j{}^* \dot{\alpha}_{j'}{}^* e^{-in(\eta+\eta')}\}. \tag{29.18}$$

The sum is over all the values of j, j', and n. Using Eq. (27.4) we may write (29.18) in the form

$$T = \tfrac{1}{4}m \left\{\dot{\alpha}_0{}^2 + \dot{\alpha}_0{}^{*2} + 2 \sum_{j=0}^{j=2N-1} \dot{\alpha}_j \dot{\alpha}_j{}^*\right\}. \tag{29.19}$$

If we set $\quad\quad \alpha_j = A_j + iB_j \quad\quad$ for $\quad j > 0$. $\tag{29.20a}$

In the $j = 0$ mode, all the particles are displaced in phase and this corresponds to the translation of the lattice (chain) as a whole. There is a single real mode, since

$$\dot{\alpha}_0{}^2 + 2\dot{\alpha}_0 \dot{\alpha}_0{}^* + (\dot{\alpha}_0{}^*)^2 = (\dot{\alpha}_0 + \dot{\alpha}_0{}^*)^2 = 4\dot{A}_0{}^2 \tag{29.20b}$$

which defines A_0 and $B_0 = 0$. This mode does not appear when one uses the fixed boundary condition (29.2c). It does not affect the potential energy and is of no interest to us. The kinetic energy, hence, has the form

$$T = \frac{1}{2}m \sum_{j\neq 0} \left\{\left(\frac{dA_j}{dt}\right)^2 + \left(\frac{dB_j}{dt}\right)^2\right\}. \tag{29.21}$$

Next, consider the potential energy. Since

$$u(n) - u(n-1) = \frac{1}{\sqrt{2(4N-1)}} \sum_j \{\alpha_j e^{in\eta}(1-e^{-i\eta}) + \alpha_j^* e^{-in\eta}(1-e^{i\eta})\}.$$

$$(29.22)$$

The total potential energy associated with the deformation of the chain has the form

$$V = \tfrac{1}{2}\gamma \sum_n [u(n) - u(n-1)]^2 \qquad (29.23)$$

$$= \frac{\gamma}{4(4N-1)} \left\{ \sum_{j,j'} \sum_n \alpha_j \alpha_{j'} \, e^{in(\eta+\eta')} (1-e^{-i\eta})(1-e^{-\eta'}) \right.$$

$$+ \alpha_j \alpha_{j'}^* \, e^{in(\eta-\eta')} (1-e^{-i\eta})(1-e^{i\eta'})$$

$$+ \alpha_j^* \alpha_{j'} \, e^{-in(\eta-\eta')} (1-e^{i\eta})(1-e^{-i\eta'})$$

$$\left. + \alpha_j^* \alpha_{j'}^* \, e^{-in(\eta+\eta')} (1-e^{i\eta})(1-e^{i\eta'}) \right\}. \qquad (29.24)*$$

The sum over n simplifies the equation as follows:

$$V = \frac{\gamma}{2} \sum_j \alpha_j \alpha_j^* (1-e^{-i\eta})(1-e^{i\eta})$$

$$= 2\gamma \sum_j \alpha_j \alpha_j^* \sin^2 \tfrac{1}{2}\eta$$

$$= \tfrac{1}{2} m \sum_j \omega_j^2 (A_j^2 + B_j^2); \qquad (29.25)$$

using an equation similar to Eq. (29.12). In (29.25) the term $j=0$ is omitted. The cross terms, i.e., terms in $u(n)\, u(n-1)$, in the potential energy have thus been eliminated by means of substitution (29.16). Furthermore, no mixed terms appear in the kinetic energy. The A's and B's have the dimension of length. A further simplification occurs when

* The same result is obtained if one writes $\alpha_j \alpha_j^* + \alpha_j^* \alpha_j$ for $2\alpha_j \alpha_j^*$ where one does not permute the order of the A's and B's.

we introduce the reduced coordinates, namely,

$$q_j = \sqrt{m} A_j \quad \text{for} \quad 1 \leqslant j \leqslant 2N-1$$
$$= \sqrt{m} B_{|j|} \quad \text{for} \quad -1 \geqslant j \geqslant -(2N-1). \tag{29.26}$$

Hence, j has $4N-2$ values for the $4N-2$ *internal* modes. Finally, the following simple Hamiltonian is obtained for the chain

$$\mathscr{H} = \tfrac{1}{2} \sum_j \{\dot{q}_j{}^2 + \omega_j{}^2 q_j{}^2\} \tag{29.27}$$

since $\omega_j{}^2 = \omega_{-j}{}^2$. Equation (29.27) pertains to "particles" of unit mass; the canonical momentum conjugate to q_j is just

$$p_j = \frac{\partial T}{\partial \dot{q}_j} = \dot{q}_j \tag{29.28}$$

and $\mathscr{H}$ can be written in terms of the p's and q's as follows

$$\mathscr{H} = \tfrac{1}{2} \sum_j (p_j{}^2 + \omega_j{}^2 q_j{}^2). \tag{29.29}$$

In view of this form, we know that every q can be excited independently. The displacement corresponding to a single mode is obtained from (29.16) and is given by

$$u(n) = \left[\frac{2}{(4N-1)m}\right]^{1/2} q_j \begin{cases} \cos n\eta_j & \text{for} \quad j \geqslant 1 \\ \sin(n\eta_j + \pi) & \text{for} \quad j \leqslant -1. \end{cases} \tag{29.30}$$

The cosine modes arise from the A's of Eq. (29.26), and the sine terms arise from the B's. The phase of π has no real importance. The frequency of these modes is determined from Eq. (29.12) using the appropriate values of η.

The above derivations are given here for physical clarity. The problem is quantized by using the q's and p's of (29.29). The *thermodynamical* properties of the lattice are obtained from a canonical ensemble, using again these same variables. The actual displacement can only be obtained from (29.30). Thus, at absolute zero, the expectation value of a q_j is obtained from the ground-state eigenfunction (see Eq. 30.9). The displacement of the nth particle is determined from these values of the q's and the "coupling coefficients"—that is,

$$\left[\frac{2}{m(4N-1)}\right]^{1/2} \begin{array}{ll} \cos n\eta_j & \text{for } j \geqslant 1 \\ \sin(n\eta_j+\pi) & \text{for } j \leqslant -1 \end{array} \qquad (29.31)$$

of Eq. (29.30).

One may form an n by n matrix using the terms in the potential energy (29.23) and reduce the finding of the frequency to the solution of an eigenvalue matrix problem. The only nonvanishing terms in the matrix in our simple problem are the $V_{n,n-1}$, V_{nn}, and $V_{n,n+1}$ terms. The coupling coefficients can be shown to bet he eigenvectors associated with the matrix. Hence, the functions given by (29.31) are components of an orthonormal set of eigenvectors. (For more details, see Born and Huang, p. 173.) Perhaps a more appropriate name for the "coupling coefficient" (which has been used elsewhere in physics) is the eigenvector.

In the specific heat problem, one requires the partition function, which is determined entirely from the frequencies. Hence, one may be content in determining the frequency spectra, as was done in the previous section. When dealing with electron-phonon interactions, one requires the actual displacements, and one therefore needs to know the coupling coefficients. In principle, one may determine these coefficients in a straightforward and general manner, and the presence of a lattice perturbation will not affect the results. In practice, these developments lead to involved mathematics, and the details are rarely carried through. We shall carry through this type of a calculation for an extremely simple case in Section 30a.

c. *Local Modes—Linear Chain*

We return to the problems of Section 29a, where only the frequencies of the modes are computed.

Consider the case when $m' \neq m$; then one may write

$$m' = m(1-\epsilon) \qquad (29.32)$$

with the restriction $\epsilon > 0$, that is, $m' < m < M$. Now the relation

$$(1-\epsilon)m\frac{d^2 u(0)}{dt^2} = \gamma[u(1)-2u(0)+u(-1)] \qquad (29.33)$$

must be added to Eq. (29.2a). The solutions must satisfy (29.2a, b, c), and (29.33). The chain has been split in two parts. At one end, boundary condition (29.2c) applies; the other is restricted by (29.33). The $n < 0$ is a mirror image of the $n > 0$ region. This is automatically fulfilled for an antisymmetric mode, since $u(-1) = -u(-1)$ and one may set $u(0) = 0$. It will now be shown that solutions for the symmetric modes can have the form

$$u(n) = A_j \exp(i\omega_j t) \sin(2N - n)\phi_j, \quad n \text{ (even)} > 0 \quad (29.34a)$$

$$u(n) = B_j \exp(i\omega_j t) \sin(2N - n)\phi_j, \quad n \text{ (odd)} > 0 \quad (29.34b)$$

and

$$u(n) = u(-n). \quad (29.34c)$$

Equations (29.34) satisfy the boundary conditions (29.2c) since particles $n = \pm 2N$ are not displaced for any ϕ. The difference between (29.3) and (29.34) is that in the latter, the ϕ's are not fixed by (29.3c), as previously, but are determined by (29.33). The A's and B's depend on ϕ by a relation similar to (29.6). Substituting into (29.2a) and (29.2b), we obtain (the subscript j is omitted):

$$(m\omega^2 - 2\gamma)(M\omega^2 - 2\gamma) - 4\gamma^2 \cos^2\phi = 0 \quad (29.35)$$

from which (29.5) follows; it holds for *any* values of ϕ. Equation (29.33) gives

$$(1 - \epsilon)m\omega^2 A \sin 2N\phi + \gamma[2B \sin(2N - 1)\phi - 2A \sin 2N\phi] = 0, \quad (29.36)$$

which, with the use of Eq. (29.6) can be reduced to the form

$$-(M\omega^2 - 2\gamma)\epsilon m\omega^2 \sin 2N\phi + 4\gamma^2 \cos(2N\phi)\cos\phi\sin\phi = 0. \quad (29.37)$$

Substituting the expression for ω obtained from (29.35) into (29.37) results in the equation:

$$\cot(2N\phi) - \epsilon(\operatorname{cosec} 2\phi) K_{\pm}(\phi) = 0 \quad (29.38)$$

where

$$K_{\pm}(\phi) = \frac{1}{m}[M + m \cos 2\phi \pm (m^2 + M^2 + 2mM \cos 2\phi)^{1/2}]. \quad (29.38a)$$

Equation (29.38) determines the values of ϕ, which satisfy Eqs. (29.2a), (29.2b) and (29.33), provided the displacements are given by (29.34a and b). If $\epsilon = 0$, Eq. (29.38) states that $\cot 2N\phi = 0$, and ϕ satisfies the requirements placed on the symmetric mode of the perfect crystal— namely, Eq. (29.8a and b). When $\epsilon > 0$, we must solve (29.38) for ϕ. In Fig. 29.4, we have plotted $K_{\pm}(\phi)$; Fig. 29.5 plots $\operatorname{cosec} 2\phi K_{+}(\phi)$ against ϕ. In Fig. 29.6, we indicate the method one may use to find solutions of ϕ. The

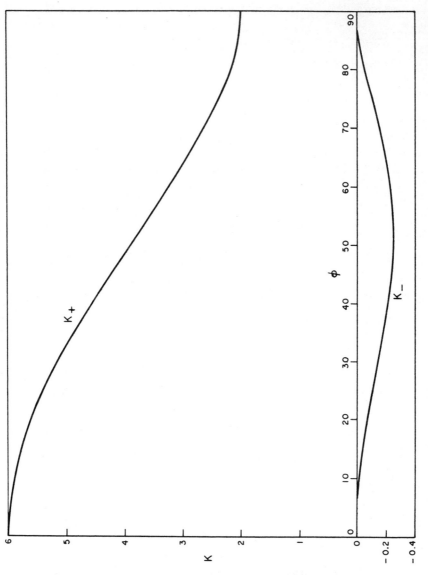

Fig. 29.4. Plot of K_+ and K_- against ϕ for $m=1$ and $M=2$. Note difference in the scale for positive and negative values of K.

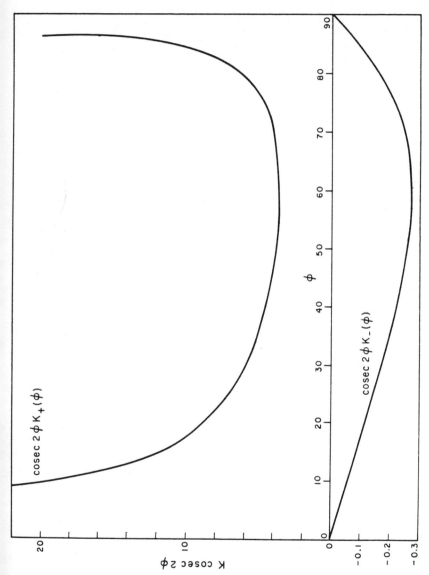

FIG. 29.5. Plot of cosec $2\phi K_{\pm}(\phi)$ against ϕ for $m = 1$ and $M = 2$. Note difference in scale for positive and negative values of the y-axis.

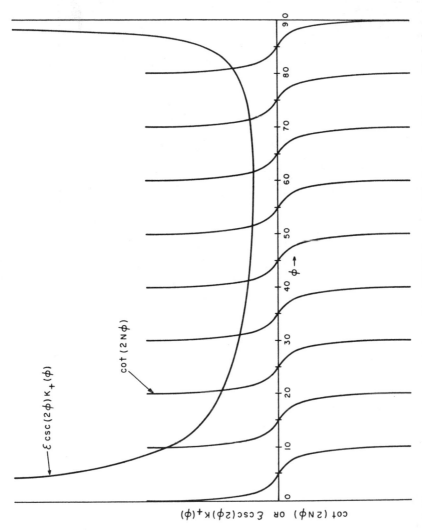

Fig. 29.6. Graphical method to find the solutions of Eq. (29.38) for $m=1$, $M=2$, and $\epsilon=0.5$. Since $N=9$, there are 35 modes: 17 are symmetric; 9 are obtained from $K_-(\phi)$; 8 are obtained from $K_+(\phi)$. Thus, one mode is missing.

solutions are now slightly different from those obtained for the perfect lattice. As $\phi \to 0$, $K_+(\phi)$ has a finite value, and

$$\epsilon \csc 2\phi \, K_+(\phi) \to \epsilon K_+(0) \frac{1}{2\phi} \qquad (29.39a)$$

while

$$\cot (2N\phi) \to \frac{1}{2N} \frac{1}{\phi}. \qquad (29.39b)$$

Since $1/N \ll \epsilon K_+(\phi)$ for any reasonable values of the parameters involved, there is a missing frequency or a missing mode. It corresponds to the top of the optical branch—that is, $j = 1$. For a general discussion of the appearances of local modes and their properties see Maradudin, Montroll, and Weiss (S).

To find an additional mode, we try a solution of the form

$$u(n) = A\,e^{i\omega t}\,e^{-n\psi} \qquad n \text{ (even)} \geqslant 0 \qquad (29.40a)$$

$$u(n) = B\,e^{i\omega t}\,e^{-n\psi} \qquad n \text{ (odd)} > 0, \qquad (29.40b)$$

where again

$$u(-n) = u(n). \qquad (29.40c)$$

This is a local mode, since it is damped as one proceeds away from the m' particle.

The reader will note these equations can satisfy (29.2c) *only* when $N \to \infty$. For this condition, $(1/2N) \to 0$, one may be certain that there is a missing mode. We may obtain an exact solution for the mode described above. The algebra is straightforward, although somewhat involved. Some additional details are given in the paper of Mazur, Montroll, and Potts (S), although their treatment has been slightly modified by the introduction of Eqs. (29.40). Using (29.40), (29.2a and b), and (29.33), we obtain (29.5) and (29.6) with $\cos\phi$ replaced by $\cosh\psi$.* Equation (29.38) is replaced by

$$1 - \epsilon K_+(\psi)\,\operatorname{cosech} 2\psi = 0 \qquad (29.41)$$

where

$$K_+(\psi) = \frac{1}{m}[M + m\cosh 2\psi + (m^2 + M^2 + 2mM\cosh 2\psi)^{1/2}]. \qquad (29.41a)$$

Equation (29.41) is exact, provided (29.40) is used. It can be put into the form

$$(1 + \epsilon^2)\sinh 2\psi - 2\epsilon\cosh 2\psi = \frac{2\epsilon M}{m}. \qquad (29.42)$$

---

* Since ψ is real, only the positive sign can be used in (29.5).

One may solve for $\sinh 2\psi$ to obtain the result

$$\sinh 2\psi = \tfrac{1}{2}(1-\epsilon^2)^{-2}\left\{\frac{4\epsilon M}{m}(1+\epsilon^2)+\frac{4\epsilon}{m}[m^2(1+\epsilon^2)^2+4\epsilon^2(M^2-m^2)]^{1/2}\right\}.$$
$$(29.43)$$

Using this value of $\sinh 2\psi$, we may return to the equation which is equivalent to (29.5) and obtain the relation which determines the frequency of the local mode

$$\frac{Mm}{\gamma}\omega^2 = m+\frac{1}{(1-\epsilon^2)}\{2M+[m^2(1+\epsilon^2)^2+4\epsilon^2(M^2-m^2)]^{1/2}\}. \quad (29.44)^*$$

If ϵ is small, (29.44) simplifies to

$$\omega^2 = \omega_L^2[1+\epsilon^2(M/m)+0(\epsilon^4)] \qquad (29.45)$$

$$\omega_L^2 = \frac{2\gamma}{mM}(M+m). \qquad (29.45a)$$

According to Fig. 29.2, there is a mode missing from the top of the optical branch when we are dealing with a perfect linear chain. As stated, there is no actual displacement related to this mode [see Eqs. (29.3) and (29.4)]; this justified its omission. The frequency of this fictitious mode is ω_L. The technique developed here for the imperfect lattice omits the mode that corresponds to $j=1$ (for the perfect lattice) but adds the mode $j=0$ previously omitted. It is now a local mode that is concentrated about the m' imperfection. If N is not too large and ϵ is very small, it is conceivable that a solution of (29.39) exists for $\phi <\pi/2N$, as well as Eq. (29.42). This paradox arises because we have assumed an infinite chain in solving for the local mode. For finite N, u of Eq. (29.40a) does not obey (29.2c), and more complex solutions are required. This problem is entirely of a theoretical nature, since in any actual crystal, N is very large and the symmetric mode for $j=1$ never appears. When $N \to \infty$, there is no frequency gap between the modes, since the frequency distribution forms a dense set. Hence, there is no actual discontinuity in the frequency as $\epsilon \to 0$. This problem is illustrated in Fig. 29.7.

Bjork (S) has indicated that in the locations where the amplitude of the local mode is large, the amplitudes of the crystal modes are small. Since the local mode is clustered about the $n=0$ particle, the symmetric modes tend to be damped in this region of the chain. Hence, at $n=0$, the vibration is primarily characterized by the local mode. The actual problem is

---

* We can evaluate $(m^2+M^2+2mM\cosh 2\psi)^{1/2}$ by the use of Eqs. (29.41) and (29.42).

quite complex, since there is almost an infinite number of crystal modes, and one may not be sure that the net effect of the very large number of crystal modes is less important than the effects of the small number of local modes. The dampening is illustrated in Fig. 29.8. The particles around m' are displaced less as $\phi \rightarrow 10$ degrees.

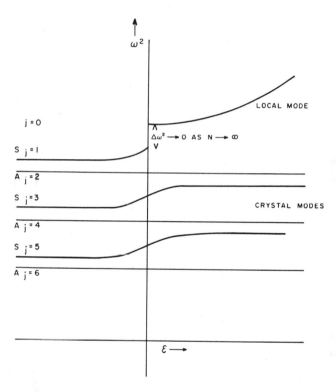

FIG. 29.7. Sketch of the effect of changing ϵ on the frequency distribution of the normal modes associated with a diatomic chain. Only the high-frequency optical modes are considered. We may assume that the top of the optical band is given by the mode $j=1$ for $\epsilon=0$. The local mode starts a new band with a simple discrete mode which has a new character.

We have shown above that the crystal modes can be concentrated about a single frequency (see Fig. 29.3); hence, the presence of a single dominant frequency as measured experimentally is not sufficient reason for one to assume that one is dealing with localized modes.

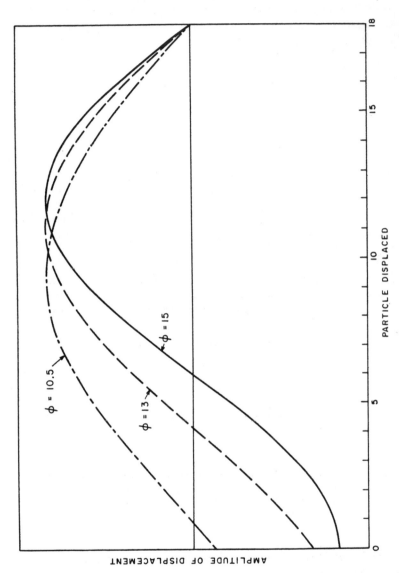

Fig. 29.8. Amplitude of the particle displacement as a function of the particle position for various values of ϕ, possible solutions of Eq. (29.38) with various values of ϵ. The maximum change in ϕ is 5 degrees for the case considered (see Fig. 29.6). N is assumed to equal 9. Note that the amplitude of the zeroth particle decreases as ϕ changes from 15 to 10 degrees and that, at the lower value, the modes "tend to avoid" the imperfection.

d. Local and Crystal Modes in General

Here the concepts of the preceding sections are generalized. The division between crystal and local modes is certainly correct. Further, the classification of modes into optical and acoustical is valuable. In a three-dimensional crystal, one may further group the modes into transverse and longitudinal. The latter classification is only meaningful for modes of long wavelength, and it becomes less useful as the wavelengths approach the interatomic dimensions.

The clustering of modes discussed at the end of Section 29a has been verified in many detailed calculations which are more realistic than the one made here. Figure 29.9 shows the mode distribution for KCl when the long-range polar forces and the short-range repulsive forces are employed.

What we observe experimentally depends on the means used to detect the modes. For example, in an extremely low-temperature specific heat measurement, one detects only the low-frequency modes, since the higher frequency vibrations are not excited. If one detects the modes by measuring the mobility of an electron in the conduction band (long wavelength), the information obtained will be regarding the long wavelength longitudinal optical modes. These modes have an electric dipole associated with them which causes a periodic variation in the scalar potential. This interacts strongly with electrons in the conduction band (see Section 7c).

At a negative-ion vacancy, one will be dealing with local and crystal modes. The transverse optical modes (long wavelength) cause a variation in the vector potential which influences the trapped electron through its spin and angular momentum, if it has any. One might assume that an electron trapped at a negative-ion vacancy would interact primarily with the scalar potential set up by the local modes. Since there is an order of 10^{23} crystal modes, one may not be sure that the net effects of the crystal modes are less important than the effects of the limited number of local modes.

The problem of developing a theory of electron-phonon interactions for all the modes becomes extremely involved. Such calculations may be carried through without too much difficulty under some simplifying assumptions. We shall not develop the problem in such a manner here, but shall limit the considerations to a few (usually two) localized modes. This will permit us to carry through the details, and the results can be generalized to a larger number. The results of the more complete theory (see Markham, S) will be summarized in Section 31a.

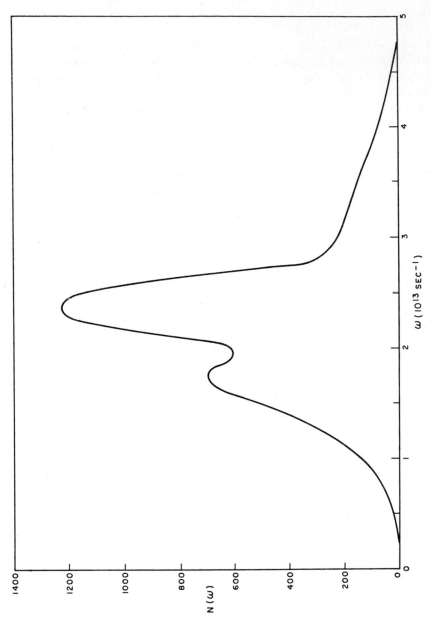

FIG. 29.9. Vibration spectra of KCl based on the calculation of Karo (S).

Since a light particle will produce a local mode, it is natural to look for such modes in alkali halides where a light H^- ion has replaced a heavier Cl^- or Br^- ion. The replacement of Cl^- by H^- produces absorptions in the ultraviolet known as the U-band. One may apply Smakula's formula and easily calculate the concentration of the U-center; further, one may produce F-centers by ultraviolet irradiation of the crystals with light in the U-band (see footnote, Section 7c).

Schaefer (S) was successful in finding localized modes due to the U-center, that is, the H^- ion. He studied eight alkali halides and located several very sharp peaks. These peaks were strongly temperature dependent. For example, in KCl the peak is (at $55°$ K):

$$6.19 \times 10^{-2} \quad ev$$

or a frequency of

$$1.5 \times 10^{13} \quad sec^{-1}.$$

This is several times the highest frequency shown in Fig. 29.9 and indicates that Schaefer was indeed looking at a local crystal mode in the infrared. These modes broaden with rising temperature, but the mechanism must be different from the ones to be described in the following sections. The reason for the difference is that if a phonon were created or destroyed there would be a much larger shift in frequencies than that observed.

REFERENCES

R. L. Bjork, *Phys. Rev.* **105**, 456 (1957).

M. Born, *Proc. Phys. Soc.* (*London*) **54**, 362 (1942).

A. M. Karo, *J. Chem. Phys.* **33**, 7 (1960).

A. A. Marududin, E. W. Montroll, and J. H. Weiss. "Theory of Lattice Dynamics in the Harmonic Approximation," Academic Press, New York, 1963.

J. J. Markham, *Rev. Mod. Phys.* **31**, 956 (1959).

P. Mazur, E. W. Montroll, and R. B. Potts, *J. Wash. Acad. Sci.* **46**, 2 (1956).

G. Schaefer, *Phys. Chem. Solids* **12**, 233 (1960).

A. H. Wilson, "The Theory of Metals," Cambridge Univ. Press, London and New York, 1953.

30. Configurational Coordinate Diagrams

Most unfortunately, the developments of the rigorous configurational coordinate concepts are confined to treatises that are considered extremely advanced (such as that of Born and Huang, or the original paper of Born and Oppenheimer (S)). Actually, these developments have a unique elegance that completely justifies the complexities found in their first reading. Here a very special and idealized problem is developed, in which one may write down most of the steps. The author hopes that this text will aid the beginner in understanding the very basic treatments given by Professor Born and his co-workers. Their treatments have laid the theoretical foundation for the field being discussed. This text should in no way be considered a substitute for the reading of the original paper and the developments given by Born and Huang.

We should like to develop general methods which give equations with parameters. These constants will be obtained from experimental measurements or crude calculations.

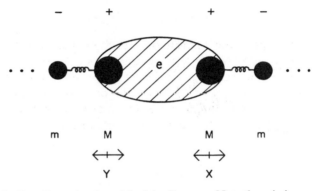

FIG. 30.1. One-dimensional model of the F-center. Note the missing central ion at $n=0$. The shaded area represents the "distribution" of the trapped electron.

a. The Born-Oppenheimer Technique and the Adiabatic Approximation

As a pedagogical tool, consider the one-dimensional model of the F-center illustrated in Fig. 30.1. In the model considered here, the particles in the chain have charges associated with them. The central negative particle is missing. For simplicity, only the interactions between the nearest neighbors are considered. It is assumed that the scalar potential, at a point x, is completely determined by the position of particles at $n= \pm 1$. Their coordinates will be denoted by X and Y. To make the model concrete, X and Y will be measured from the equilibrium position for the imperfect crystal—that is, when there is no trapped electron at $n=0$.

Consider the form of the wave function associated with the system made of the electron whose position is at x, particle $+1$ of mass M whose equilibrium position is at $X=0$ (when the electron is missing) and of particle -1 again of mass M whose displacement from equilibrium is denoted by Y.* The concepts developed here are completely general, and rigorous derivations are given elsewhere (Born and Huang; Markham, 1959S).

The Hamiltonian associated with the model depicted in Fig. 30.1 is:

$$\mathscr{H} = -\frac{\hbar^2}{2M}\left(\frac{\partial^2}{\partial X^2}+\frac{\partial^2}{\partial Y^2}\right)-\frac{\hbar^2}{2m_e}\frac{\partial^2}{\partial x^2}+V(X,Y;x). \qquad (30.1)$$

The first two terms are the kinetic energy associated with the nuclei, T_n, while the next is t, that associated with the electron. The last is the potential. V is assumed to have the form

$$V(X,Y;x) = \tfrac{1}{2}\gamma X^2+\tfrac{1}{2}\gamma Y^2+e^2|A+X-x|^{-1}+e^2|A+x-Y|^{-1}. \qquad (30.1a)$$

A is the distance between particles. The first terms are the spring-like interactions of the particle ± 1 with the ions at ± 2 (which are not allowed to move). The last two terms are the Coulomb energy between the electron at x and the ion at ± 1. The exact form of V is not of interest, since we are trying to establish a technique that is independent of its form. If ions ± 1 are now held fixed, (30.1) reduces to

$$h_e(X,Y) = -\frac{\hbar^2}{2m_e}\frac{\partial^2}{\partial x^2}+V(X,Y;x) = t(x)+V(X,Y;x). \qquad (30.2)$$

A solution of the Schrödinger equation associated with Hamiltonian (30.2) must exist. Let this solution be

$$\phi_n(X,Y;x) \qquad (30.3a)$$

for the eigenfunction of the nth *bound* state whose eigenvalue is

$$\epsilon_n(X,Y). \qquad (30.3b)\dagger$$

ϵ includes the spring energy. In a real crystal, the spring energy does not exist and V is the net potential energy of all the electron-nuclear interactions as well as all the internuclear potentials.

* The equilibrium positions are determined in the absence of electron-lattice interactions. This will be discussed shortly. The change in the distances between particles due to the missing ion is neglected.

† States exist where ϵ does not have a minimum but these will not be considered here.

The adiabatic approximation assumes that the total wave function associated with $\mathscr{H}$ has the form

$$\Psi(n, v) = \chi_T(X, Y)\phi_n(X, Y; x). \tag{30.4}*$$

n denotes the eigenstates of ϕ, while v denotes those associated with χ_T. ϕ_n is a function of three variables, although the coordinates of the ions enter into it in a different manner. It is Ψ_I of Chapter IX. Using the above equations one may obtain the following differential equation for the χ_T's:

$$\frac{-\hbar^2}{2M}\left\{\frac{\partial^2}{\partial X^2}+\frac{\partial^2}{\partial Y^2}\right\}\chi_T(X, Y)\phi_n(X, Y; x)+\epsilon_n(X, Y)\chi_T(X, Y)\phi_n(X, Y; x)$$

$$= E\chi_T(X, Y)\phi_n(X, Y; x), \tag{30.5}$$

where E is the total energy. If one neglects the dependence of ϕ_n on X and Y and uses Taylor's expansion, one obtains the following equation

$$-\frac{\hbar^2}{2M}\left(\frac{\partial^2}{\partial X^2}+\frac{\partial^2}{\partial Y^2}\right)\chi_T+\{\tfrac{1}{2}\epsilon_{xx}(n)(X-X_n)^2+\epsilon_{xy}(n)(X-X_n)(Y-Y_n)$$

$$+\tfrac{1}{2}\epsilon_{yy}(n)(Y-Y_n)^2\}\chi_T = [E-\epsilon_n(X_n, Y_n)]\chi_T. \tag{30.6}$$

X_n and Y_n are the values of X and Y where

$$\left[\frac{\partial\epsilon_n}{\partial X}\right]_{X_n, Y_n} = \left[\frac{\partial\epsilon_n}{\partial Y}\right]_{X_n, Y_n} = 0 \tag{30.6a}$$

while

$$\epsilon_{xx}(n) = \left[\frac{\partial^2\epsilon_n}{\partial X^2}\right]_{X_n, Y_n} \quad \text{etc.} \tag{30.6b}$$

In (30.6), the eigenvalues of h_e act like the potential energy for the Hamiltonian associated with the nuclear motions. Equation (30.6a) determines the equilibrium position of the ions. It should be stressed that X_n and Y_n depend on the state of the electron because of (30.3) and (30.6a). This is the case of *strong* electron-phonon interactions.

$\phi(X_n, Y_n; x)$ is the electronic wave function when the nuclei are held fixed at their equilibrium positions. Chapter IX discusses this wave function and its eigenvalues. If one wants to carry through this calculation from first principles, one must, of course, know the ϕ's and the ϵ's. Here only their existence is considered, to see to what conclusions one is led. This tends to separate the problem into two parts; although this is not

---

* The Ψ used in Chapter X is not related to Ψ_I of Chapter IX in any way. We hope that no confusion will arise.

strictly possible or desirable, the complexity of the problem nevertheless
requires it at present.

Equation (30.6) can be simplified by the introduction of the normal
reduced coordinates. The algebra is particularly simple when $\epsilon_{xx} = \epsilon_{yy}$. In
this case, the reduced normal coordinates are given by

$$X - X_n = \frac{1}{\sqrt{2M}}[q_1(n) + q_2(n)] = \frac{1}{\sqrt{2M}}(q_1 + q_2) \qquad (30.7a)$$

$$Y - Y_n = \frac{1}{\sqrt{2M}}[q_1(n) - q_2(n)] = \frac{1}{\sqrt{2M}}(q_1 - q_2) \qquad (30.7b)$$

The Hamiltonian now takes the form

$$\left[-\frac{\hbar^2}{2}\frac{\partial^2}{\partial q_1{}^2} - \frac{\hbar^2}{2}\frac{\partial^2}{\partial q_2{}^2} + \frac{1}{2}\{\omega_1{}^2(n)\,q_1{}^2 + \omega_2{}^2(n)\,q_2{}^2\} \right]\chi_T = [E - \epsilon_n(0,0)]\chi_T$$

$$(30.8a)$$

where

$$\omega_1{}^2(n) = \frac{1}{M}\epsilon_{xx}(n) + \frac{1}{M}\epsilon_{xy}(n),$$

$$\omega_2{}^2(n) = \frac{1}{M}\epsilon_{yy}(n) - \frac{1}{M}\epsilon_{xy}(n). \qquad (30.8b)$$

The *angular frequency* of the lattice vibrations are denoted by ω while the
frequency of a photon is denoted by ν. A phonon is the energy $\hbar\omega$ (that is,
when the energy goes from $\hbar\omega(\nu + \frac{1}{2})$ to $\hbar\omega(\nu + \frac{3}{2})$ we shall assume that a
phonon is created. Equation (30.8a) is split into two normal modes, q_1
and q_2. We note that the coefficients coupling the q's to the reduced
coordinates $\sqrt{M}(X - X_n)$ and $\sqrt{M}(Y - Y_n)$ give the following matrix:

$$\begin{pmatrix} \dfrac{1}{\sqrt{2}} & \dfrac{1}{\sqrt{2}} \\[2mm] \dfrac{1}{\sqrt{2}} & -\dfrac{1}{\sqrt{2}} \end{pmatrix}.$$

It is unitary. This is a general requirement if the cross terms are to drop
out of (30.8a). It gives unique coupling coefficients when there are no
degenerate modes. One may show that the transformation in Section 29b
has similar properties. Equation (30.8a) can be written in the form

$$\left[-\frac{\hbar^2}{2}\frac{\partial^2}{\partial q_1{}^2} + \frac{1}{2}\omega_1{}^2(n)\,q_1{}^2 \right]\chi_T + \left[-\frac{\hbar^2}{2}\frac{\partial^2}{\partial q_2{}^2} + \frac{1}{2}\omega_2{}^2(n)\,q_2{}^2 \right]\chi_T$$

$$= [E - \epsilon_n(0,0)]\chi_T \qquad (30.8c)$$

where $\omega_1 \neq \omega_2$. Since the q's are a linear combination of X and Y, the equilibrium conditions, Eqs. (30.6a), take the form

$$\frac{\partial \epsilon_n}{\partial q_1} = \frac{\partial \epsilon_n}{\partial q_2} = 0 . \tag{30.8d}$$

Equation (30.8c) can be solved, since it consists of two simple harmonic Hamiltonians. χ_T is a product of two functions, namely:

$$\chi_T = \chi_{v_1}^{(1)}(q_1) \chi_{v_2}^{(2)}(q_2) . \tag{30.9}$$

The solutions for the ground, first, and second excited states of one of the χ's have the form

$$\chi_0(q) = \left(\frac{\omega}{\pi\hbar}\right)^{1/4} \exp\left\{-\frac{\omega q^2}{2\hbar}\right\} \tag{30.9a}$$

$$\chi_1(q) = 2q \left(\frac{\omega}{4\pi\hbar}\right)^{1/4} \exp\left\{-\frac{\omega q^2}{2\hbar}\right\} \tag{30.9b}$$

$$\chi_2(q) = (4q^2 - 2) \left(\frac{\omega}{64\pi\hbar}\right)^{1/4} \exp\left\{-\frac{\omega q^2}{2\hbar}\right\} \tag{30.9c}$$

where the angular frequency ω takes the values ω_1 and ω_2.

The eigenfunction associated with the system can now be written in the form

$$\Psi_A(n, v) = \chi_T(q_1, q_2) \phi(q_1, q_2; x) \tag{30.10}$$

which is known as the *adiabatic approximation*, since ϕ adjusts itself to changes of the q's. An alternate approximation,

$$\Psi_S(n, v) = \chi_T(q_1, q_2) \phi(0, 0; x) , \tag{30.11}$$

is known as the *static approximation*. Now ϕ is fixed with regard to changes in the q's. Both forms are only approximate solutions of (30.1). Equation (30.11) applies to very shallow traps and traps in nonpolar solids; hence consideration will be limited to (30.10) (see Markham, 1956S).

What we have developed is completely general for any eigenstate, n, of the Hamiltonian h_e provided a minimum exists. Our interest is in the transition between two eigenstates. Let one of these be the ground state and the other be the first excited state. We refer everything to the ground state and write ω_1 for $\omega_1(g)$, ω_2 for $\omega_2(g)$, q_1 for $q_1(g)$, etc. Equation (30.8c) applies to the ground state. It can be written in the form

$$\left[-\frac{\hbar^2}{2}\frac{\partial^2}{\partial q_1{}^2} - \frac{\hbar}{2}\frac{\partial^2}{\partial q_2{}^2} + \epsilon(q_1, q_2)\right]\chi_T = E\chi_T \tag{30.12}$$

where

$$\epsilon(q_1, q_2) = \tfrac{1}{2}\omega_1^2 q_1^2 + \tfrac{1}{2}\omega_2^2 q_2^2 + \epsilon(0,0); \tag{30.12a}$$

$$E = \epsilon(0,0) + (v_1 + \tfrac{1}{2})\hbar\omega_1 + (v_2 + \tfrac{1}{2})\hbar\omega_2; \tag{30.12b}$$

and

$$v_i = 0, 1, 2, 3, \cdots$$

The corresponding equation for the excited state is

$$\left[-\frac{\hbar^2}{2}\frac{\partial^2}{\partial q_1^2} - \frac{\hbar^2}{2}\frac{\partial^2}{\partial q_2^2} + \epsilon'(q_1, q_2) \right]\chi_T' = E'\chi_T'. \tag{30.13}$$

ϵ' does not have the simple form of Eq. (30.12a) when expressed in terms of q_1 and q_2, since these coordinates are not the normal ones associated with the excited state. This arises from the dependence of the normal coordinates on the equilibrium position of the nuclei. Due to the change in the electronic wave function, $X(g) \neq X(u)$ and $Y(g) \neq X(u),$* and

$$\left[\frac{\partial \epsilon'}{\partial q_j} \right]_{0,0}$$

is not necessarily zero. ϵ' may be expressed as follows:

$$\epsilon'(q_1, q_2) = \epsilon(q_1, q_2) + \Delta\epsilon(q_1, q_2) = \epsilon(0,0) + \tfrac{1}{2}\omega_1^2 q_1^2$$
$$+ \tfrac{1}{2}\omega_2^2 q_2^2 + \Delta\epsilon(0,0) + \epsilon_1 q_1 + \epsilon_2 q_2. \tag{30.14}$$

Here

$$\epsilon_j = \left[\frac{\partial(\epsilon' - \epsilon)}{\partial q_j} \right] = \left[\frac{\partial \epsilon'}{\partial q_j} \right]_{0,0}. \tag{30.14a}$$

This is a first-order expansion. In (30.14a), the differential is evaluated at $q_1 = q_2 = 0$, the equilibrium position for the ground state. By Feynman's theorem (see Born and Huang, p. 189) we may find a simple physical interpretation of ϵ_j. Using (30.2), it follows that

$$\epsilon_1 = \frac{\partial}{\partial q_1}\epsilon'(q_1, q_2) = \frac{\partial}{\partial q_1}\int \phi_u^*(t+V)\phi_u \, d\tau$$

$$= \int \frac{\partial V}{\partial q_1}|\phi_u|^2 \, d\tau. \tag{30.15}†$$

This indicates that ϵ_1 is just the negative of the generalized force $-\partial V/\partial q_1$ averaged over the electron distribution $|\phi_u|^2$. It does not have the dimension of force, since q has the dimension of length (mass)$^{1/2}$.

* g and u refer to the ground and upper state.
† The last step is justified by Feynman's theorem.

Substitution of (30.14) into (30.13) results in

$$[T_n + \epsilon' - \epsilon(0,0)]\chi_T'$$

$$= \left[-\frac{\hbar^2}{2}\frac{\partial^2}{\partial q_1^2} - \frac{\hbar^2}{2}\frac{\partial^2}{\partial q_2^2} + \frac{1}{2}\omega_1{}^2 q_1{}^2 + \frac{1}{2}\omega_2{}^2 q_2{}^2 + \Delta\epsilon(0,0) + \epsilon_1 q_1 + \epsilon_2 q_2 \right]\chi_T'$$

$$= [E' - \epsilon(0,0)]\chi_T'. \tag{30.16}$$

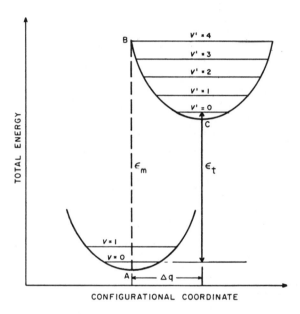

Fig. 30.2. Configurational coordinate diagram for an imperfection with one degree of freedom.

The energy in the excited state is now measured relative to $\epsilon(0,0)$ of the ground state. In Fig. 30.2, we consider the situation for one of the modes. Point A corresponds to the value $q_1 = q_2 = 0$. The energy of the lowest vibrational eigenvalue associated with the ground electronic state is given by the line marked $v = 0$. The energy of the first excited vibrational state is marked $v = 1$, etc.; $\Delta\epsilon(0,0)$ is the difference in energy between points B and A, while $\Delta\epsilon(q)$ is the difference between the curves for a given value of q. In general for all the modes, $\epsilon_m(a) = \Delta\epsilon(0,0)$.

To determine the equilibrium point for the upper curve, we have to return to (30.8d) and use ϵ'. The following value for the equilibrium position of the upper state

$$q_1 = -\epsilon_1/\omega_1{}^2 = \Delta q_1 \qquad (30.17)*$$

results. Now the transformation,

$$q_1(u) = Q_1 = q_1 - \Delta q_1, \qquad (30.18)$$

gives

$$\epsilon' - \epsilon(0,0) = \tfrac{1}{2}\omega_1{}^2 Q_1{}^2 + \tfrac{1}{2}\omega_2{}^2 Q_2{}^2 + \epsilon_t, \qquad (30.19)$$

where

$$\epsilon_t = \Delta\epsilon(0,0) - \tfrac{1}{2}\omega_1{}^2(\Delta q_1)^2 - \tfrac{1}{2}\omega_2{}^2(\Delta q_2)^2. \qquad (30.19a)$$

ϵ_t is the amount of energy it takes to transform the system from the ground state of the lower level to the ground state of the excited level (points A to C). This energy is known as the thermal energy for the transition.

The problem treated here is simple enough that one could have deduced its results visually from the coordinate diagram. The presentation here is an attempt to arrive at the results in a systematic manner from the developments of Born and Oppenheimer. The next higher terms in the expansion of ϵ' would have given a change in the frequency of the modes. Further terms would indicate that the Q's are linear combinations of both the q's, and that the concept of configurational coordinates breaks down unless there is only one local mode of importance to the center. This situation, however, seems extremely unlikely.

All the developments in this section are based on the assumption that ϕ commutes with the kinetic energy operator associated with the ions. This, of course, is an approximation, and we shall very briefly consider its limitations in a later section.

REFERENCES

M. Born and R. Oppenheimer, *Ann. Physik* **84**, 457 (1927).
J. J. Markham, *Phys. Rev.* **103**, 588 (1956).
J. J. Markham, *Rev. Mod. Phys.* **31**, 956 (1959).

* We assume that $\Delta q > 0$, that is, $\epsilon_1 < 0$; this of course is not necessary for the arguments but is done for convenience.

31. The Franck-Condon Principle and the Shape of an Absorption and an Emission Band

To understand the elementary ideas behind the Franck-Condon principle, consider the equation for the absorption of light, derived earlier [Eq. (4.10)]:

$$\alpha = a \frac{8\pi^3}{3} \frac{e^2}{hc} \nu |\langle \Psi'|\mathbf{r}|\Psi\rangle|^2 N_0. \tag{31.1}*$$

Note that $g(\nu)$ has been omitted since here Ψ represents a *total* wave function of the system, electronic plus the vibrational part. The difference in Eq. (31.1) is in the wave functions. To gain an understanding of this problem we shall let the temperature be absolute zero and the Ψ states are made of products of χ_0's times ϕ. The Bohr frequency condition must apply, hence

$$\alpha(\nu_0) = \text{Av } a \left\{ \frac{8\pi^3 e^2}{3hc} \sum_{v'} \int \nu |\langle \Psi'|\mathbf{r}|\Psi\rangle|^2 \delta(\nu - \nu_0) \, d\nu \right\} \tag{31.2}$$

where Av means an average over a narrow set of phonon levels where the Bohr frequency condition applies. This is assured due to the δ-function. Equation (31.2) does not assume that only a single phonon is involved in the process. The δ-function selects only those transitions where the Bohr condition applies.

For $T > 0$, we have to include a Boltzmann factor to take care of the distribution of the population in the various levels. This situation will be considered shortly. The absorption band is thus a series of lines that ideally are infinitely narrow. Actually, every line has a breadth due to a large variety of interactions. The absorption is thus a series of bands that merge into a single broad one. This is illustrated in Fig. 31.1.

It is convenient to introduce the oscillator strength, Eq. (4.3a), to integrate over δ, and write:

$$\alpha(\nu) = \frac{\pi e^2}{mc} afN_0 \frac{1}{\Delta\nu} \sum_{v'}^{\Delta\nu} |\langle \chi_{T'}|\chi_T\rangle|^2. \tag{31.3}$$

The frequency dependence of the right-hand side arises from v'. The sum is limited by the Bohr condition so that ν is in the range $\nu \pm \frac{1}{2}\Delta\nu$. We now consider that only one mode interacts with the center—that is, only

* $\mathbf{r}$ is the radius vector since now we are considering a three-dimensional problem; f is given by (4.3a).

one $\epsilon_j \neq 0$—since our major interest is for instructional purposes. When more than one mode has to be considered, then the problem must be handled with greater care—see Markham (S).

In the most general case, f is a function of the frequency and the q's. The assumption will now be made that the matrix element in f is independent of the q's. This is called the *Condon approximation*. Further, the frequency dependence of f will be neglected. This is a simplification that cannot be completely justified. Thus the frequency dependence of α (the shape factor) arises from the matrix element in Eq. (31.3).

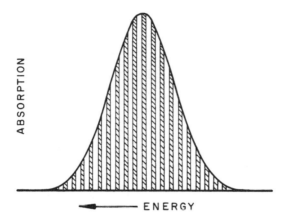

FIG. 31.1. Schematic diagram showing the broadening due to the emission or absorption of phonons.

To see how this happens, consider the case when the system is in the lowest vibrational state. If $\Delta q = 0$, the only allowed transition (nonzero value of the matrix) is to $v' = 0$ (see Fig. 31.2a). When $\Delta q \neq 0$, transitions to higher excited states occur ($v' = 0, 1, 2, \cdots$); see Fig. 31.3a and b. When $\Delta q = 0$ (for $v' > 0$), the positive " area " in the product $\chi' \chi_0$ equals the negative, and the sum is zero. When $\Delta q \neq 0$ (Fig. 31.3b), the positive area does not equal the negative, and the matrix element has a nonzero value.

The case illustrated in Fig. 31.3a gives a single line corresponding to the energy ϵ_t. If Δq is very small, then one main line is obtained with some satellites, since now the matrix elements, $|\langle \chi_1' | \chi_0 \rangle|^2$, $|\langle \chi_2' | \chi_0 \rangle|^2$, etc., are finite.* This situation corresponds to the case illustrated in Fig. 31.2b.

* The prime on the χ_v' is omitted.

When $\hbar\omega$ is small, it may be impossible to resolve the fine structure, and the experimental data will give only the envelope curve, which will be referred to as the "*band shape.*" Hence, the energy of the absorbed photon is determined by the vibrational matrix elements. The foregoing conclusions can be established by the use of Fig. 31.3a and b.

Consider next the case when Δq is large, specifically case (c) in Fig. 31.2. Transitions to vibrational levels much smaller than $v' = S$ are essentially

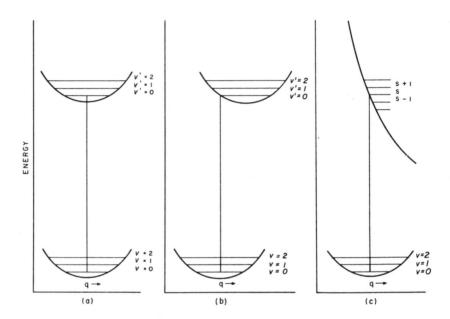

FIG. 31.2. The configurational coordinate diagram showing the effect of various Δq's.

forbidden, since χ_0 is finite only where χ_v' is zero. For levels whose value of v' is considerably larger than S, χ_v' oscillates, and the product, $\chi_v'\chi_0$ averaged over q is zero. The nature of the χ's [see Pauling and Wilson (S), p. 73] suggests the matrix element will be largest for the "vertical transition." Actual calculations show, however, that the nondiagonal matrix elements do not completely vanish, and that they, in part, determine the shape.

In the extreme case, when Δq is large, one is tempted to neglect the quantization process altogether and consider only vertical transitions whose probabilities are determined by $|\chi_0(q)|^2$. This assumption is made since $\chi_v{}'$ does not oscillate near the classical turning point, that is, the value of q where $\frac{1}{2}\omega^2(q-\Delta q)^2 = \hbar\omega(v'+\frac{1}{2})$ for $v'>0$. χ_0 has a Gaussian shape. For other values of q, $\chi_v{}'$ oscillates a great deal and these values of q do not contribute to the integrals—that is, $\int \chi_v{}'(q)\chi_0(q)\,dq$.

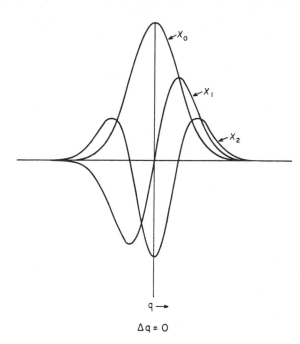

FIG. 31.3a. Plots of χ_0, χ_1, and χ_2, showing the symmetry and the effect of changing the equilibrium position; $\Delta q=0$.

In view of the sum over v' in (31.3), the energy of the absorbed photon must have the value

$$\epsilon = h\nu = \epsilon_t - \tfrac{1}{2}\omega^2 q^2 + \tfrac{1}{2}\omega^2(q-\Delta q)^2$$
$$= \epsilon_t + \tfrac{1}{2}\omega^2(\Delta q)^2 - \omega^2\,\Delta qq \qquad\qquad (31.4)$$
$$= h\nu_m - \omega^2\,\Delta qq \qquad\qquad\qquad\quad (31.4a)$$
$$= \epsilon_m - \omega^2\,\Delta qq. \qquad\qquad\qquad\quad (31.5)\text{*}$$

In (31.4), we have completely neglected the quantum nature of the energy values. It seems questionable to include $-\tfrac{1}{2}\omega^2 q^2$ associated with the

* For convenience, Δq is assumed to be positive. This is not a necessary requirement for the derivation.

ground state when we know that the energy of the system in that state is independent of q. Actually, we shall soon use (31.5) for situations where $\theta > 0°$ K, and the above limitation is less true. This term is extremely small, since (30.9a) confines q to small values. ν_m and ϵ_m are associated

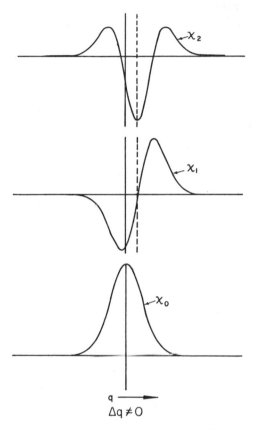

FIG. 31.3b. Plots as in Fig. 31.3a when $\varDelta q \neq 0$.

with the maximum absorption probability (see Fig. 30.2). We further assume that the probability of absorbing a photon of energy ϵ is proportional to the probability of finding the system at q. This can be obtained from Eq. (30.9), namely,

$$\Gamma(q) = \chi_0{}^2(q) = \left(\frac{\omega}{\pi h}\right)^{1/2} \exp\left\{-\frac{\omega q^2}{\hbar}\right\}, \qquad (\theta = 0°\,\text{K}). \quad (31.6)$$

The above assumptions are known as the *Franck-Condon approximation*. This principle requires: (1) that the q's do not change during a transition; and (2) that the momentum associated with the degrees of freedom does not change. The latter requirement actually is the same as requiring that all the energy be potential in both the ground and the excited states; hence, there are only "vertical transitions" in Figs. 30.2 and 31.2. For details see Herzberg (S, 194 ff.), Condon and Morse (S), or Condon (S). The requirement that the momentum or velocity not change occasionally is not stressed but it is a very important part of the principle.

The Franck-Condon principle should be distinguished from the Condon approximation made earlier. We stress that (31.6) applies only when the system is initially in the lowest vibrational state. To obtain the shape factor, we must replace the configurational coordinate q by the energy of the absorbed photon. From Eq. (31.5):

$$q = \frac{1}{\epsilon_1}(\epsilon - \epsilon_m) \tag{31.5a}$$

where (30.17) has been used (ϵ_1 being associated with the q). Hence, we obtain

$$g_l(\epsilon) = [2\pi\hbar^2 \omega^2 S]^{-1/2} \exp\left\{-\frac{1}{2(\hbar\omega)^2}\frac{1}{S}(\epsilon - \epsilon_m)^2\right\}, \qquad (\theta = 0°\,\text{K}) \quad (31.7)^*$$

where

$$S = \frac{1}{2}\frac{\epsilon_1^2}{\omega^2}\frac{1}{\omega\hbar} = \frac{1}{\hbar\omega}\left[\frac{1}{2}\omega^2(\Delta q)^2\right]. \tag{31.7a}$$

S is known as the Huang-Rhys S-factor, and was introduced into the theory by these authors in their original purely quantum mechanical treatment of the subject (Huang and Rhys, S). [Pekar (S) used $2S$, which he denotes by d.]

S is the ratio of the potential energy when our oscillator is displaced Δq to the energy of a single phonon $\hbar\omega$. This is the reason for denoting the level vertically above $\Delta q = 0$ by S in Fig. 31.2. The introduction of more modes and allowances for the changes in the frequencies makes this definition somewhat more complex but does not change the basic idea. The experimental shape curve is obtained by plotting α against the photon energy. It should be similar to Eq. (31.7) because of (31.3). This theory gives a Gaussian curve shape. The frequency dependence of f has been neglected. Such a plot is shown in Fig. 31.1.

---

* Γ and g give the probability in unit intervals of q and ϵ; hence, the coefficient in front of the exponent is important. g_l is g at low temperatures.

We note that

$$\int_0^\infty g(\epsilon)\, d\epsilon = 1 \qquad (31.8)$$

provided ϵ_m is large, so that one may replace the lower limit by $-\infty$. A form of Eq. (31.7) was used in Section 3. We are interested in the width at half height. For this purpose, it is useful to define the point at half absorption (see Section 3) to the violet, ϵ_v and to the red ϵ_r of ϵ_m. Then

$$H(0)^2 = (\epsilon_v - \epsilon_r)^2 = [8\ln 2](\hbar\omega)^2 S; \qquad (\theta = 0°\,\mathrm{K}). \quad (31.9)$$

The equations developed so far assume that only one vibrational mode is involved in the problem. If two modes are included, (31.5) has to be replaced by

$$\Gamma(q) = \left(\frac{\omega_1}{\pi\hbar}\right)^{1/2}\left(\frac{\omega_2}{\pi\hbar}\right)^{1/2} \exp -\left\{\frac{\omega_1}{\hbar}q_1{}^2 + \frac{\omega_2}{\hbar}q_2{}^2\right\} \quad \text{at} \quad \theta = 0°\,\mathrm{K} \quad (31.10)$$

and (31.4) is replaced by

$$h\nu = \epsilon_t + \tfrac{1}{2}\omega_1{}^2(\varDelta q_1)^2 + \tfrac{1}{2}\omega_2{}^2(\varDelta q_2)^2 - \omega_1{}^2\,\varDelta q_1\,q_1 - \omega_2{}^2\,\varDelta q_2\,q_2. \quad (31.11)$$

Equation (31.11) gives

$$\epsilon = \epsilon_m + \epsilon_1 q_1 + \epsilon_2 q_2. \qquad (31.11a)$$

If the variable q_2 is replaced by

$$\frac{1}{\epsilon_2}[\epsilon - \epsilon_m - \epsilon_1 q_1],$$

one may integrate over q_1 holding ϵ fixed. Again Eq. (31.7) is obtained except that S, the Huang-Rhys factor, has the form

$$S = \frac{1}{2}\frac{1}{\omega\hbar}\frac{1}{\omega^2}(\epsilon_1{}^2 + \epsilon_2{}^2) \qquad (31.12)$$

where the assumption that $\omega_1 = \omega_2$ has been made. If $\omega_1 \neq \omega_2$, the expression for S becomes more complex.

Thus, Eqs. (31.7) and (31.8) do not depend on the assumption of a single configurational coordinate. One may generalize (31.9) to any number of coordinates. No difficulty arises in this generalization if a single "effective" frequency exists. This problem has recently been treated in detail (Markham, S).

For a mode to contribute to the shape, it must be displaced during the transition, that is, its ϵ_j or $\varDelta q$ must not be zero. If a single effective frequency exists, the modes for which $\varDelta q \neq 0$ must all have approximately this frequency. We have seen that the modes in an actual crystal (see Figs. 29.3 and 29.9) pile up, and the net behavior of the crystal modes may resemble a single one, a situation that also occurs when one is dealing with local modes.

Let us next consider what happens when the temperature is finite. The probability of finding an oscillator in state v is given by

$$p(v) = e^{-v\beta}(1 - e^{-\beta}) \tag{31.13}$$

where

$$\beta = \frac{\hbar\omega}{k\theta}$$

(see Seitz, 1940, p. 100). Here, k is the Boltzmann constant, and θ is the absolute temperature. The probability of finding an oscillator in state v at position q is thus given by

$$p(v)\chi_v^2(q)$$

and the net probability has the form

$$P(q) = \sum_v p(v)\chi_v^2(q). \tag{31.14}$$

It is possible to evaluate (31.14) in a straightforward but lengthy fashion (see, for example, Markham, S).*

The result has a relatively simple form:

$$P_\theta(b) = b\frac{1}{\sqrt{\pi}}\exp\left\{-\frac{1}{b^2}q^2\right\} \tag{31.15}$$

$$b = \left(\frac{\hbar}{\omega}\right)^{1/2}\coth^{1/2}\frac{\hbar\omega}{2k\theta}. \tag{31.15a}$$

Note that at low temperatures, $\Gamma = P$. At high temperatures, P takes the form

$$P = \left(\frac{2k\theta}{\pi\omega^2}\right)^{1/2}\exp\left\{-\frac{\omega^2 q^2}{2k\theta}\right\}, \tag{31.15b}$$

which is the one obtained from Boltzmann's statistics where one considers only the potential energies of the oscillator. One can see that (31.15) resembles (31.6) and that the only change is the temperature factor, a^2, which equals $\hbar/\omega$ at $0°$ K, but approaches $k\theta/\hbar\omega$ at high temperatures.

* Namely, Eq. (9.35) of Markham's paper.

Equations (31.7) and (31.9) are replaced by the relations

$$g(\epsilon) = \left[2\pi\hbar^2\,\omega^2\,S\coth\frac{\hbar\omega}{2k\theta}\right]^{-1/2}\exp\left\{-\frac{(\epsilon-\epsilon_m)^2}{2(\hbar\omega)^2\,S\coth\dfrac{\hbar\omega}{2k\theta}}\right\} \quad (31.16)$$

and

$$H^2 = 8\{\ln 2\}(\hbar\omega)^2\,S\coth\left(\frac{\hbar\omega}{2k\theta}\right). \quad (31.17)$$

Equation (31.16) applies to any number of modes, provided a *single* effective frequency exists, so that (31.15) applies to every mode involved in the process. At high temperatures

$$\coth\frac{\hbar\omega}{2k\theta} = \frac{2k\theta}{\hbar\omega}\,. \quad (31.18)$$

Hence, it follows that

$$g_h(\epsilon) = [4\pi\hbar\omega S k\theta]^{-1/2}\exp\left\{-\frac{(\epsilon-\epsilon_m)^2}{4\hbar\omega S k\theta}\right\} \quad (31.19a)$$

and

$$H^2 = 16(\tfrac{1}{2}\omega^2\,\Delta q^2)\,k\theta\ln 2. \quad (31.19b)*$$

At low temperature, one recovers Eq. (31.7). Equation (31.19b) was originally derived by Mott and Gurney, p. 113. A more detailed treatment has been given by Klick and Schulman (S).

Closely related to this problem are the absorption and emission which occur when one dissolves thallium in an alkali halide. Williams, using a suggestion of Seitz, has calculated a configurational coordinate diagram for two levels of the Tl^+ ion, the ground and the first excited state. He assumes that the Tl^+ ion replaces a K^+ ion in KCl and that there is an interaction between it and the immediate environment.

Williams (S) assumed that a breathing mode existed around the Tl^+ ion—that is, that the six nearest neighbor Cl^- ions vibrate in phase radially (along the line that connects Tl^+ to Cl^-). This assumption most probably is an oversimplification which, however, does not modify the essential ideas. Many problems related to these calculations have not been completely resolved. Williams's calculations, nevertheless, indicate a unique agreement between theory and experiment; this gives a sound experimental and theoretical basis on which to proceed.

---

* One may attempt to alter Eq. (31.19) by changing Eqs. (31.4) and (31.5). Such attempts are open to question since we know that the Franck-Condon principle applies only *approximately*. Further, the use of Eq. (31.15) is questionable.

We shall refer to the technique just developed by the name Williams-Hebb (S), since these two authors were the first to introduce (31.15) into this type of a calculation. The use of configurational coordinates and transition probabilities, as well as of the Condon approximation, are basic to any calculation of band shapes. One may make an exact calculation using quantum mechanics without the use of the Franck-Condon principle [Huang and Rhys (S) or Pekar (S)]. One may even omit the use of the Condon approximation [Meyer (S); for details, see Markham (S)]. The Franck-Condon principle and Eq. (31.15) are further approximations that have been used extensively by Williams and by Klick.

The steps taken to obtain (31.9) and (31.16) to (31.19) cannot possibly be justified. Since they have been used a great deal in the literature, it is well to discuss them here.

The first approximation is the assumption that one may consider only vertical transitions—namely, transitions of type A to B in Fig. 30.2. The quantum restrictions (selection rules) for the transition between vibrational states are strict in case (a) of Fig. 31.2, but are only approximate in the two other situations. Indeed, one may not assume without detailed calculations that the transition probability from $v = 0$ to $v' = S + 1$ equals the transition probability from $v = 0$ to $v' = S - 1$; actually, they do not.

The second approximation is in the steps used to obtain $g(\epsilon)$. These errors are not great at very low temperatures, but the use of (31.15) combined with (31.4) means that we replace the energy of the higher vibrational modes by energy of the coordinate curve. We have applied (31.5) to transitions from excited vibrational states through the use of Eq. (31.15). This equation was obtained by summing the probability of finding the system at q over *all* the vibrational energy levels. The energy of a state is composed of both potential and kinetic energy, whereas Eq. (31.5) considers only the difference in the potential energies. A further important approximation was made in the use of (30.14), where higher order terms were neglected. If the major terms of the type $\partial^2(\epsilon' - \epsilon)/\partial q_j^2$ were included, there would be a frequency change between the ground and the excited states. The Williams-Hebb approximation becomes more involved, but can still be used. The next larger order terms destroy the simple relations between the q_j's and the Q_j's.

a. Summary of Some Exact Calculations

These problems will be pursued a little further by quoting the results of some simple exact calculations. The arguments are too involved to be given in full detail (see Dexter, S, and Markham, S). Assume again that the system is initially in the ground state $v=0$ (absolute zero). One may now calculate exactly the transitions to vibrational levels in the excited state provided there is no change in the *single* effective frequency. The result is

$$\left[\int \chi'_{v'}\chi_0\, dq\right]^2 = e^{-S}\frac{S^v}{v'!}.\tag{31.20}$$

The frequency dependence of (31.20) on energy arises through the value of v',

$$\epsilon = \epsilon_t + v'\hbar\omega.\tag{31.21}$$

Since expression (31.20) was first given by Pekar in relation to this problem, it has been called Pekarian; it is actually a *Poisson* distribution, and the latter designation will be used here. It equals unity when $S=0$ and $v'=0$. This can be seen from Fig. 30.2. When $S \neq 0$, one may prove the relation

$$\sum_{v'} |\langle \chi'_{v'}|\chi_0\rangle|^2 = 1.\tag{31.22}$$

The sum of (31.22) is equivalent to an integration over the energy. Experimentally, one observes the envelope of (31.20).* To make the problem solvable, we have neglected secondary terms which smooth out the fine structure (see Fig. 31.1). Equations (31.20) and (31.22) indicate that the actual transition probabilities are equivalent to the g introduced previously.

Equation (31.20) shows that the true absorption curve is not the one given by (31.7); indeed, (31.20) is not a symmetric curve. Its maximum occurs at

$$v' = S \qquad \text{(nearest integer)}.\tag{31.23}$$

To show this, one may use Sterling's approximation and differentiate with respect to v'. The Poissonian curve has a long tail to the violet, as can be seen from Fig. 31.4. One should stress that the lack of symmetry of the curve arises from the transition matrix elements themselves, and is not due to any asymmetry in the *potential* energy *curves*. This means that the technique used in obtaining (31.7) cannot be *fully* justified.

At high temperatures, the exact model gives a completely symmetric Gaussian shape if terms beyond ϵ_j are omitted. One may obtain (31.17) rigorously for any value of θ. The rigorous quantum-mechanical calculations do not actually develop expressions for H; rather, they give moments

---

* This statement applies to the F-center but not to all color centers, some of which show fine structure at low temperatures.

of the distribution* which can be related to H, provided the shape is known. One may again show that (31.17), (31.20), and (31.22) apply to any number of modes. Here we are assuming that a *single effective* frequency can be defined and where there is no *change* in the phonon frequencies. If several effective frequencies exist, expressions corresponding to (31.17) have been derived (see Markham, S).

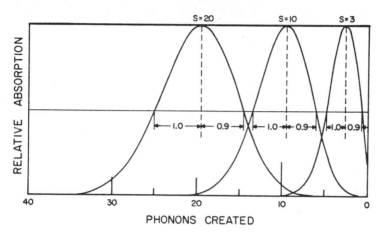

FIG. 31.4. Three Poissonian curves for various values of S. Note the lack of symmetry. Actually, for large values of S the curve becomes symmetric.

b. Emission Curve Shapes

The probability of spontaneous emission is given by Einstein's A coefficient which, at a point defect in a solid, has the form

$$A_d = \left\{\frac{n(n^2+2)^2}{9}\right\} \frac{64\pi^4 e^2 \nu^3}{3 \ hc^3} |\langle \Psi'|\mathbf{r}|\Psi\rangle|^2. \tag{31.24}$$

The above expression for A_d is derived and discussed in the Appendix to this chapter. A_d is caused by the zero-point vibrations of the electromagnetic waves. These are distorted by the crystal, and the relation between the local field and the macroscopic field is assumed to be the same as that considered previously (Section 4).

The matrix element in (31.24) will produce an emission shape. We may

---

* The moments of the distribution are defined by the relation $M_n = \int_0^\infty \epsilon^n \alpha(\epsilon)\,d\epsilon$. The square of the width at half height, H^2, is proportional to $(M_2/M_0)-(M_1/M_0)^2$. The factor of proportionality for a Gaussian curve is 5.54.

again introduce a δ-function so that the Bohr condition, Eq. (4.2), is obeyed. From Eq. (31.24) we may obtain the following expression for the emitted energy in intervals of $\Delta\nu$:

$$S_e(\nu) = a' \frac{64\pi^4 e^2}{3} \frac{1}{c^3 \Delta\nu} \sum_{\nu'}^{\Delta\nu} \nu^4 |\langle \Psi'|r|\Psi\rangle|^2 \tag{31.25}$$

where the sum over ν has the same meaning as it did previously [$S(\nu)$ is the photon energy emitted at frequency ν]. a' is the expression in the curly brackets of Eq. (31.24). Introducing the oscillator strength of Eq. (4.3) the following shape curve for emission is obtained:

$$S_e(\nu) = a' \frac{8\pi^2 he^2}{mc^3} \nu^3 f_e \frac{1}{\Delta\nu} \sum_{\nu'}^{\Delta\nu} |\langle \chi_{T'}|\chi_T\rangle|^2 \tag{31.26}$$

where f_e is the oscillator strength for the emission process. The relation of f_a (oscillator strength for absorption—Section 4) and f_e are unknown at present. There are many reasons, both experimental and theoretical, to believe they are not equal. One might be an order of magnitude smaller— we assumed them equal in Section 7 to simplify the calculation. If the ν^3 term in front of the sum in Eq. (31.26) is ignored, the emission shape is again determined by the matrix elements. The problem of the effect of the ν^3 term in (31.26) or the ν^4 term in (31.25), as well as of the ν term in (31.1), requires more careful attention than it has received so far. Preliminary consideration has been made using a method developed by Lax (S) [see Markham (S)].

Emission occurs after the system has come to an equilibrium in the excited state. This assumption can be made, since the thermal equilibrium is established in a matter of 10^{-12} or 10^{-11} sec, while the photon emission occurs after 10^{-8} sec. Thus, the role of the χ_T's has been interchanged. In the simplest theory, the shape is again Gaussian. More complex calculations give a Poissonian curve where the tail is on the infrared side; this is the mirror-image effect often referred to in the literature.

We may summarize the "state of the art." The techniques developed here are certainly approximate and do not agree completely with exact calculations on simple models. The moments of the distribution can be obtained for more complex models using more exact theory, although they are lengthy and involved. The shape has not been calculated rigorously for more involved models, although such studies would be of great value. In a later section, we shall see that the experimental results demand more exact calculations than are presently available.

The second method will be referred to as the quantum mechanical approximation.* It uses configurational coordinates. It can include a finite shift (more than infinitesimal) in the equilibrium positions between the ground and the excited state, and can be made to include changes in the frequencies. It uses the Condon approximation and effectively allows for the Franck-Condon principle. Actually, it goes beyond the Franck-Condon principle and makes rigorous calculations of the matrix elements. It could be used without making the Condon approximation. In the original development by Pekar (S) and by Huang and Rhys (S), the Δq's were assumed to be very small; hence, the name "linear approximation" has been applied to this model (see Dexter). It has been shown recently that these limitations can be removed using some developments by Lax (S) and by O'Rourke (S). For details, see Markham (S).

c. The Calculations of S

An effect of major importance has been discovered independently in the calculations of S by McCombie, Matthew, and Murray (S) and by Casselman and the author (S). Let us examine ϵ_j, which enters into S in the following manner

$$S = \frac{1}{2}\frac{1}{\hbar\omega_e{}^3} \sum_j \epsilon_j{}^2, \tag{31.27}$$

where one assumes that an effective phonon frequency exists and that it is not affected by the electronic transitions. From Eq. (30.15) we have:

$$\epsilon_j = \int |\phi_u|^2 \frac{\partial}{\partial q_j} V(X, Y; x)\, d\tau_r. \tag{31.28}$$

ϕ_u and V are functions of the ionic and electronic positions. It was indicated that the q's are related to the ionic position by means of a unitary transformation—Eq. (30.8c). In Eq. (31.28) the simple model of Section 30 has been employed. In general, for the one-dimensional linear chain of equal masses (we include the displacement of all particles now and not just the nearest neighbors) the total displacement is given by

$$u(n) = m^{-1/2} \sum_j e(n|j)\, q_j, \tag{31.29}$$

where n refers to the particle and j to the mode. The e's can be considered as eigenvectors of a matrix equation; for details, see Born and Huang, p. 173. Hence, we shall call them eigenvectors—they are really components of eigenvectors—and the effect discussed here may

---

* The first method is the one that uses Eq. (31.15), disregarding the fact that all the levels in the sum of Eq. (31.14) do not have the same eigenvalues.

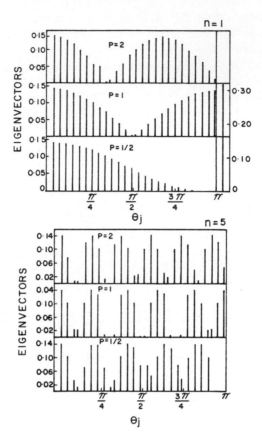

Fig. 31.5. Plot of the eigenvectors of various symmetric modes (value of θ_j) for $n=1$ (lower plot) and $n=5$ (upper plot) (after Casselman and Markham, S).

be referred to as the *eigenvector effect*. Substituting Eq. (31.29) into (31.28) results in

$$\epsilon_j = \frac{1}{m^{1/2}} \sum_n e(n|j) \int |\phi_u|^2 \frac{\partial V}{\partial u(n)} \, d\tau. \tag{31.30}$$

One may evaluate $\partial V/\partial u(n)$ and the integral by making some simplifying assumptions regarding the potential function. Thus S depends on the eigenvectors.

The e's have been calculated for a chain of 101 particles where the mass of the center particle m' is different from the mass m of the other one. The eigenvectors depend on

$$P = m'/m. \tag{31.31}$$

The equations that determine the e's are similar to those discussed in Section 29. The results of a calculation are shown in Fig. 31.5.* The effect of the variation of P is indicated in Fig. 31.5. We conclude that right next to an imperfection the e's will not have the value they have at a perfect site in the crystal ($P = 1$). This leads one to consider the imperfection as a "molecule" rather than as an imperfection imbedded into a perfect lattice. This in part justifies the approaches discussed at the end of Chapter IX. Perhaps the most important point to stress is that the eigenfunction effect occurs independently of the value of P—that is, independently of the presence of a local mode, $P < 1$. The symmetry for $P = 1$ (no imperfection) occurs because symmetrical boundary conditions have been used.

This is a general effect which is not limited to the one-dimensional case. The equations above must be generalized.

REFERENCES

T. N. Casselman and J. J. Markham, *Phys. Chem. Solids* **24**, 669 (1963).

E. U. Condon, *Phys. Rev.* **28**, 1182 (1926); **32**, 858 (1928).

E. U. Condon and P. M. Morse, "Quantum Mechanics." McGraw-Hill, New York, 1929.

D. L. Dexter, *Solid State Physics* **6**, 353 (1958).

G. Herzberg, "Molecular Spectra and Molecular Structure," Vol. I. Van Nostrand, New York, 1950.

K. Huang and A. Rhys, *Proc. Roy. Soc. (London)* **A204**, 403 (1950).

C. C. Klick and J. H. Schulman, *Solid State Physics* **5**, 97 (1957).

M. Lax, *J. Chem. Phys.* **20**, 1752 (1952).

J. J. Markham, *Rev. Mod. Phys.* **31**, 956 (1959).

C. W. McCombie, J. A. D. Matthew, and A. M. Murray, *J. Appl. Phys. Suppl.* **33**, 359 (1962).

H. J. G. Meyer, *Physica* **21**, 253 (1955).

R. C. O'Rourke, *Phys. Rev.* **91**, 265 (1953).

L. Pauling and E. B. Wilson, "Introduction to Quantum Mechanics." McGraw-Hill, New York, 1935.

S. I. Pekar, "Research in Electron Theory of Crystals." M.S., A.E.C. tr-5575. U.S. Dept. of Commerce.

F. E. Williams, *J. Chem. Phys.* **19**, 457 (1951).

F. E. Williams and M. H. Hebb, *Phys. Rev.* **84**, 1181 (1951).

32. NONRADIATIVE TRANSITIONS

We have carefully omitted discussing anything regarding the steps between (30.5) and (30.6) and have, for all practical purposes, neglected

---

* Actually the calculations were done for the symmetric modes since this effect does not show up in the antisymmetric modes of the *particular* example employed by Casselman and co-worker. Further Eq. (30.8d) did not actually apply and Eq. (30.15) became more complex.

the dependence of ϕ_n on X and Y. Additional terms appear, depending on the assumed form of the eigenfunction (30.10) or (30.11). For the adiabatic approximation, the terms omitted are

$$-\frac{\hbar^2 \chi_T}{2}\left(\frac{\partial^2 \phi_n}{\partial q_1{}^2}+\frac{\partial^2 \phi_n}{\partial q_2{}^2}\right)-\hbar^2\left(\frac{\partial \chi_T}{\partial q_1}\right)\left(\frac{\partial \phi_n}{\partial q_1}\right)-\hbar^2\left(\frac{\partial \chi_T}{\partial q_2}\right)\left(\frac{\partial \phi_n}{\partial q_2}\right). \quad (32.1)$$

We have expressed the kinetic energy in terms of the q's. Equation (32.1) may be taken into account by two means. First, one can use it to modify the eigenfunctions, Eq. (30.10). In that case, the corrected eigenfunctions are linear combinations of $\Psi_A(n,v)$ in (30.10). Alternatively, we may still use Eq. (30.10) and consider that (32.1) induces nonradiative transitions between the eigenstates. These transitions are given by the Schrödinger time-dependent perturbation theory. A complete treatment of this problem has not yet been given. The first type of approach has been made by Born and Huang, while the second method has been employed by Meyer (S) and by Kubo (S). These extremely important problems will not be pursued further here.

REFERENCES

R. Kubo, *Phys. Rev.* **86**, 929 (1952).
H. J. G. Meyer, *Physica* **20**, 1016 (1954).
H. J. G. Meyer, *Physica* **21**, 253 (1955).

33. EXPERIMENTAL RESULTS

One might assume that one could readily obtain data to test Eqs. (31.16), (31.17), and (31.20) in the available experimental literature. Unfortunately, this is not the case. The most studied absorption band is probably the F absorption. As we stressed earlier, the F-center is greatly affected by slight exposures to light and improper quenching after additive coloration. The values of H reported in the literature are not always self-consistent. Five detailed studies of H for absorption have been made, using different alkali halides, by Mollwo (S), Russell and Klick (S), Konitzer and Markham (S), Markham and Konitzer (S), and Stungis, Markham, and Noble (S). The analysis of Mollwo is of historic interest only.

The data of Russell and Klick were analyzed in terms of (31.17), and were found to agree with the theory for KCl, KBr, KI, NaCl, and LiF. A comparison of the data of Mollwo and those of Russell and Klick with the more recent data indicates that these studies were made on bleached or poorly quenched crystals. Most probably, the data do not pertain exclusively to transitions between the two bound states and the theory developed here does not apply.

The most detailed attempt to correlate the theory with experiment so far has been done on KCl and RbCl, where measurements were made at temperatures below 400° K. The data will now be presented. First,

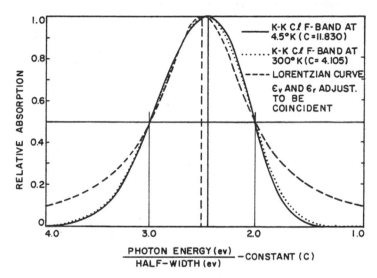

FIG. 33.1. Comparison of the shape of the F-band at two temperatures with a Lorentzian curve. The scale is arbitrarily adjusted so that the half-points occur at the same values. The vertical line corresponds to the peak and shows that the F-band is not a symmetric curve (after Konitzer and Markham, S).

consider the shape of the band. If one allows for the temperature broadening by making ϵ_v and ϵ_r coincide, the measurements indicate that the band shape is temperature independent. The method employed was to divide ϵ by H, and to divide the absorption by α_m—the maximum value of the absorption. Then by shifting the origin of the axis associated with ϵ/H, one may make the points ϵ_v and ϵ_r coincide for any temperature. A set of curves is shown in Fig. 33.1 for KCl. It indicates that the shape is temperature independent, whereas Fig. 33.2 shows that the asymmetry observed is approximately Poissonian. A Lorentzian curve,* as well as a

---

* We take the Lorentzian curve in the form

$$\text{const}\, H^2[H^2 + (\epsilon - \epsilon_m)^2]^{-1}.$$

Gaussian curve, has been included. This means that the absorption curve is approximately Poissonian and that it is temperature independent.

This explains the shape at low temperatures on the simple model suggested in Section 31. It does not, however, explain the shape at high temperatures. One may make rough calculations (Williams-Hebb method) on more complex models and obtain an "explanation"; these simplified calculations, however, do not give the correct results on the simplest model at low temperatures. Hence, we do not know what

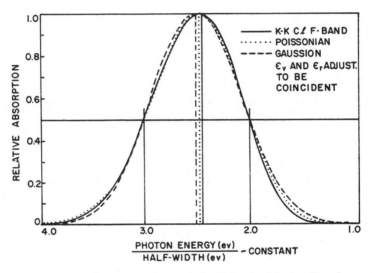

FIG. 33.2. Comparison of the shape of the F-band with the Gaussian and the Poissonian shape; $S = 30$ (after Konitzer and Markham, S).

reliance can be placed on this type of calculation. This is a problem that has not been successfully solved theoretically.

Next, Eq. (31.17) should be tested. In obtaining (31.17), a Gaussian shape was assumed. More detailed calculations, both theoretical and experimental, indicate that (31.17) may be used in spite of the fact that the shape is almost Poissonian. To establish the relation between H and θ, one may write (ω is the *effective* frequency):

$$H^2(\theta) = H^2(0) \coth\left(\frac{1}{2}\frac{\hbar\omega}{k\theta}\right) \qquad (33.1)$$

where $H(0)$ can be defined from Eq. (31.17), that is, $H^2(0) = 8(\hbar\omega)^2 S \ln 2$. Since $H(0)$ can be obtained from low-temperature measurements (say

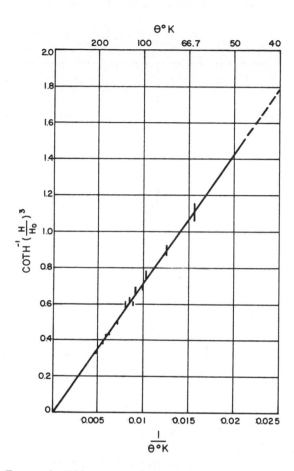

Fig. 33.3. *F*-center in KCl. Arc hyperbolic cotangent plot of the measured values of the half width versus the reciprocal of the temperature. From the graph, the frequency of the modes that broaden the *F*-band can be determined (after Konitzer and Markham, S); ($\omega = 2\pi(2.96) \times 10^{12}$ sec^{-1}; 0.0122eV).

at 4° K), ω is the only unknown in Eq. (31.1). Although it is important to evaluate this unknown, we are *primarily* interested in knowing if the data really obey Eq. (33.1). The question is: Does Eq. (31.17) actually describe the experimentally observed facts? To test this, arc coth$[H^2(\theta)/H^2(0)]$ is plotted against $1/\theta$. Such a plot for the *F*-center in KCl is shown in Fig. 33.3 using the data of Fig. 3.7a. Figure 33.3 indicates a completely satisfactory agreement with the equation. From the slope of the plot, we may obtain ω, namely,

$$\omega = 2\pi \times 2.96 \times 10^{12} \quad \text{sec}^{-1}. \tag{33.2}$$

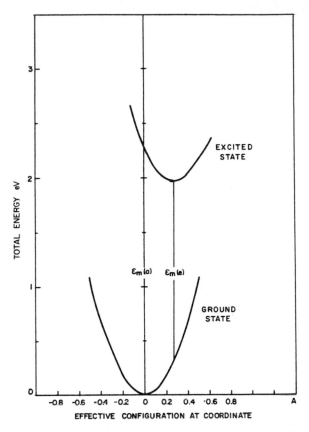

FIG. 33.4. Configurational coordinate diagram for the F-center in KCl assuming no frequency change. This is the simplest assumption to make. The effective frequency of the ground state is assumed and $\epsilon_m(a)$. The values for emission do not agree with the experimental ones. Effective mass was assumed to equal the total mass of the nearest neighbor ions.

This corresponds to a phonon energy of 0.0122 ev. S may be obtained from this value of ω combined with $H(0)$. Its value is 28.4 for KCl.

Using this value and (31.7a), $\varDelta q$ may be calculated. The result is 5.67×10^{-20} cm gm$^{1/2}$. This gives a value of 0.28 A for the displacement of the coordinate, if we assume that the effective mass associated with the center equals the mass of six potassium ions (nearest neighbors). Using the above value of ω, $\varDelta q$, and ϵ_m, the configurational coordinate diagram shown in Fig. 33.4 for the F-center in KCl was made.

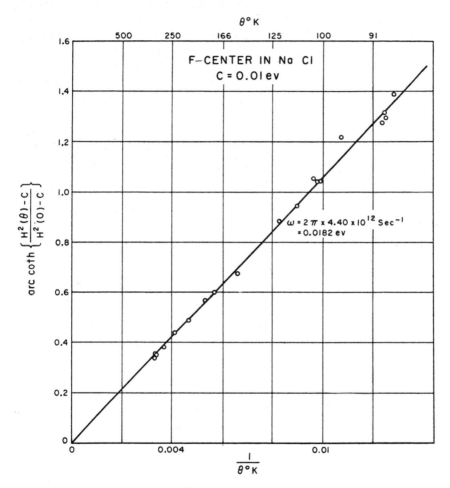

FIG. 33.5. The F-center in NaCl. Arc hyperbolic cotangent plot of the measured value of the half-width versus the reciprocal of the temperature. Note that a constant has been subtracted (after Markham and Konitzer, S).

The reader will note that the predicted value for the emission maximum (that is, 1.26 ev; Table 8.1) does not agree with the observed value. The reason for this is that it has been assumed that there was no change in the phonon frequency between the ground and the first excited state. This assumption is not justified. As stressed previously, to do this calculation correctly, we need to include higher order terms in Eq. (30.14), as well as in the definition of S, Eq. (31.7a). Russell and Klick (S) have obtained a more realistic diagram using calculations similar to the one given in the first part of Section 32. They combined their absorption data and the emission measurements of Botden, van Doorn, and Haven (S).

A plot similar to Fig. 33.3 for the F-center in NaCl is given in Fig. 33.5. Note that we have had to subtract a constant from $H^2(\theta)$ to obtain a line that goes through the origin. It is not known if one generally has to add a constant. At present, the meaning of the constant is in some doubt. From the values in Figs. 33.3 and 33.5, one sees that the modes important for the F-center broadening are in the middle frequency range (see Fig. 29.9) and are not the longitudinal optical modes of infinite wavelength, as was originally assumed by Pekar and by Huang and Rhys.

The temperature dependence of ϵ_m has not been discussed here since the treatment requires the inclusion of higher order terms in Section 30. This can be done using quantum mechanical approximations (see Markham, S); the results, however, are not very satisfactory. The temperature dependence of ϵ_m has not been satisfactorily solved.

TABLE 33.1. EFFECTIVE PHONON FREQUENCIES FOR ABSORPTION AND EMISSION[a]

Frequency	NaCl	KCl	RbCl	KBr	KI
$\frac{1}{2\pi}\omega_{\text{eff}}(a) \times 10^{-12}$ sec^{-1}	4.40	2.96	2.45	2.80	2.55
$\frac{1}{2\pi}\omega_{\text{eff}}(e) \times 10^{-12}$ sec^{-1}	5.90	4.55	3.33	3.75	3.25

[a] After Gebhardt and Kühnert, S.

A curve similar to Figs. 33.3 and 33.5 has been obtained by Stungis and coworkers (S) for RbCl, $[\omega = 2\pi(2.43 \times 10^{12}$ sec$^{-1})]$. In this case, the curve goes through the origin. Very recently Gebhardt and Kühnert (S) have reported ω for absorption and for emission obtained on six alkali halides. They did not use the type of plot described here, perhaps because their temperature points were limited. The data are given in Table 33.1. Lüty and Gebhardt (S) have used a hyperbolic cotangent plot to evaluate

$\omega_{\text{eff}}(e)$ for KCl. Their plot goes through the origin which indicates that Eq. (33.1) applies also to emission. Gebhardt, in a private communication, has indicated to the author that some corrections are required to the emission data.

REFERENCES

T. P. J. Botden, C. Z. van Doorn, and Y. Haven, *Philips Res. Rept.* **9**, 469 (1954).
W. Gebhardt and H. Kühnert, *Phys. Letters* **11**, 15 (1964).
J. D. Konitzer and J. J. Markham, *J. Chem. Phys.* **32**, 843 (1960).
F. Lüty and W. Gebhardt, *Z. Physik* **169**, 475 (1962).
J. J. Markham, *Rev. Mod. Phys.* **31**, 956 (1959).
J. J. Markham and J. D. Konitzer, *J. Chem. Phys.* **34** 1934 (1961).
E. Mollwo, *Z. Physik* **85**, 56 (1933).
G. Russell and C. C. Klick, *Phys. Rev.* **101**, 1473 (1956).
G. E. Stungis, J. J. Markham, and G. Noble, *J. Chem. Phys.* **40**, 3634 (1964).

APPENDIX

THE A AND B COEFFICIENTS

In the appendix we discuss Eq. (31.24) and relate it to Smakula's formula. An expression for A associated with the emission from a point imperfection has been given by Lax, but it was not related to Smakula's equation. One may regard Smakula's formula as an experimental equation which defines an oscillator strength, f. The true connection between the experimental f and the matrix element depends on the absorption shape and the local field. The local field problem has not been solved in a satisfactory manner, but the same corrections will be used for both the A and B coefficients. The correct A coefficient is arrived at by the use of the semiclassical approach given by Gordon and by Klein. The theory employed will be in the form presented by Seitz (1940, p. 215).

One cannot obtain an expression for the spontaneous emission from the theory developed by Gordon and by Klein. One can, however, make certain judicious modifications and obtain the correct value. This derivation is not completely rigorous, although the results are correct. The discussion starts by "deriving" the usual A coefficient for an atom in a vacuum. The energy that induces the downward transition is due to the zero-point vibration of the electromagnetic waves. The probability of a transition per unit of time from state u to g is given by

$$P = \frac{8\pi^3 e^2}{3h^2} \mathbf{r}_{ug}^2 \rho_v \qquad (E1)$$

where $\mathbf{r}_{ug}$ is the matrix element coupling the states which appeared before. The energy density of the modes at frequency ν is ρ_ν. It can be obtained in the usual manner (Seitz, 1940, p. 108) where only transverse vibrations have to be considered. One obtains:

$$\rho_\nu = \frac{8\pi}{c^3} \nu^2 \left(\frac{1}{2}h\nu\right) = \frac{4\pi}{c^3} h\nu^3 . \tag{E2}$$

Equation (E2) assumes that the energy associated with every degree of freedom is $\frac{1}{2}h\nu$. The volume of the enclosure does not enter into ρ_ν, as can be shown from an argument presented in Slater (p. 460). Combining (E1) and (E2), the desired coefficient is obtained except for a factor of 2, namely,

$$A' = \frac{32\pi^4}{3} \frac{e^2 \nu^3}{hc^3} \mathbf{r}_{ug}^2 . \tag{E3}$$

The missing factor of 2 arises because the transition probability in a quantized field is proportional to $(n+1)$ where n is the initial state eigenvalue. For large n, this number is proportional to the energy $(n+\frac{1}{2})\nu h$, but it is just twice this value when the ground state is involved. The actual coefficient is, therefore

$$A = \frac{64\pi^4}{3} \frac{e^2 \nu^3}{hc^3} \mathbf{r}_{ug}^2 \tag{E4}$$

which is the result obtained from the rigorous derivation due to Dirac.

To relate this value to an imperfection in a dielectric (with dielectric coefficient n), we must find the connection between the energies of the modes and the actual local field at the imperfection, since it is this field which induces the downward transition. The usual expression for the energy of a macroscopic field in a dielectric (plane waves) gives:

$$\left\langle \frac{n^2 E^2}{4\pi} \right\rangle_{av} = \frac{1}{2}h\nu . \tag{E5}$$

Hence, the macroscopic field is $1/n^2$ times the vacuum field for the same energy of oscillation. Further, we introduce the Lorentzian correction,

$$E_L = \tfrac{1}{3}(n^2+2) E . \tag{E6}$$

From Eqs. (E5) and (E6), the correction for the presence of the dielectric is obtained. Effectively, the energy of a given mode of vibration is

$$(1/9n^2)(n^2+2)^2 (\tfrac{1}{2}h\nu) . \tag{E7}$$

Finally, we must employ the true velocity of light (in the medium) in (E2) so that the actual ρ_ν has the form

$$\rho_\nu(\text{local}) = \frac{4\pi h\nu^3}{c^3}\frac{n}{9}(n^2+2)^2 \qquad (E8)$$

and the corrected coefficient is:

$$A_d = \frac{n}{9}(n^2+2)^2\frac{64\pi^4}{3}\frac{e^2\nu^3}{hc^3}\,\mathbf{r}_{ug}^2 \qquad (E9)$$

or

$$A_d = \frac{n}{9}(n^2+2)^2\frac{8\pi^2}{c^3}\frac{e^2\nu^2}{m}f, \qquad (E10)$$

where Eq. (4.3a) has been used. In the black body, the ratio of the A to B coefficients is

$$\frac{A}{B} = \frac{8\pi h\nu^3}{c^3}. \qquad (E11a)$$

In view of the fact that the actual modes in the dielectric must be employed, this ratio for a point imperfection should be

$$A/B = 8\pi h\nu^3\left(\frac{n}{c}\right)^3. \qquad (E11b)$$

If Eq. (E10) is correct, one should be able to obtain (E11b) from (E10) and Smakula's equation. The latter, per imperfection, has the form

$$\alpha_m H = \frac{(n^2+2)^2}{n}\frac{2}{9}\frac{e^2}{mc}f. \qquad (E12)$$

The number of upward transitions at an imperfection is given by

$$B\rho_\nu' = \int \frac{1}{h\nu}\alpha I\,d\nu = \frac{1}{h\nu}a_s\alpha_m\Delta\nu I. \qquad (E13)$$

B is one of Einstein's coefficients appropriate for a dielectric, and ρ_ν' is the mean energy density induced in the medium by the light of intensity I falling on the sample (not the local one). a_s is Smakula's constant (see Section 3); it equals $\pi/2$ for a Lorentzian shape, which is implicit in (E12). One must relate I to ρ_ν' so as to obtain an expression for B. In a medium of unit permeability, the relation is

$$\frac{\rho_\nu'}{I} = \frac{n}{c} \qquad (E14)$$

or

$$B = \frac{\pi}{9} \frac{(n^2+2)^2}{n^2} \frac{e^2}{h\nu m} f.$$ (E15)

Now, by dividing (E10) by (E15), we obtain the desired ratio, Eq. (E11b). This does not really prove our derivation, but only indicates that our A is consistent with Smakula's formula, from which f is determined. Actually, in the derivation, we have assumed that B(emission) = B(absorption). This is not required, since we may calculate B(emission) from Eqs. (E10) and (E11b), in which case the two B's may not be equal. This seems to be the case in reality (see Section 8).

GENERAL REFERENCES

A. Abragam, "The Principles of Nuclear Magnetism." Oxford Univ. Press, London and New York, 1961.

M. Abraham and R. Becker. "The Classical Theory of Electricity and Magnetism." Hafner, New York.

E. R. Andrew, "Nuclear Magnetic Resonance," Cambridge Univ. Press, London and New York, 1955.

H. A. Bethe and E. E. Salpeter, "Quantum Mechanics of One- and Two-Electron Atoms." Academic Press, New York, 1957.

M. Born and M. Göppert-Mayer, *Handb. Phys.* **24.2**, 623 (1933).

M. Born and K. Huang, "Dynamical Theory of Crystal Lattices." Oxford Univ. Press, London and New York, 1954.

E. U. Condon and G. H. Shortley, "The Theory of Atomic Spectra." Cambridge Univ. Press, London and New York, 1953.

R. Fowler and E. A. Guggenheim, "Statistical Thermodynamics." Cambridge Univ. Press, London and New York, 1960.

J. S. Griffith, "The Theory of Transition—Metal Ions." Cambridge Univ. Press, London and New York, 1961.

W. Heitler, "The Quantum Theory of Radiation." Oxford Univ. Press, London and New York, 1954.

G. Joos, "Theoretical Physics." 3rd ed. Hafner, New York.

N. F. Mott and R. W. Gurney, "Electronic Processes in Ionic Crystals." Oxford Univ. Press, London and New York, 1940.

L. I. Schiff, "Quantum Mechanics." McGraw-Hill, New York, 1955.

F. Seitz, "The Modern Theory of Solids." McGraw-Hill, New York, 1940.

F. Seitz, *Rev. Mod. Phys.* **18**, 384 (1946).

F. Seitz, *Rev. Mod. Phys.* **26**, 7 (1954).

J. C. Slater, "Quantum Theory of Matter." McGraw-Hill, New York, 1951.

C. P. Slichter, "Principles of Magnetic Resonance." Harper and Row, New York, 1963.

R. A. Smith, "Wave Mechanics and Crystalline Solids." Chapman and Hall, London, 1961.

J. H. Van Vleck, "The Theory of Electric and Magnetic Susceptibilities." Oxford Univ. Press, London and New York, 1932.

Author Index

A

Abragam, A., 160, 166, 170, 171, 184, 186, 187, 190, 194, 197, 199, 200, 201, 233, 243, 388
Abraham, M., 169, 388
Abrahams, E., 197, 198, 201, 225, 262, 278
Adrian, F. J., 205, 297, 298, 309, 313, 322, 324, 325, 328, 329
Alexander, J., 147, 148, 156
Allard, J. G., 261, 262, 263, 288
Amperè, A. M., 161
Anderson, S., 259, 288
Andrews, E. R., 186, 388
Apker, L., 64
Avakian, P., 10, 26

B

Barnes, R. G., 168, 180
Bates, L. F., 256, 258
Bates, R. T., 33, 35, 257, 258
Becker, K. H., 94, 95
Becker, R., 169, 388
Bethe, H. A., 159, 160, 161, 167, 170, 171, 231, 388
Bjork, R. L., 348, 353
Bleaney, B., 259, 288
Bloch ,F., 183, 184, 190, 192, 201, 233
Bloembergen, N., 193, 201, 233, 243
Blum, H., 221, 230, 232, 261, 262, 280, 281, 285, 286, 287, 288, 325, 326, 329
Blumberg, W. E., 272, 288
Born, M., 1, 5, 7, 73, 300, 312, 331, 338, 339, 342, 353, 354, 355, 359, 361, 378, 388

B

Botden, Th. P. J., 81, 86, 89, 91, 95, 384, 385
Brachman, M. K., 68, 87
Brandenberger, J., 12, 26
Breit, G., 227, 232, 248
Bron, W. E., 281, 288
Bronstein, L., 3, 4, 5, 7
Brown, F. C., 65, 66, 70, 72, 73, 86, 87, 94, 95, 96, 139, 140, 157
Bupp, L. P., 141, 157, 256, 258
Burnstein, E., 142, 156
Butler, W. D., 12, 26

C

Casimir, H. B. G., 179, 180
Casler, R., 147, 148, 156
Casselman, T. N., 212, 219, 295, 297, 375, 376, 377
Castle, J. G., 280, 288
Castner, T. G., 154, 156, 236, 238, 239, 241, 243, 273, 275
Christensen, S. H., 261, 266, 281, 283, 284, 288
Compton, W. D., 56, 57, 152, 156
Condon, E. U., 159, 160, 161, 167, 174, 206, 207, 208, 218, 257, 367, 377, 388
Costikas, A., 132, 133

D

Debye, P., 331
Delbecq, C. J., 58, 106, 107, 108, 109, 112, 113, 154, 155, 156
Dexter, D. L., 32, 35, 112, 113, 295, 297, 324, 325, 329, 371, 375, 377

389

Subject Index

In this index, attempts have been made to state where the *major* terms are defined and to refer to subjects that have been treated in detail (note the use of the letters, ff). In a section where terms are referred to repeatedly, only one entry is made.

A

a, 310
$a(n,j)$, 300
a_j, 224
$a_n (r - R_j)$, 300
a_s, 21ff, 30, 31
A-band, 141
A-coefficient (Einstein's), 373, 385ff
acoustical branch, 334ff
additive coloration, 50, 58ff, 82, 91, 97, 256, 270, 292
adiabatic, 35, 183, 260, 266
adiabatic approximation, 354ff, 358, 378
adiabatic Hamiltonian, 199
adiabatic passage, criterion for, 192ff
   rapid, 185, 189
angular momentum, 161, 177
antisymmetric mode, 334ff
axis of symmetry, 248, 249, 251, 252

B

$b(\mathbf{k})$, 299
$b(n, \mathbf{k})$, 299
$b(n, \mathbf{k};\mathbf{r})$, 299
B-center (band), 15, 33, 141, 282, 283, 284

B-coefficient (Einstein's), 384ff
bandshapes, experimental results, 378ff
bleaching, 45, 127, 140ff
   of F-center and EPR, 281ff
   at high temperature, 140ff
   at low temperature, 96ff
Bloch, the function, 299
   the mechanism of broadening, 198ff, 234, 274
   the phenomenological equation, 185, 266, 274
Bohr, the frequency condition, 362, 374
Boltzmann, the factor, 362, 369
Born-Mayer, the force, 315, 316
Born-Oppenheimer, the technique, 320, 354ff
Born-von Kármàn, the boundary conditions, 299, 336, 337
breadth of the absorption bands, 331
breathing mode, 370
Breit-Rabi, the equation, 228, 230
Brillouin, the perturbation theory, 211

C

Ca^{+2} effect of, 44
Cd^{2+} effect of, 44
$Cu^{2+}6H_2O$, 172ff, 201, 205, 209
Cl_2 -ion, 153
chemical potential, 60
closure theorem, 204
colloid, 5, 58, 61, 63, 64
comparison of the two solutions of EPR, 189ff